Count Not the Dead
The Popular Image of the German Submarine

"Iron coffins," "grey wolves," and "steel sharks" – cast in images such as these, submarines have been icons of Germany's maritime tradition. In books and films, submarines have been used to promote political goals and to justify and explain an intriguing and sometimes ambiguous past. A fascinating look at nearly one hundred years of propaganda and literature, *Count Not the Dead* explores the cult and culture surrounding one of the most mythologized weapons of war.

Basing his study on some 250 German novels, memoirs, fictionalized histories, and films (including *Das Boot*), Michael Hadley examines the popular image of the German submarine and weighs the values, purposes, and perceptions of German writers and filmmakers. He considers the idea of the submarine as a war-winning weapon, the exploits of the "band of brothers" who made up the U-boat crews, and the hopes that U-boats embodied in two world wars against the Allies. Analysed in context, the U-boat emerges as a central factor and metaphor in Germany's ongoing struggle with its political and military past.

In *Count Not the Dead* Hadley explores the complex relationships between political reality and cultural myth, and draws important conclusions about the way in which Germans have interpreted their past and how these views are being changed by present concerns.

MICHAEL L. HADLEY is Professor of Germanic Studies, University of Victoria.

Count Not the Dead

*The Popular Image of
the German Submarine*

MICHAEL L. HADLEY

Naval Institute Press
Annapolis, Maryland

Published and distributed in the United States of
America by the Naval Institute Press, 118 Maryland
Avenue, Annapolis, Maryland 21402-5035.

Library of Congress Catalog Card Number 95-67165

ISBN 1-55750-134-3

Printed in Canada on acid-free paper

This book has been published with the help of a grant
from the Canadian Federation for the Humanities, using
funds provided by the Social Sciences and Humanities
Research Council of Canada.

Und Siegesboten kommen herab: die Schlacht
Ist unser! Lebe droben, o Vaterland,
   Und zähle nicht die Toten! Dir ist,
      Liebes! nicht *einer* zu viel gefallen.

And harbingers of victory soft descend: the battle's
Ours! Endure on high, O Fatherland,
   Count not the dead! for Thee
      Beloved! not *one* too many has fallen.

Friedrich Hölderlin, "Tod fürs Vaterland," 1796

Cited by Propaganda Minister Goebbels,
Christmas 1942, and by Admiral Rolf
Johannesson on burying the dead of the
battleship *Bismarck,* April 1944

1914–1918	199 U-boats lost
	5249 submariners fallen
1939–1945	739 U-boats lost
	30,003 submariners fallen

From a bronze tablet, U-boat Memorial,
Möltenort–Kiel

Contents

Preface

"Iron coffins," "grey wolves," and "steel sharks" – cast in these images, German submarines and their exploits fill the pages of almost one hundred years of Germany's naval lore. Captured in literature and film, these "monsters of the deep" have fascinated generations of readers and viewers. Submarine stories have been used to promote political goals and have helped to justify and explain an intriguing and sometimes ambiguous past. They contribute to the core mythology of Germany's maritime tradition.

Germany's national experience of underwater warfare has spawned a vast amount of fiction and non-fiction by Germans and non-Germans alike. Memoirs, academic tomes, novels, films, and pulp-trade hits have romanticized, fantasized, analysed, and criticized. Evidence suggests that no other weapon of war has been as closely identified with German culture as the submarine. Although one readily associates such inventions as the Stuka dive-bomber, the v-2 rocket, and the Panzer tank with Germany, none of these weapons has generated so much popular and scholarly writing both at home and abroad. Certainly, none of them has given rise to an established literary tradition. That distinction rests with the German submarine, the "u-boat," with all the cultural baggage the name evokes. Indeed, popular imagination outside Germany would have us believe that two types of craft have been engaged in the history of underwater combat: submarines and u-boats. According to this perception, one type was driven largely by "stout-hearted men" for noble causes, the other by "cunning Germans" for sinister and pernicious ends. This distinction explains why Germany's technical term for "undersea boat" has been adopted by other languages as an expression of fascination, awe, and wartime opprobrium.

This book marks the first attempt to navigate the rocky waters of the U-boat's literary record. It is based on a study of some 250 novels, memoirs, and fictionalized histories published in German, as well as a sequence of major films, which substantially helped to create and promote what German submariners still refer to as the "U-boat spirit." Regarded by Germans as a "miracle weapon" during the two world wars, U-boats radiated a special aura, for in both conflicts they almost managed to bring Britain and her Allies to their knees. The U-boat was recognized as the decisive weapon of war and was mythologized like none other before or since. Its narrative tradition is rooted in well-documented fact. Indeed, operational histories and analyses attest not only to the weapon's effectiveness, but to the daring, skill, and courage of those who took it to sea. The tenacity with which German submariners faced the uncertainties and terrors of undersea warfare against enemies who ultimately defeated them is no less impressive.

Significantly, no U-boat narrative belongs to the canon that scholars have established for the literature of war. Popular works on war have, of course, been a staple of this century. But the prevailing European mind-set of continentalism has led scholars to identify the term "war" with "land war," and "war novel" with "land-war novel." Thus, naval war and its attendant questions of morality and maritime prestige have been excluded from the formula. Yet army literature and U-boat literature present essentially different arguments about Germany's experience of war.

Narratives about the war at sea, for example, can indulge in a kind of romanticism untenable in books about war on land, where the debris of mortal combat scars the earth. According to naval myth, warfare on the high seas is "clean." Navies neither occupy territory nor subjugate peoples; they simply pass through vast tracts of contested ocean and remain distant from the politics that drive the war at home. Sailors are never involved in deportations or pillage, and the bloody battle between ships on the high seas leaves neither trace of carnage nor sites for national shrines. The myth therefore holds that participants in naval wars are untouched by politics and untainted by the political results of "purely naval" action carried out in the service of national policy. An examination of naval literature reveals how self-deceptive and self-serving this myth can be. In choosing to overlook naval literature, scholars have ignored a revealing body of writing that, however flamboyant, nevertheless documented and promoted Germany's efforts to wrest for herself a place in the sun. Significantly, the most telling naval literature does not concern itself with capital ships in surface warfare in the grand Mahanian manner of big-ship, big-gun, blue-water navalism, but with Germany's major naval weapon in two world wars, the submarine.

For the historian, German books about the U-boat communicate a reality quite different from the vicarious adventure and uplifting sentiments most stories were designed to deliver. Seen as cultural artifacts, these works reveal the changing meanings that the image of the German submarine projects. They shed light on the telling links between propaganda and popular culture, and on the ensuing tensions between tradition and reform that surfaced within Germany's postwar armed services. On a larger scale, the image of the German submarine in literature and film affords some important conclusions about the way in which Germans have interpreted their past and how far present concerns change these views.

This book, then, explores the popular image of the German submarine in books and film. In examining literary and sub-literary portrayals, I weigh the values, purposes, and perceptions of German writers and film-makers, though without filtering them according to their aesthetic distinctions and achievement. Literary pretensions are not germane to this study; nor indeed is literary analysis. Critics will find little in U-boat literature on which to hone their skills. Among other things, and with rare exception, the recycled language of U-boat narratives labours under an exhaustion of descriptive metaphor similar to that which has been observed of twentieth-century British seafaring works.[1] Given the importance of the U-boat record, I have chosen to treat each text simply as an artifact, as one more piece in the fascinating puzzle that makes up the historical mosaic of this compelling subject.

Literature, of course, is an imitation of nature. It draws on the human imagination to create in some ideal form a new reality that does not exist in actual life in precisely that sequence or manner. Writers reorder and reshape; they sometimes indulge in the conjurer's tricks of smoke and mirrors. This certainly holds for the subliterary forms of pulps and dime novels as well. One might therefore ask what value lies in probing the popular image of the German submarine and in examining mere appearances. Precisely this: appearances belong as much to what we conveniently call historical reality as do verifiable facts. In short, our perceptions of things as they "really" are take shape in our minds in various ways. They are determined as much by our own immediate experiences and the intellectual musings these trigger as they are by enticing images, misconceptions, salty yarns, and damned lies.

The popular image of the German submarine offers us an important case study of these complex relationships. Here the u-boat emerges in three dimensions: as a fateful weapon of war, as a cast of mind, and as the embodiment of a particular "band of brothers." In writing this book, I have reflected more upon the imitation of nature than upon the u-boat as it actually was. In a real sense, this tension between appearances and reality, between nature and imitation, confronts us with a central problem of historiography, where even at the best of times the sea returns false echoes and the periscope sometimes fogs.

Acknowledgments

Mr Horst Bredow, director of the U-Boat Archives in Cuxhaven, Germany (Stiftung Traditionsarchiv Unterseeboote), has long been a mainstay of my research into German submarines. He has given me full access to his extraordinary collection of books and records, permission to quote therefrom, and the benefit of his experience. Both he and his wife, Annemie, have always offered me a home away from home as an archive guest. To them I owe much.

Over the years, numerous former members of Germany's U-Boat Arm have shared their memories and reflections with me. In doing so, they have put a human face on fading documents and distant events, and have helped clarify complex issues. I especially acknowledge Mr Hans Meckel and Dr Jochen von Knebel-Doeberitz, both of whom had served on the staff of Grand Admiral Dönitz, and Admiral Paul Hartwig, wartime skipper of U-517, who reached flag rank in the post-war German navy.

To Vice-Admiral Klaus Rehder, former Commander-in-Chief, Fleet, Federal German Navy, and to his successors Vice-Admiral Dieter Franz Braun and Hans-Rudolf Boehmer, I owe not only the singular honour of having been invited on three occasions to participate in the German fleet's annual Historical-Tactical Conference, but opportunities both ashore and afloat of familiarizing myself with the modern German navy, its personnel, ships, and traditions.

The Canadian navy has helped me as well. While serving as Maritime Commander in Halifax, Vice-Admiral Robert George arranged for me to be posted for my Reserve training in 1990 to a familiarization tour aboard the Oberon-class submarine HMCS *Okanagan* – an operational vessel closest to a Second World War German VIIC U-boat. His purpose of making this now shorebound, former surface-navy sailor a more authentic raconteur of life beneath the waves was fulfilled by all members of the submarine's crew, who unstintingly shared the lore of their trade.

McGill-Queen's University Press has kindly granted permission to draw upon occasional material that I had published previously under its imprimature.

I am grateful to two colleagues, one a military historian and the other a professor of German literature, for having critiqued the original manuscript: Dr Roger Sarty, Senior Historian, Director of History, National Defence Headquarters, Ottawa; and Dr Peter Liddell, Department of Germanic Studies, University of Victoria, Victoria, BC. Their specialist perspectives helped me in balancing the claims of at least two disciplines. I would also like to thank my editor, Rosemary Shipton, for her many insights and advice.

Finally, I especially thank my wife and life's companion, Anita Borradaile Hadley. Not only has she supported me with her discerning editorial work on this manuscript and others, but for many years has both shared and encouraged the research adventures of this arm-chair submariner.

Ultimately, however, I am responsible for the material and judgments of this book. I am also responsible for all translations from the German, which, unless otherwise indicated, are my own.

Research was supported by grants from the University of Victoria and from the Pacific and Maritime Strategic Studies Group of the University of Victoria, with support from the Military and Strategic Studies program of Canada's Department of National Defence.

MLH
"Stormhaven"
Victoria, BC

Stylized painting from 1936 by marine artist Claus Bergen

1906: full-speed trials of Seiner Majestät Unterseeboot u-1. Note tall wind-scoops fore and aft and open hatches.

1912: postcard, "Tomorrow I must leave." Sentimental verse celebrating the cosmic significance of a sailor's farewell

1913: postcard with German Imperial Battle Flag and the Austrian national colours. Luther's battle hymn, "A Mighty Fortress is our God!" was based on Psalm 46.

1913: postcard, "Just get to know the German people!" A cute little lad in the popular sailor suit takes his U-boat to sea.

1914: U-boat postcard with imperial naval pennant: "The glossy sea is our field, / The German sub bears us far; / And our hate is ripe and full / Woe unto you, England, watch out!"

1914: postcard, "The heroic deed of U-9," on sinking three British cruisers in a single hour on 22 September. Reissued in 1934 to mark the twentieth anniversary

1914: jingoistic postcard, "The Town of Rüdesheim salutes U-9," surmounted by Germania. Sponsored by the regulars of the "Old German Inn"

"A Hero's Grave: In German hearts, in German flood, / He now rests safe and secure."
Postcard commemorating the loss of war hero Otto Weddigen, skipper of U-29, on
18 March 1915

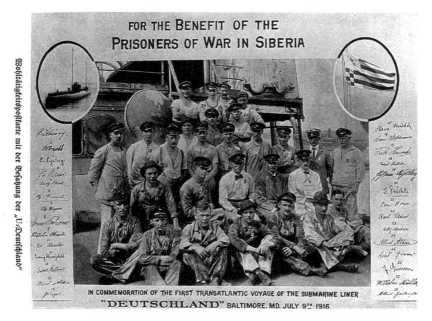

1916: postcard commemorating the transatlantic voyage of the submarine freighter
U-Deutschland, ostensibly issued to raise charitable funds in the United States for German
POWs in Siberia.

Family traditions: Bosn's Mate Hör and his father.
Note the young seaman's Iron Cross, won aboard
U-9, and his father's Iron Cross for 1870/71.

Family traditions: father and son in Hitler's navy. Staff Signal Chief Max Schuch (left)
and Leading Signalman Werner Schuch of U-264

1915: postcard, "U-boats Away!" Verses extol battle against "England, the tyrant of the seas."

„Unsere kühnen Unterseeboote".

Dichtung und Tonweise von OTTO GROLL.

„Volldampf voraus!" Durch Sturmgebraus
Das „U"-Boot zieht zum Kampf hinaus.
Ein Fisch von Stahl, so klein und schmal;
Doch furchtbar seinen Gegnern all'.
Den Mannen drauf — ein Jeder Held —
Das Hurra aus der Kehle gellt.
„Die ganze Kraft nun eingesetzt!
Wir siegen oder sterben jetzt!"
    Ihr Feinde ringsum, zeigt Euch nur!
    Wir folgen mutig Eurer Spur.
    Ihr sollt jetzt fühlen deutsche Kraft
    Wie sich der „Michel" Freiheit schafft.

„Tauch ab, tauch auf!" Es ruft die Pflicht!
Am Horizont der Feind in Sicht.
Ein Zittern hebt des Schiffes Leib.
Gott schütze unser Kind und Weib.
Ein „Los" erschallt, „Torpedo flieg!"
Durch Deine Kraft bring' uns den Sieg.
Bis Schiff auf Schiff vom Briten-Bund
Versenkt liegt auf dem Meeresgrund.
    Ihr Feinde ringsum, zeigt Euch nur!
    Wir folgen mutig Eurer Spur.
    Ihr sollt jetzt fühlen deutsche Kraft
    Wie sich der „Michel" Freiheit schafft.

1 (Erschien für Klavier, Gesang und Orchester)
Alleinvertrieb: OTTO GROLL, Dresden, Holbeinstr. 50

1915: postcard, "Our bold submarines." A death-or-glory poem warning the enemy that "German might" will win freedom of the seas by destroying the British fleet.

1917: U-cruiser U-117 that fought off the East Coast of Canada and the United States. Note the 15 cm (5.9-inch) gun.

1917: the crew of U-117 on the foredeck. Note the accordionist, lower left.

Count Not the Dead

Introduction:
The Seeds of Tradition

"No weapon has fascinated the Germans so much as the U-boat, the poor man's truncheon," a journalist wrote in 1985.[1] "No other German weapon in World Wars One and Two has had such a mystical aura," wrote another.[2] All evidence confirms such views. During both wars, and during the interwar years as well, the U-boat was mythologized more than any other weapon of war. It became identified with raw maritime prestige and national destiny. Germans had gone to sea in submarines from 1906 until 1919, and again from 1935 until 1945, for a total of twenty-three years. As a partner in NATO, the modern Federal German Navy has been going to sea in submarines for an additional forty years. Yet the public continues to view the postwar generation of German submariners in the context of the "grey wolves" that fought – and lost – in both world wars. At the root of this identification lies a number of complex issues forming the German experience of undersea warfare.

Germany's U-boat experience has several dimensions: technical, tactical, political, strategic, social, and literary. Indeed, one could argue that this sequence – from technical to literary – fairly represents the stages through which the national experience emerged. According to this pattern, the needs of maritime defence first stimulated technical responses and tactical experiments; military and political leaders then grappled with the opportunities and challenges presented by the new weapon on the larger stage of national interests; sailors of the Submarine Service developed their own doctrines and mystique; and, finally, imaginative writers struggled with the cultural legacy. Writers were driven by various motivations. Some made genuine efforts at comprehending national history, while others sought to create a politically useful past. Others were simply out to make a buck.

These aspects of u-boat history did not really develop in a totally linear and sequential fashion. They impinged laterally on one another and ultimately folded in upon themselves. In so doing, they both created and reflected new mind-sets – in themselves the stuff of new experience. Clearly, any thoroughgoing attempt at elucidating Germany's experience of underwater warfare must account for complex and conflicting dynamics. A literary survey of the submarine offers a similar challenge. Since the earliest days of the First World War, popular literature and media portrayals have played a major role in determining our perception of submarines. Books and articles for mass audiences have attempted to wrest spiritual victory from the major defeats of the two world wars; they have struggled to communicate powerful images and persuasive ideas in the service both of "historical reality" and "naval tradition."

Rooted in both mythology and fact, traditions are easily enough traced in military and naval culture where they are celebrated daily in uniforms, emblems, and rituals. The threads of tradition are much more elusive in national cultures, but they are no less powerful. Reichskanzler Theobald von Bethmann Hollweg brooded about the influence of popular sentiment in 1917 at the beginning of unrestricted u-boat warfare: "publicly the German people's attention was drawn to their possession of an infallible weapon, [and] u-boat warfare could not be wrested from the nation's heart." His judgment was prophetic as far as the popular imagination in Germany was concerned.

At the level of popular consciousness, the propaganda image of the German submariner as some kind of legendary hero – or villain – did not begin to change until the release of the film *Das Boot* in 1981. This evocative, intensely human production managed to move even audiences of Germany's former enemies to empathize with the u-boat's crew. In the film they discovered for the first time a Nelsonian "band of brothers" who no longer fitted the stereotype of the iron-willed and amoral "Prussian" sailor. Among the many legacies that Admiral Horatio Nelson had bequeathed to naval tradition in the wake of his victory at the Battle of Trafalgar (1805) was his concept of the vital bond among seafarers; the officers in particular formed a special brotherhood that transcended other social orders – and indeed all national boundaries. Yet so uncomfortably ambivalent were the impressions that some viewers saw the film as a tacit adulation of Third Reich glory.

German audiences fared little better. The sometimes conflicting public reaction in Germany to both the film version of Buchheim's *Das Boot* and the subsequent TV series – as well as to the founding of U-boat technical museums in Kiel and Bremerhaven – underscores a critical fact: Germany's experience of underwater warfare embraces even those who have neither been to sea nor experienced war. They have experienced the past vicariously, for that is the way in which memory, tradition, and literature work. The seeds of Germany's naval tradition broke ground in the latter part of the nineteenth century under pressures from both the industrial revolution and the politics of national expansion. Significantly, it fell to a defeated Grossadmiral Tirpitz to identify the emotions surrounding those beginnings as he pondered his career in the most massive fleet that Germany had ever known.

Grossadmiral Alfred von Tirpitz concluded his memoirs in 1919 after fifty-four years of naval service. By then Germany had lost the Great War (1914–18) and had been torn by revolution. Her emperor, Wilhelm II, had abdicated and slipped incognito across the Dutch border; her captured fleet had scuttled itself while interned in the British naval anchorage at Scapa Flow. Unrestricted U-boat warfare had almost brought Britain to her knees, but had ultimately failed. How was Germany to cope with her shattered dreams, and the navy to recapture its lost honour? How could Germans wrest even some vestige of spiritual victory from such abject defeat? One answer seemed to lie in seeking the meaning of those pivotal points in their history. This is what Tirpitz – naval officer, patriot, and "father of the German fleet" – set out to do.

One fundamental link with glory and honour had been clear from the beginning: the imperial connection. Tirpitz recalled the ceremonial transition from a Prussian coastal defence force to a high seas navy: "When the beautiful flag with the eagle was taken down on our ships in 1867, and the flag of the North German Bund, fashioned more after the British model, was hoisted in its place, we midshipmen felt the disappearance of the Prussian colours with some pain. But we sensed a great historical turning-point and emptied our glasses with mixed feelings. The year 1871 thrust the Prussian memory back even further; we became Imperial officers, and the navy got the black-white-red kokarde."[3]

These imperial colours – the black and white of Prussia, and the red of the Hanseatic League – would endure throughout the history of three of Germany's navies until the end of 1945. Imperial in structure and imperial in mind, the German fleet itself was actually a

creation of empire. Unlike the German army, which stressed particu-
larist values and the virtual independence of its many provincial corps
– the Prussian and the Bavarian, for example – the navy was a symbol
of national unity.[4] Only through a powerful fleet, it was argued, could
Germany compete with other European nations and claim international prestige.

Spawned in the years of the Battleship Race of the 1890s and
reemphasized in the 1940s, this proclamation of navalism underscored not only the role of surface ships, but later that of submarines
as well. Navalism was the overriding strategic concept of the day. It
insisted that large battle-fleets and concentration of force would
decide who controlled the oceans; it contended that the possession of
select bases on island or continental peripheries were more valuable
than the control of large land masses. Ultimately, navalism was the
belief that national prestige without seapower was impossible. The
prophet of this doctrine was the United States Navy's Captain Alfred
Thayer Mahan, whose epoch-making book, *The Influence of Seapower
upon History* (1890), had transformed him into what a Canadian
scholar has called "the principal philosopher of seapower, a naval
Mohammed."[5] Mahan's work was a bestseller throughout Europe, and
the kaiser saw to it that copies were placed aboard every ship in the
Imperial Fleet.[6]

Through a number of transformations in strategic thinking, which
early naval leaders either could not or did not foresee, the U-Boat Arm
became the successor to the battleship fleet. Even today a few veterans
of the Second World War occasionally betray hints of nostalgia for the
era of Kaiser Wilhelm II and speak with wistful deference and self-
irony of their brotherhood as "kaisertreu" – faithful to the kaiser. Thus,
when submarines entered service in the early 1900s, they were grafted
onto a navy already imbued with the mystique of imperial power.

What did it mean to be an imperial navy? The kaiser's personal
influence was, of course, of paramount importance. He saw himself
as the embodiment of the naval service. He nurtured the paternalistic
relation with his fleet and involved himself in many aspects of his navy,
from policy to the everyday routines which, in other navies, were
normally dealt with at lower levels of command. His delight in wearing
uniforms, particularly that of admiral, is legendary. In the early days
this habit was innovative and caused some stir.[7] His regular case-reviews
of the Honour Courts – summary trials that examined officers charged
with offences against the Code of Service Discipline – reveal just how
closely he monitored the comportment of even his most junior officers. He became personally involved in such cases as that of a Reserve
sublieutenant of an auxiliary minesweeper charged with having

"caused a stir while in uniform by speaking to a female of doubtful morals"; a company commander of a naval gunnery unit who was running a pig farm on the side; and junior officers who had become engaged to girls below their social class. The kaiser's judgment on such cases of immorality and offence to the officer class invariably meant dismissal from the navy.[8] The message was clear: naval service meant prestigious service.

Both at home and abroad, members of the force were acquiring an increased sense of their role in the projection of imperial power. Throughout the 1870s and 1880s, Germany undertook surveys and explorations in distant waters. The aspiring empire deployed the East Asia Cruiser Squadron, jostled for colonial possessions, and exercised gunboat diplomacy. Once exotic territory like South and Central America, the Caribbean, the South Seas, China, and the Philippines became familiar to German seamen.[9] By the end of the 1890s the German navy had become a vehicle of German culture abroad. Endorsing earlier plans for a fleet and support base in China, for example, Tirpitz had recommended Kiautschau as a natural location. On 27 January 1898 a cabinet order placed the military occupation forces and the whole administration of the Kiautschau-area under the direct control of the Reichskanzler through the state secretary of the Imperial Naval Office. As a retired admiral much later recalled with pride, the navy was thereby made responsible not only for security and development of naval forces in the Far East, but also for trade.[10] And as was always the case in imperial expansion, trade imported culture in its wake. If sailors shared this sense of the navy's national purpose, it only remained for the populace to feel it as well.

The ground was evidently well prepared. In November 1895 Georg Wislicenus, a passionately committed naval officer, published his famous illustrated book on German seapower, *Deutschlands Seemacht, sonst und jetzt.*[11] It turned out to be what today's media would call a blockbuster of a book.[12] Its overwhelming success took everyone by surprise: the author, the foreign office, the admiralty, and even the prestigious firm of Brockhaus which had published it. As Admiral Hugo Pohl of the Imperial Naval Office later observed, Wislicenus had written what was in the hearts of many Germans, and bookdealers' profits seemed to indicate that the philosophy of navalism had already permeated all geographical regions and all social levels of Germany. (With the exception of Admiral Tirpitz, naval authorities had seemed unaware of the national mood – the ambitions already at large among the populace.) The first edition sold out within six weeks, and Brockhaus quickly put a second printing onto the market at Christmas 1895. The prized editions quickly turned Wislicenus and his ideas into household words. Yet the naval officer had an abrasive manner. He grated on the nerves of his conservative naval colleagues by declaring that British seapower was a menace, and by vehemently attacking the parochial naval policies of the German Reichstag which failed to address the challenge. He specifically blamed the Imperial Naval Office for having huddled too long in its "armoured ivory tower of pure military thought" and thus being unable to reap any political harvest. Tirpitz agreed. He grasped the opportunity and ran with it.

The Tirpitz era of navalism is noted for its mobilization of the national press in what has been called the great "bandwagon" days of public relations.[13] Immediately after assuming the position of state secretary of the Imperial Naval Office in 1897, Tirpitz had created the Press and Information Branch – Abteilung für Nachrichtenwesen und allgemeine Parlamentsangelegenheiten – which formed the nucleus of the later Naval Intelligence Service. Known as N (for Nachrichten-büro), it coordinated the preparation of parliamentary papers, promoted the Naval Bills, and published popular works on sea power for civilian consumption. Information published by the anonymous N developed into the periodical *Nauticus: Jahrbuch für Deutschlands See-interessen*, which argued the economic and political cause for the non-military reader. Marshalling a broad spectrum of officers, writers, and well-known academics to his banner, Tirpitz launched the modern era of military propaganda. The German Navy League, which had been spreading the gospel of navalism and naval prestige, had more than 600,000 members by 1901 and provided a broadly based and dynamic corps of converts through which Tirpitz could sell his message. Britain's Navy League, by contrast, had only 15,000 members that year.[14]

The books, periodicals, articles, and photo-reports that Tirpitz's staff produced for mass consumption successfully promoted the concept of Germany as a seafaring nation with a vital need for a powerful navy.[15] The annual fleet manœuvres formed the basis for stirring reports; most of them were totally fictionalized versions of what had actually taken place. The navy's own information officers contrived the stories with a modicum of truth in order to feed the curiosity of civilian reporters who could not otherwise be controlled. In this way press censorship influenced, shaped, and in some cases even stage-managed public opinion in order to "increasingly interest the public in the institutions and needs of the Kriegsmarine."[16] The navy, in modern terms, had become a media event.

By 1901 no fewer than eleven Berlin newspapers, and thirty-one in the provinces, subscribed to the ready-made stories churned out by N.[17] These papers were based not only in the port cities of Hamburg, Kiel, Danzig, Cuxhaven, and Wilhelmshaven, but inland as well;

they included Augsburg's *Augsburger Abendzeitung,* Cologne's *Cölnischer Volkszeitung,* Münich's *Allgemeine Zeitung* and *Neueste Nachrichten,* Stuttgart's *Schwäbischer Merkur,* and Kassel's *Casseler Tageblatt.* Pamphlets and articles on the autumn fleet manœuvres provided photos, sketches, and commentaries, and spoke of thousands of onlookers thronging to see the nation's naval grandeur; they promoted the importance of big-ship fleets, Mahanian concepts of naval power, and home-grown concepts of glory and prestige.

The whole promotional campaign had been undertaken on the kaiser's explicit instructions.[18] In an address to the German Society of Naval Architects in November 1901, he had described the modern warship as not merely a triumph of mechanical skill; it was more essentially "a consummate expression of human purpose and of national character."[19] By September 1911 Berlin's *Charlottenburger Tages-Zeitung* could proclaim with other publications that "the German fleet has become the subject closest to the nation's heart."[20]

The images – or clichés – about German power at sea were projected not only at home. A report in Toronto's *Saturday Night,* for example, described a Canadian's impressions of life aboard a German liner in 1912 and transferred to commercial shipping all the cultural baggage from warship journalism; in doing so it reiterated the so-called Prussian virtues of military precision, military system, and iron discipline. Reprinted in a range of German papers such as *Die Post* and *Neue Preußische Kreuz-Zeitung,* the article was collected by German Naval Intelligence and placed before the kaiser. Marginal notes in the kaiser's own hand reveal his pleasure at the image his citizens were projecting.[21] He must have been particularly heartened to read the Canadian journalist's words: "If one wants to see military precision at its highest level one must travel on a steamer of a German line. One cannot shake off the impression that the kaiser himself is on board, urging everyone on to perfection."[22]

Where was the submarine in all this discussion? In 1859 a publishing house in southern Germany published the first major book on submarines: Ludwig Hauff's *Die unterseeische Schiffahrt* [Underwater seafaring]. This new invention, the subtitle announced, had been "invented and put into practice by Wilhelm Bauer."[23] Excited at the prospect of new scientific horizons, Hauff introduced his superbly documented and popularly written text as follows: "Eight years ago, on 1 February 1851, an event took place in Kiel harbour which filled the world with astonishment and admiration. It was the first – unfortunately unsuccessful – experiment of Wilhelm Bauer, a subaltern in the artillery, with the submersible fire-ship (Brandtauchschiff) he invented. So important is this invention that it will not only compare with electrical telegraphy, but might even surpass it."

Hauff had been following Bauer's work closely and had gotten to know him well. Often working alone, Bauer had borne the scorn of the implacable clique of professional "experts" and government officials. Conservative to the core, they were convinced of the impossibility of his scheme and therefore spurned his ideas. Not the least of Bauer's difficulties, according to Hauff, was "the scholarly conceit and arrogance that looked down scornfully or with mild disdain upon the invention of a 'nameless' man who was 'merely a corporal.'" This attitude of myopic superiority foreshadowed the painfully slow acceptance of submarines by military and naval thinkers. For as Hauff had documented for the period up to 1859, "German governments and German citizens either could not or would not do anything for the invention" – despite the favourable judgments of scientific and technical commissions. Given the experimental nature of the newfangled underwater weapon, and given the fact that Germany had no navy at the time, this reticence is perhaps not surprising. The best the king of Bavaria could do was to pay Bauer's travel costs to help him market his invention abroad.

Bauer took his plans to England – followed in spirit, if not in person, by the admiring Hauff. His exploits rarely excited comment in either the British or the German press. The idea of undersea voyages would not be popularized until Jules Verne's science-fiction hit, *Twenty Thousand Leagues under the Sea* (1870). The possibility of underwater navigation struck most observers in these early days as an entirely crackpot idea. The *Kentish and Surrey Mercury*, however, was a strikingly prescient exception. In an unusually lengthy, three-column article published on 24 March 1855, the British reporter concluded: "We are old enough to have heard [of] gas lighting, railroads, electric telegraphs and transatlantic steamer routes being scornfully derided and declared impossible. But we have also had the experience of seeing them carried out. Why should not Wilhelm Bauer be right too?"[24]

Hauff saw to it that German readers noted such British interest. In fact, that was a major purpose of his book on underwater seafaring. He urged his countrymen not to reject the inventions of "native sons" who would carry Germany into the industrial revolution. Should they fail to do so, Hauff implied, Germany would be fast outpaced by a much more progressive Britain. Hauff prophesied a promising future for Bauer's "immeasurably important invention"; he knew it would "be further developed and be perfected, and become one of the most important inventions ever." Public recognition was slow in coming. By the time the popular press had become interested, combat submarines were beginning to emerge in a number of navies.

In 1903 Germany's Catholic illustrated magazine *Stadt Gottes: Illustrirte Zeitschrift für das katholische Volk* devoted a section to the new naval craft. At first glance this seems an unlikely vehicle for disseminating naval ideas. But conservative sectors of the populace, to many of whom the *Stadt Gottes* [City of God] appealed, had long since been persuaded that naval expansion was the surest means for securing influence in both national and world affairs. Indeed, the Catholic Centre party had specifically allied itself with Tirpitz's aggressive naval bills. In doing so, its leader "looked beyond the religious and regional character of his party and fancied that the naval issue could make it the premier national party in Germany."[25] That achieved, the party could also extend the influence of the Catholic Church. This is but one of many examples in which political parties, special-interest groups, and both the Protestant and Catholic churches saw navalism as the yellow-brick road to political success.

In 1903 *Stadt Gottes* printed drawings of Wilhelm Bauer's *Brandtaucher* and described its origins and development. There was also a photograph of the launching of the American submarine *Shack*, and another captioned "the latest English submarine." The opening lines established both the tone and direction of the argument:

Submarines are small warships capable of travelling beneath the surface of the sea in order to approach an enemy ship unnoticed and hurl their mine-ordnance (torpedoes) against it. When we published an article several years ago about the historical development and contemporary status of underwater vessels, it was mostly the French and North Americans who were seriously concerning themselves with the construction of submarines for war purposes.[26]

Germany and England had now joined the competition. The *Stadt Gottes* pointed this out, but failed to explain that this was the era of the battleship armaments race. Both countries were now preoccupied in building these massive vessels. This was the naval weapon that, according to the best-informed wisdom of the day, provided the only means of winning the classical 'decisive sea battle.' With one crushing blow, it was thought, a fleet of battleships would decide the fate of nations. No country wanting its place in the sun could afford to be without them. For this reason, no country regarded the submarine as an offensive weapon; it was at best a secondary means of inshore maritime defence. Battleships, by contrast, cast an aura of power and grandeur in which submarines – and submariners – could not yet bask.

This attitude was not solely due to the internationally accepted Mahanian "capital ship" theory of naval strategy; it reflected the technical infancy of the U-boat.

Two years later, in February 1905, the German Navy League's official publication *Die Flotte* printed one of the first articles on the introduction of the U-boat to the fleet.[27] Entitled "News from Our Battle Fleet," it included photographs of a U-boat under construction and explained its basic features. Even so, the piece was notably lacking in enthusiasm: "Even today, the utility is quite limited. Darkness and sea state make it almost completely blind, and its short range doesn't permit it to go far from its support base. The modern submarine can therefore only be regarded as an imperfect weapon which only has prospects of success under specific conditions and for limited purposes like harassment of a blockading fleet."

By this time the Spanish submarine designer Raimondo Lorenzo d'Équevilley had been developing his designs in Germany. Like his German counterpart Wilhelm Bauer, he had been led by a series of rejections to move throughout Europe in search of a sponsor. He found an enterprising mentor in Friedrich Krupp. d'Équevilley is recognized as "the midwife of the German submarine" and remained on Germany's design team throughout the Great War. But in the early years he had to work hard to sell an idea that had clearly come of age. In 1905 he published *Untersee- und Tauchboote* [Submersible and Diving Boats] to inform the general reader – and doubtless his best potential customers – of the history and current status of these experimental naval craft. He regarded them as revolutionary; so revolutionary, in fact, that they might one day make surface fleets redundant and useless. Submarines might even become instruments of peace. "As exaggerated as it may sound," he confidently wrote, "who knows whether the appearance of undersea boats may put an end to naval battles" altogether. It was neither Germany nor Bauer who reaped the Spaniard's accolades for submarine experiments. To his mind "the honour for discovering this new branch of seafaring which will be of decisive significance for the history of the world, falls primarily upon France."[28] The judgment is fair, for France was a leader in innovative ship design at the time. Far more important, in retrospect, was the fact that d'Équevilley's views were being voiced in Germany – and in German – at a time when German industrial and naval thinkers were ready to respond.

Three years later, Admiral Tirpitz's journal for naval propaganda, *Nauticus* (1908), published a major survey of the concepts and technology of the submarine. Since its founding in 1899 the annual *Nauticus* had had a clearly defined mission. Its authors were bent upon marshalling broad popular support for navalism in the service of Germany's maritime interests. Having achieved such a large measure of success, the editors of the issue for 1908 could, with disarming frankness, put all their cards on the table. As their preface explained:

The first issues of *Nauticus* appeared at the time of the first naval bills, and were designed as aggressive promotional material [Agitationsmittel] in support of the great task of the time – namely convincing the German people of the truth that a defence capability at sea is a condition of life for any state that wants to thrive and not fritter its paltry existence away. Since its appearance in 1899 it has, in step with the German people's increasing understanding of the significance of maritime interests, become more a factual educational publication [Aufklärungsmittel] on all areas touching upon the principles of our development of sea power.[29]

The editors' claim to having shifted accent from aggressive promotion [Agitationsmittel] to popular education [Aufklärungsmittel] should be viewed cautiously. Navalism remained a major focus of *Nauticus*. In time, Germany would be forced to realize that it could compete neither financially nor strategically with Britain's fleet. This ultimately meant falling back upon the naval weapon of the secondary power: the submarine. It is an irony of history that the submarine would become the "capital ship" of the future.

Working independently and largely in secret, the European nations were gradually reaching some agreement on the nature and role of submarines. The article on "The Current Status of Submarines" which *Nauticus* published in 1908 claimed that "the period of groping and experimenting" was now definitely over. The authors further declared: "A remarkable feature of recent times is that the nimbus of secrecy which had earlier surrounded the submarine politics of the leading nations like a thick veil has to a considerable degree now been lifted." Lack of press coverage in the past on submarine navigation had not been due to any official or public disinterest in the fascinating topic. The reason for this new openness, *Nauticus* argued, was the involvement of private industry in submarine development. From this point onward, German u-boats would have a public image.

Nauticus recognized the enormous distance that still had to be covered in both technology and tactics before the submarine's potential could be fully realized. Exploiting this potential was merely a matter of perfecting its technology; in the light of industrial advances, the day of the u-boat was merely a matter of time. One thing was already abundantly clear: "The undersea boat has gained access to all the navies of the world – not as an object of experimentation, but as a fully fledged weapon of war." Germany herself was already well on the way: she had built submarines for Russia under contract. On 4 August 1906 the first combat submarine for the German fleet was launched at Friedrich Krupp's Germania Werft shipyards. On 14 December 1906 the U-boat was commissioned as *Seiner Majestät Unterseeboot 1* (SM U-1).

As is so often the case, exploration of the new weapon's potential lagged behind technical developments. The commanding officer of *Seiner Majestät Uboot U-11*, Kapitänleutnant Walter Forstmann, was the first submariner to fully grasp its offensive operational possibilities. His double-hulled high-seas craft had been commissioned on 21 September 1910; by the end of 1912 it had completed the first successful long-range trials under his command. He would become an ace during the First World War. In an unpublished paper, "The Use of Our High Seas Submarines 1911–1912," Forstmann developed his ideas in the context of a possible war against England: submarines would take the offensive.[30] The paper remained an internal document.

Ironically, it fell to a piece of British science-fiction to publicize just what German submarines could do. A mere eighteen months before the outbreak of war, Sir Arthur Conan Doyle published in *The Strand Magazine* his prescient short story "Danger! A Story of England's Peril." His fantasy tale told of the British blockade of a foreign land that was quite transparently Germany; it told of the Royal Navy's swift capture of the enemy's surface fleet and the landing of British troops on his coast. According to conventional strategic theory, that should have spelled the end of the war. But the outcome of Doyle's political tale did not follow naval convention: Britain was ultimately defeated by the action of eight small enemy submarines. They had starved her out by conducting unrestricted warfare against merchant shipping, thereby cutting off her lines of supply. Germany's underwater sea-power – "the navy of one of the smallest Powers in Europe," according to the fictional narrator – had flouted the accepted maxims of naval war. The submarines had done so by isolating the vital centre of the British Empire through direct attacks that entirely evaded the might of the British surface fleet. Ironically, Doyle's sci-fi prophecy almost came true. As he wrote when introducing a republication of his story in August 1918 – three months before hostilities ended – "The great silent battle which has been fought beneath the waves has ended in the repulse of an armada far more dangerous than that of Spain" in 1588.[31] In an example of history imitating fiction, the attacks by Germany's undersea "armada" had begun in 1914 with but ten U-boats – only two more than Doyle's story had envisioned.[32]

Much of the U-boat lore in Doyle's entertaining yarn anticipated subsequent German iconography. Like many future German U-boat memoirists, Doyle's fictional captain-narrator took his readers on dangerous combat missions that he executed with daring and dash. Action was of the essence. Prefiguring many a real combatant who followed, he regarded the political machinations of the statesmen whose policies he served as irrelevant to his trade: "A naval officer has nothing to do with politics," the skipper explained. He therefore exonerated himself from all responsibility except for the purely technical matter of conducting warfare at sea. After all, "I only came upon the scene after the ultimatum [to go to war] had been actually received." And like the real U-boat skippers whose actions he foreshadowed, Doyle's captain also knew that he must sometimes push against the legal and moral boundaries of naval warfare in order to succeed. In the fictional narrator's words: "It is desperate business to gain the upper hand, and one must use one's brain in order to find the weak spot of one's enemy. It is not fair to blame me if I have found yours. It was my duty."[33]

That, too, would be a major theme in U-boat literature. For like the Royal Navy and its colonial offspring, successive German navies had fully accepted Admiral Horatio Nelson's dictum: "Duty is the great business of a sea officer; all private considerations must give way to it however painful it is." Nelson's message would be evoked by generations of German sailors who, in the aftermath of two world wars, sought to explain and justify the roles they had played. They saw themselves only as soldiers who had done their duty. For many of them, years of often painful analysis would pass before they fully grasped all that the concept of duty implied. In the process of self-examination, wartime certitudes about duty, loyalty, patriotism, and service would frequently emerge as the disquieting ambiguities of a later age.

1 U-boats in the Imperial German Navy, 1914–18

Kapitänleutnant Freiherr von Forstner published his first memoir of the war in 1916 after the submarine had already proved itself an impressive weapon. The German U-boat in particular had demonstrated its ability to destroy warships and merchant vessels alike, and to trigger a disconcerting psychological malaise in the enemy camp. To its opponents, the U-boat seemed to bear out the oft-quoted conviction of a British observer of 1902 that the submarine was "underhanded, unfair and damned un-English." German writers, of course, saw the matter differently. In words reminiscent of U-boat skipper Walter Forstmann's internal paper of 1912, one German wartime observer of the U-boats' earliest major successes confirmed the crafts' major strength. They were no longer backup weapons for second-rate maritime nations, but "invisible weapons of attack."[1] This was ideal material for the martial epic.

Freiherr von Forstner's memoir, *Als U-Boots-Kommandant gegen England* (1916), was a major work in the Ullstein War Book series. For the price of one mark, as the title page announced, the reader could share in the experiences of "a submarine commander against England." It was obviously written to win popular support and new recruits in a continentally minded country with limited access to the sea. "Neither the German people nor the enemy," von Forstner wrote, had "expected the U-boat to count for so much."[2] He was gratified that laity and professionals alike had now recognized the primacy of U-boat warfare. In simple and often naively graphic terms he initiated the reader into the mysteries of undersea adventures in combat against an implacable foe. He projected the image of the dashing, competent German sailor, justly defending his homeland against the ravages of the arch-enemy England. He sought recruits: "It would especially delight me to have awakened in many a youthful reader the joy and love for the fine and interesting service in the Imperial Navy, particularly so if our beloved U-Boat Arm were brought closer in human terms to many readers. We might then hope that the nervousness or disinclination towards water still current in many circles ... would increasingly disappear from our German Fatherland, and that no longer would anxious mothers be concerned about directing their sons to undertake service in the navy."[3]

Von Forstner's next work, *U-Bootsleben* [U-boat Life, 1916], continued the public-relations campaign by providing a coloured picture-book extolling "the romantic life on board our diving-boats." For just 80 Pfennig the reader could own fine reproductions of naval artist Bössenroth's "splendid pictures." In fact, from the impressionistic painting entitled *Abenddämmerung am U-Boots-Hafen in Kiel* [Twilight in Submarine Harbour at Kiel] to the more realistic *U-53 in 18 Seemeilen Fahrt* [U-53 at 18 Knots] and *Vereistes Boot* [Ice-covered Submarine], the reproductions are really very fine indeed.

What had occasioned this rise in the u-boat's fame and fortune? The commencement of hostilities in August 1914 had brought in its wake a radical shift in German naval strategy. No longer holding large surface units in readiness as a deterrent fleet-in-being, the German navy began deploying its warships to probe British defences and to entice the Royal Navy into a confrontation. Although the German army was arguably the most powerful in the world, the navy had been comparatively weak and unready. Shocked by shortcomings in tactical leadership that had led to the loss of three light cruisers, a destroyer, and 700 men in a confrontation with British surface forces off Heligoland on 28 August 1914, the kaiser had taken control of fleet units into his own hands.[4] Both the kaiser and Admiral Scheer recognized that the only means at Germany's disposal for forcing Britain to sue for peace lay in commerce warfare. This meant avoiding confrontation with warships and striking against merchant shipping. Gripped by Britain's stranglehold on German trade, the German navy resorted to the weapons that conventional thinking had regarded as secondary – submarines and mines. It ultimately developed the submarine cruiser, a new engine of war without legal precedent in international law. Germany's new "infallible weapon" soon produced its own mythology. "Silent and secretly, as befits the nature of our weapon," a submariner wrote, "we entered the Great War. Ours was no grand exodus like that of the army who went to war fêted by an enthusiastic populace."[5]

Undaunted and as yet unsung, German submariners faced the enemy alone.

This mythology was all the more readily accepted because most Germans did not regard themselves as waging a war of aggression. From the popular perspective in Germany, the war had all been Britain's doing. A raft of German writings informed the German public that the jealousy and aggression of England, the Perfidious Albion of the propaganda war, had caused this fateful shift. With characteristic simplicity, one submariner wrote in his popular history about the "leviathan" submarine cruiser *U-Deutschland*. "In the peace of a German harvest summer of 1914 the war-trumpets sounded shrill and startled our diligent people from ploughshare and workman's bench. Envious neighbours had been looking askance at the growth of German power potential."[6]

Publishers throughout the land turned to the patriotic and apparently lucrative task of enlightening the German public about naval matters. Their media were the Groschenhefte, the pulp penny-books sold at newspaper kiosks, book stalls, and tobacconists. One of the leading series was produced by the famous Berlin publishing house founded by the Jewish patriot Leopold Ullstein (1826–1899); its pocket-sized booklets were written to stir up the readers' patriotism and to awaken their heroic thoughts and emotions. Ullstein's War Book series was a staple throughout the 1914–18 conflict and continued unabated during the interwar years and into the Second World War. The series became a tradition among nationalist and conservative sectors of German society. Indeed, Ullstein products had become such a mainstay of mass-market publishing that the Nazis expropriated the firm in 1934 (while "resettling" the Jewish owners).[7] The takeover was not primarily because the firm was Jewish, but rather because large sectors of the populace not only delighted in the action-packed plots of its books, but trusted in them as authoritative and right-thinking. It was, in short, a truly "national" German firm. Marketed under the guise of keeping German readers – including soldiers in the trenches – informed of what the nation's warriors were doing, they remained unalloyed propaganda.[8] Germany's early submarine successes gave Ullstein and other publishers the very heroes they needed to rally public support for the war. The government's own propagandists were of course involved as well. Submarines were a new and exciting weapon, and their skippers radiated adventure and romance.

But for the men actually carrying out underwater warfare, the business was often nasty, swift, and harsh. In a brief action on 15 September 1915 that was never picked up in Germany's popular press, for example, Germany lost U-boat U-6 in one of the first recorded torpedoings by a British submarine.[9] U-6 was a cramped, damp 500–ton vessel, driven on the surface by four 225 HP two-stroke gasoline engines. Her volatile fuel was already being superseded in the fleet by diesel. U-6 had set out on patrol from the island base of Helgoland six days earlier and had sunk but three small vessels for a meagre "bag" of 800 tons. Confident that they were alone and undetected on the late afternoon of the 15th, her skipper set course westward to the Scottish coast in order to intercept British trade. Scarcely had captain and navigator left the bridge to decend into the tower when the officer-of-the-watch glimpsed a periscope a bare 150 meters to port. A churning and swirling of water then caught his eye as two torpedoes streaked towards him in rapid succession. Ordering his helm hard over, he watched aghast as one of the lethal "eels" raced by his bow, while the second struck him savagely just forward of the tower. It was all over in seconds. Only the five crewmen on the upper deck survived the blast; they were fished from the sea by the Royal Navy's submarine E-26. The sea had closed over a Flander's Field charnel-house of shattered bodies and twisted machines, and suggested in its primeval surge that war at sea was surgically clean. The ocean swell betrayed no trace of battle.

Yet the opening gambits of the war in 1914 did provide Germany with some spectacular U-boat successes. Significantly, and quite unexpectedly, these were not against unarmed merchantmen, but against powerful surface warships that conventional wisdom claimed were immune from underwater attack. On 5 September 1914 Kapitänleutnant Otto Hersing's U-21 made history by launching the first submerged torpedo attack of the war, sinking the British light cruiser HMS *Pathfinder* near Scotland's Firth of Forth; on 22 September 1914 Kapitänleutnant Otto Weddigen's U-9 created the first piece of enduring combat iconography by destroying three of the Royal Navy's 12,200–ton Bacchanti-class cruisers in a single hour: HMS *Cressy*, *Aboukir*, and *Hogue*. In doing so, Weddigen vindicated the submarine as an offensive weapon and provided his country with a naval hero when it sorely needed one. Every aspect of the attack was a new venture and would be described in surprisingly accurate detail in postwar literature.

Surfacing that morning near the Maas Lightvessel after having ridden out the previous day's storm submerged, Weddigen and his crew found calmer weather and clearer visibility. Captain, engineer, and the watch-officer Johannes Spieß (who also would become a famous skipper) were taking in the morning air after a fetid night and were bracing themselves against the heavy swell. It was 0545, just before sunrise. As the U-boat began charging her batteries with her notoriously smoky gasoline engines, Spieß cursed the billowing exhaust that could betray her presence. Weddigen reduced speed in order to cut down the smoke and went below, leaving Spieß to carry out a lazy zigzag course along the Dutch coast, some twenty miles from the town of Scheveningen. The crew were anxious to catch their first glimpse of the enemy; anxious, too, to avenge the loss of their "chummy ship" U-15, which had been rammed and sunk by the cruiser HMS *Birmingham* in August. Thus when the first target hove into sight over the horizon, Spieß all-too-readily identified it as one of the "Birmingham-class." That meant a light cruiser. U-9's crew went swiftly to battle-stations. A series of automatic commands triggered well-drilled responses: battening hatches, flooding tanks, switching from petroleum engines to batteries, arming torpedoes. And in all this controlled swirl of activity, the last navigational fix and target bearing were taken to begin setting up the first outlines of the tactical picture. Poised at periscope depth despite the swell that could thrust her exposed hull to the surface, U-9 waited for the target to approach. It soon became clear that not one cruiser, but three were heading their way, steaming in line ahead. No U-boat had ever faced such a threat before, and only one had ever fired a torpedo in hopes of killing such Goliaths. So new was both the situation and the technology that no one really knew for certain what would happen when the fight began. Would U-9 survive against such massive surface power? And if she could get in close enough for a kill, would the explosion of her torpedoes against the cruisers' hulls destroy her as well? These questions were by no means idle. The officers all knew the fate of U-15 and they knew that U-21 had been severely shaken by the explosion when torpedoing HMS *Pathfinder* from a range of 1200 meters. It was generally accepted that at a virtually lethal range of 500 meters they could expect heavy bow damage and the possible destruction of her diving planes. In a series of short, snappy periscope sights, Weddigen coolly calculated his chances and decided to strike the cruiser steaming in the middle of the column. Weddigen cautioned the crew to take the boat down to fifteen meters and stay there once he had fired, for the range was "rather tight." It was, in fact, just under 500 meters.

As Spieß later recalled, these were nerve-tingling moments. At 0720 Weddigen fired the first shot. Thirty-one seconds later a dull blow announced the detonation and triggered jubilation in the U-boat. Unable to see, they could only guess what was happening by listening to the abrasive underwater sounds of cracking and wrenching soon emanating from her victim's death-agony. After a cautious wait, Weddigen brought U-9 to periscope depth to watch *Aboukir* sink. Meanwhile all available crew of U-9 were kept running between bow and stern in order to maintain diving trim in the swell. The bow had immediately become buoyant once the torpedo had fired and would only regain its displacement as the bow tube was reloaded. A quick look from close range revealed a serious miscalculation: the targets were not light cruisers at all, but huge Bacchantis. By this time U-9 was committed. At 0755, thirty-five minutes after his first shot, Weddigen made two direct hits on *Hogue* from 300 meters. But despite all efforts to tighten her turning-circle in the escape manœuvre by racing full speed ahead on one screw and full speed astern on the other, U-9 scraped her periscope along *Hogue*'s hull. There was just time to reload when HMS *Cressy* loomed into range. At 0820, precisely one hour after the first shot, Weddigen fired his two stern torpedoes and struck from a range of 1000 meters. *Cressy* died slowly, and Weddigen fired his last torpedo into her as a coup de grâce. Spieß's final periscope glimpse of the scene was especially vivid. Up until now U-9 had been witnessing the destruction of machines and had not yet seen men die: "But now life entered this tragic theater. The giant with his four stacks rolled slowly but inexorably over onto his port side, and like ants we saw black swarms of people scrambling first onto one side and then onto its huge flat keel until they disappeared in the waves. A sad sight for a seaman. Our task was now done, and we had to see to getting ourselves home as quickly as possible … When we blew tanks and surfaced at 0850 there was no enemy to be seen. The sea had closed over the three cruisers."[10]

For many years to come, veterans would hallow 22 September as "Weddigen Day," and heroic tales would capture much of the flavour of wartime reality. U-9's successful triple attack had been unprecedented, and many national presses – including those of Allied powers – recognized the fact. The kaiser cabled congratulations and awarded Weddigen and his crew the Iron Cross; "bundles of congratulatory telegrams," one of the officers later wrote, awaited the submarine on arrival home.[11] The crew allegedly required a special shed to keep all the gifts and letters that a grateful German public showered upon them. Admiral Scheer explained the national euphoria thus: "Weddigen's name was on everyone's lips, and especially for the navy his deed was sheer relief from the feeling of having as yet achieved so little in comparison with the heroic deeds of the army. Such a success was necessary in order to appreciate the value of the submarine for our conduct of war."[12]

Yet once the euphoria had died down, many voices began to minimize the success. The three cruisers, as the British press had correctly pointed out, had been old and should never have been deployed in the exposed area that had been Weddigen's patrol zone. Indeed, as a British submariner would observe in 1930, Weddigen's success had been in large part due to Britain's "early policy of heroic but useless sacrifice."[13] Moreover, the Royal Navy's standing orders had actually required the warships to stop to pick up survivors after the initial hit. This effectively turned the remaining two warships into stationary targets for the likes of Weddigen. But on 15 October 1914 Weddigen's U-9 again vindicated the U-boat when it torpedoed and sank the modern 7800–ton cruiser HMS *Hawke* northeast of Aberdeen. The U-boat's mission had covered over 1700 nautical miles and had expended virtually all her fuel. It now seemed abundantly clear that submarine technology was allowing German sailors to operate deep within British waters and to destroy heavily armed ships. Weddigen this time won the coveted Prussian award Pour le mérite.

U-Weddigen had become the stuff of legends. They persisted long after his death in action in 1915, "an event which was felt most painfully by the whole nation," as his former watch-officer recalled in 1930.[14] Myths conveniently ignored the fact that when attacking a British ship of the line on 18 March 1915 in his new boat, U-29, he had been ignominiously destroyed by an ancient maritime weapon – the ram. Ironically, the fatal blow had been struck by the bow of the obsolescent battleship HMS *Dreadnought.* Weddigen's exploits had nevertheless encouraged public and naval leadership alike. Widely disseminated throughout the country, a volatile mix of fact and fiction about submarine adventures encouraged boldness in both naval and civil circles.

Unknown to the populace, a revolution in naval strategy was underway. Whereas it had always been legal in international law for warships of one belligerant to attack warships of another without warning, this right of sudden attack had never been accorded when the victim was an unarmed merchant ship or neutral. In that case, international law required a warship to comply with the time-honoured Prize Rules of "detention and search" that secured the safety of passengers and crew. The law had been formulated in the pre-submarine days with surface warships in mind. But by insisting now that U-boats also detain and search merchant vessels on the high seas for enemy contraband, and destroy the vessel only when everyone was safely put off in boats, the rules effectively cancelled out the U-boat's unique advantage of covert action and surprise. Many Germans were convinced that the only way to defeat Britain was to attack her supply lines without warning. As Admiral Carl Hollweg explained, "the energetic execution of submarine warfare against commerce" was now to be the cutting edge of German naval power. The vaunted surface fleet was slipping into a supportive role and would spend its remaining days as a strategic checkmate, a fleet-in-being.[15] New submarine technology spawned new tactics that cut through the British blockade with a vengeance and allowed submarine deployments to widen their range deep into the Atlantic.

Up until now Germany had held its submarines stictly to the Prize Rules for fear of provoking the neutral United States into joining the battle on Britain's side. This was practically a self-defeating stance, for the United States was Britain's leading supplier of food and *matériel*. Some German naval leaders had become frustrated at having their hands tied by "purely political" considerations when they knew that by unleashing the u-boats they could bring Britain to her knees; newspaper accounts seemed to indicate that the German public also wanted to turn its new and powerful weapon against Britain's trade routes without restraints. Plans were in hand to open unrestricted submarine warfare on 1 February 1915. Indeed, the u-boat's apparent invincibility may well have helped trigger the so-called Tirpitz questions.

In a surprise move in December 1914, Admiral Tirpitz gave an unprecedented interview to the Berlin representative of United Press during which he revealed his plans for what amounted to "total" submarine warfare against Britain. As observers of the day later recalled, Tirpitz created a "world sensation" so audacious that many suspected a "Tirpitz bluff."[16]

Tirpitz had startled many of his own countrymen, including the German foreign office and Reichskanzler von Bethmann Hollweg himself, by calling official policy into question during the interview with the foreign press. "What will America say," he demanded, "if we open u-boat warfare against all ships sailing to England and starve it out?" Entirely convinced that the United States would remain neutral rather than face the devasting power of Germany's submarine forces, he phrased his question more as a taunt. Bethmann Hollweg was appalled. In his view, Tirpitz's failure to have cleared his statement with either the government or the foreign office had forced Germany into the fateful first step towards a style of submarine warfare for which it was by no means ready. German naval intelligence advised the state secretary in a secret memorandum that the press and the public had greeted the interview with jubilation.[17] As the Reichskanzler recalled: "Publicly the enemy were warned to brace themselves for a u-boat blockade, and publicly the German people's attention was drawn to their possession of an infallible weapon. From this point on, u-boat warfare could not be wrested from the nation's heart."[18]

When inaugurating their first major submarine campaign, the German navy warned all shipping of the danger it courted when transitting selected zones: "All the waters surrounding Great Britain and Ireland ... are hereby declared a war zone. From the 18th

February onwards, every enemy merchant ship found within this war zone will be destroyed without its being always possible to avoid danger to the crews and passengers."[19] An early, shocking result was the torpedoing of the unarmed passenger liner *Lusitania* on 7 May 1915 by U-20, with the loss of 1198 lives. The subsequent sinking of the passenger ships *Falaba, Cushing,* and *Gulflight* also aroused international political protest;[20] in the words of the American ambassador to Berlin, these unprovoked and sudden attacks had caused the US government "growing concern, distress and amazement."[21] In fact, the carnage inflicted on merchant shipping by U-boats was already threatening to sever Britain's lifelines. Ultimately, the US reaction to the *Lusitania* affair and other sinkings forced the German government to reimpose restrictions and, in effect, to revert to Prize Rules war. Germany would not attempt unrestricted submarine warfare again until 1917.

Germany's High Seas Fleet played no aggressive role in this early campaign and its officers had grown frustrated and restless. The kaiser himself had to step in to keep the inactive, grumbling crews of his fleet in check. In the words of his orders of 7 September 1915, he did so "with a heavy heart." The officer corps, he asserted, would have been "extremely proud of the achievements of our U-boats" despite the political restraints that have prevented them from waging full-scale war. (He might more candidly have added that it was the supremacy of the Royal Navy's Grand Fleet that had bottled the Germans up – with the exception of the wide-ranging U-boats.) He therefore directed his officers not to get restless, but "to subordinate themselves to the will of their Supreme Warlord." In particular, they must cease undermining his supreme command with "disparaging criticism which, through unfortunately all too perceivable indiscretions, is working poisonously throughout the navy."[22] The proclamation is at once a revealing and a pathetic document, one that underscores a growing rift between two classes of sailor: those on capital ships who could only dream of real action, and those in submarines who actually fought the war. The public was already more enamoured of the latter, and popular literature was doing its part to nourish that attraction.

Otto von Gottberg's *Kreuzerfahrten und U-Bootstaten* [Cruiser Missions and U-boat Deeds] that appeared in Berlin in 1915 was one of the first popular books to extol the submarine. True to its type, this inexpensive piece of escapist, adventure literature addressed the undiscriminating reader. Gottberg began by invoking the old Tirpitz doctrine of navalism: "With full awareness the seamen rode their planks unto death, even unto undying fame itself. Surely never since men have gone down to the sea in ships has a seafaring people affirmed more joyously and firmly with their deeds [the old doctrine] navigare necesse est."[23] He then treated his reader to rousing accounts of u-boats attacking according to Prize Rules of visit and search, u-boats adapting the techniques of small surface raiders in blockading trade, seamen defending the Fatherland to the death, and – of particular importance for international politics – u-boats displaying chivalry and human concern.

Yet despite all the evidence of German chivalry and idealism, Gottberg complained, the Allies persisted in giving the Germans bad press. (This was certainly true, and no invention of Gottberg's imagination.) Allied propaganda had labelled the German submariner (and the kaiser himself) "barbarian," "pirate," and "pig." Gottberg marshalled evidence in the u-boat's defence. He argued that German sailors had always treated their enemies on the high seas with gallantry and kindness. British high-handedness and brutality, he enjoined, now forced Germans to become aggressive. Only when assailed by British propagandists, Gottberg railed, and only when Britain had contravened decency and international law by deploying u-boat decoys disguised as innocent coasters was the German submariner forced to respond in kind. "Our Volk can therefore only counsel the skippers of our diving boats [sic] to exercise less mercy and consideration than before. An English proverb – and therefore understandable to our opponent – says that 'if you have the name, you may play the game.' Whoever shows us brutish severity, where we offer kindness and leniency, must expect us to get even tougher."[24] This open challenge must have been most compelling now that the Weddigen myth was rapidly assuming firmer shape.

The first of many accounts of the "Life and Deeds of our Naval Hero" Weddigen appeared in May 1915, within two months of his loss in action. The author was his younger brother. Various publishers had been urging him to write for considerable time, but the death of the hero had removed the author's earlier reservations about publishing an account of an ascendant star before it had reached its zenith. Weddigen's life now acquired a glowing aura. No longer could one claim that his deeds had been inspired merely by "a sense of duty which anyone else in his position would have had." Rather, the "German people has now lost one of its favourite heroes – their Siegfried of the Depths – who embodies our whole heroic navy, in its fidelity, in its glorious daring." In point of fact, however, Weddigen did not embody the "whole heroic navy" at all. His success belonged solely to the u-boat men, for the surface navy had done little to attract such panegyrics. Perhaps unwittingly, therefore, the author was suggesting that the U-Boat Arm would soon personify the German navy as a whole.

Weddigen's popular image had inspired reams of poems and paeans in the popular press. His brother's booklet contains some twenty-five pages of them in both High and Low German: these range from "The Lay of Otto Weddigen and His Blue Jackets" [Das Leed van Otto Weddigen un siene blauen Jungs] in the *Oldenburger Sonntagblatt* of the North Country lowlands to "Otto Weddigen" in the more cosmopolitan *Leipziger Illustrirte Zeitung* and "The Ballad of U-29" in Berlin's satirical weekly *Kladderadatsch*. In a variety of tones and limping gaits – from prayerful sentimentality to jingoistic hyperbole – the verses praised great deeds and lamented the loss of Germany's "viking with laurels." One thing now seemed clear. The maritime prestige Tirpitz had been seeking since the prewar race with Britain to build a battleship surface fleet had now been won by the "might, majesty, dominion and power" of the German submarine. Or so the poetasters would have it.

By the autumn of 1915 Vizeadmiral Hermann Kirchhoff, also a professor of naval history, had dashed off a popular book about Weddigen and his new underwater weapon, allegedly based on Weddigen's personal diaries and notebooks.[25] As his preface explains, "Weddigen had been the first to make the arrogant Brits feel the dreadfulness of the German spirit of attack." Indeed, as Kirchhoff put it, "for the German people Weddigen embodies that seamanlike boldness, so axiomatic in U-boat skippers." He would therefore continue to "spur on other Germans to further and even bolder deeds." In a statement as true then as it is today, Kirchhoff proclaimed: "The name Otto Weddigen is inseparable from the U-Boat Arm." (Until very recently, U-boats of the Federal German Navy secured alongside the "Weddigen pier" in Kiel.)

Other writers were active that year, both in Germany and in Austria. For example, a Leipzig firm published Friedrich Otto's *Das Unterseeboot im Kampfe* [The U-Boat in Combat], while in Vienna the Austrian Navy League produced *Das U-Boot*.[26] The latter, written by two officers in Austria's "Imperial and Royal Navy," promoted the "guerrilla war of the diving boats"; like their German counterparts, they extolled "deeds of radiant ethics and greatness, of which our grandchildren in distant days will speak and sing." Maritime supremacy was being won by "the undersea vessel conceived by the technology of Germany and Austria-Hungary, and driven by death-defying blue-jackets with superior dash and skill." Perhaps not surprisingly, such hyperbole sometimes mirrored the tone of official correspondence. On 4 September 1915, for example, Admiral Gustav Bachmann briefed the kaiser on the Allied use of armed merchantmen and wrote of "our death-defying U-boat crews [facing British] pirates at sea."[27]

Public support of submarine operations remained an important buttress of Tirpitz's political strength. Unguided public opinion, however, was something he disdained. He was typical of the officer corps in feeling that one must command, not consult. On 28 July 1915 the German military attaché in Washington, Franz von Papen, had expressed this view nicely in relation to the world's largest democracy, the United States. Like previous attachés, he disparaged the "weak" form of American government wherein leaders must hearken to "public opinion, the sole barometer for the conduct of external relations."[28] From the beginning, German officials, like those in the Tirpitz public-relations force, had realized the importance of shaping public opinion. Early on, they had discovered the value of sugar-coating the message with entertainment. Thus didactic fiction remained a principal medium for commercial publishers, who were motivated as much by profit as by patriotism. This, as we have seen, had been the case with Freiherr von Forstner's two Ullstein War Books *Als U-Boots-Kommandant gegen England* and *U-Boots-Leben* (1916).

That same year, marine artist-professor Willy Stöwer published an album of his splendid prints entitled *Deutsche U-Boot-Taten in Bild und Wort* [German U-boat Deeds in Image and Word]. The pictures radiated national self-confidence and pride, and promoted the view that U-boats were going to sea not with aggressive intent, but for "the benefit of peace welfare." This was all the more reason for the public to support the German navy. Weddigen's exploits figured prominently in the iconography of battle, particularly *The sinking of HMS Aboukir, Hogue and Cressy.* Typical of such art books were its memorable and graphic captions: "Thus the English Goliaths were brought down by the German David," the editor explained. Another print, *Return of U-9 and her Heroes*, proclaimed how "proudly the Fatherland looked upon this small band of heroes under the rousing hurrahs of the crews of German warships." The artist's interpretation of historical events was never too far from the truth, despite his often sentimental style. In the latter case, for example, the whole surface fleet had in fact piped and cheered the side when greeting the inbound U-9. This was a formal salute normally accorded only the kaiser and the admiral of the fleet.

Julius Küster's *Das U-Boot: Motor-Tauch-Schiff* [The U-boat: The Motor-Diving-Ship], which treated the technical development of submarines both at home and abroad, also appeared in 1916. In what was fast becoming stock emblematics, Küster's frontispiece made his central point: framed by an oversize imperial battle flag of the German navy (Reichskriegsflagge), a U-boat plunged through heaving seas while a crippled merchantman sank in the background. The image was designed to suggest a sunburst of glorious victories made possible by a major new weapon.

The U-Boat Arm had meanwhile acquired a father figure less remote than the kaiser. The new advocate was a veritable Santa Claus of a man, Admiral Henning von Holtzendorff, chief of the German Admiralty Staff. He had for some time been advocating unrestricted submarine warfare and had pursued military goals to the virtual exclusion of their political implications. However, he was by no means politically naive. On 31 January 1916 he gave the Allies an unprecedented glimpse of himself in a press interview accorded the United Press staff correspondent in Berlin.

The admiral is a small, plump, energetic man, with thick, white whiskers and a hearty handshake. He greets you smiling, with a military bow, a firm grip and word of greeting which comes so suddenly that you forget you are in the presence of one of the kaiser's most trusted officials ... The admiral is a doer, not a talker, as evidenced by the things he has accomplished, and by the fact that this is the first time he ever talked for publication ... Asked how long he thought the war would last [he replied] "Until we are victorious."[29]

The image of the taciturn, patriarchal leader epitomizes the hero of many U-boat books. U-boat advocates were once again champing at the bit to pursue a decisive all-out undersea war such as had been attempted in 1915, and which had been "squelched" by politicians fearful of the United States. Submariners knew they had the weapon, the skills, and the courage. All that was needed was the government's political will, which many felt was too slow in coming. Such waffling rankled in the press despite the official news about "heroic" submarine successes. The submariners unnecessarily feared that their image was becoming tarnished because the government had refused to give them full rein. Von Holtzendorff complained in a private letter of 5 March 1916 to Admiral Scheer, commander of the High Seas Fleet, about the problems he faced in trying to convince the kaiser to be bold and to strike. Both the kaiser and his chancellor were rightly concerned about any action that might provoke the United States into entering the war on Britain's side, but von Holtzendorff was impatient. Germany possessed an infallible weapon, he urged Scheer. Why not use it as it was designed to be used and exploit its special advantages of stealth and surprise?

Von Holtzendorff's letter attributed the U-boats' continuing limited success to purely legal considerations that obliged them to fight according to Prize Rules. He did not mention that the international outcry against U-20's sinking of the *Lusitania* had forced the German government to confine itself once again to the old rules of detention and search. On the other hand, von Holtzendorff claimed, the Allies were resorting to the "illegal" use of provocative and unethical methods such as decoys. (Q-ships had been Britain's immediate response to Germany's early attacks-without-warning.)[30] Pretending to be harmless civilian vessels, these "scurrilous" vessels called Q-ships lured surfaced U-boats into a trap, while British merchantmen had now armed themselves in order to repel attack or rightful search. Forced by international law to fight on the surface where they were vulnerable, U-boats were virtually offering themselves as sitting targets to British Q-ship and merchant-vessel guns. At the time von Holtzendorff was writing, Q-ships had destroyed only four U-boats; the most famous of them caused the *Baralong* incident of 19 August 1915 during which British naval personnel had shot and killed German survivors of U-27 as they floundered in the sea beside their sinking vessel.[31] U-boat literature of the 1920s and 1930s would highlight this aspect of British "iniquity" and "treachery."

Von Holtzendorff felt himself under pressure from all sides – from the kaiser as well as from the press. "Newspapers harranging the U-boat war," he grumbled, "are just as false from the perspective of the conduct of the state as from that of the war itself, and have even sharpened their attacks into personal invective against the kaiser, which caused him great outrage. And I, of all people, have been made responsible for mishandling the press!"[32] As he accurately reported, the German press was now taking up the cudgel against perceived indecision at the highest levels of naval leadership. He was obviously relieved to inform Scheer that the kaiser had ordered the admiralty staff to assume responsibility for censorship and public information. From this point on, the navy would control the news and more closely shape its own image. It would also try to reshape its high-seas role. For by this time, too, old "battleship" Scheer had become more convinced than ever that "setting the submarine against English trade" offered the sole hope "for wearing down England's economic life."[33] German naval leadership – and public opinion – was gradually converted to this view.

During the first half of 1916, the underwater war took on a new dimension with the maiden voyages of the submersible merchantmen *U-Deutschland* and *U-Bremen*. They were unarmed freighters designed to run between Germany and the neutral United States. They caused such a stir in the international press that many stories from Allied and neutral countries were reprinted in Germany. These added a new cachet to the submariners' image. By early 1916 Germany was being squeezed by Britain's blockade. These "starvation tactics" forced

Germany once again to turn to submarine technology in an attempt to reach US ports and industrial resources. By remaining at sea in excess of thirty days without replenishment, combat submarines had proven their seaworthiness on extended missions from Wilhelmshaven to Constantinople without touching harbour.[34] It was clear that U-freighters could be counted on to do the same, thereby avoiding the British blockade.[35]

Despite the secrecy surrounding her planning and construction, rumours about the *U-Deutschland* had preceded her arrival in the United States. Even while she was undergoing sea-trials in the Kieler Bucht, the American German-language newspaper *New-Yorker Staats-zeitung* of 25 May 1916 had published a report about "the first submarine freighter." Sounding at the time like a chapter from Jules Verne's *Twenty Thousand Leagues under the Sea*, the article announced that she would shortly attempt to cross the Atlantic from Hamburg to New York. *U-Deutschland's* actual arrival in Baltimore in July 1916 was a grand public-relations event. Showered with congratulatory telegrams and invitations, and fêted by patriotic German-American associations, her skipper, Captain Paul König, was welcomed as Germany's hero.[36] The mayor of Baltimore gave an official dinner in honour of both the captain and the German ambassador to Washington. After-dinner speeches celebrated the importance of the *U-Deutschland* for German-American trade relations; the civic band played the stirring strains of the patriotic "Die Wacht am Rhein" and the American national anthem. This final gesture, in the U-boat skipper's words, was "a lovely symbol of friendship and understanding [for both countries] both of whom lay great store on the freedom of the seas."[37] Had Germans designed the voyage of *U-Deutschland* in order to dispel the myth of the "marauding and merciless Hun," they could scarcely have offered the American press a better package. The Germans themselves put the event to good use, with the designer of the "undersea freighter" program himself writing anonymous editorials for both the *Berliner Zeitung* and the *Voßische Zeitung*.[38]

Once *U-Deutschland* had arrived safely in Baltimore, the German Naval Information and Intelligence Office, code-named *N*, fed a great deal of material to the German press in order to boost morale on the home front. Thus the *Berliner Tageblatt* for 11 July 1916 announced the "America voyage of a German Mercantile Submarine," and in subsequent issues followed the various political and strategic speculations about *U-Deutschland's* arrival in Baltimore.[39] Twice-daily issues from 11 to 19 July 1916 covered retrospectives on the journey; they described the formidable impression she allegedly made on neutral nations, and highlighted "England's protests" against the German achievement.

The navy's pre-packaged articles proclaimed that "German technology and German daring celebrate a pioneering triumph."[40]

The German press, from illustrated magazines to serious newspapers, proclaimed her "happy return home" and squeezed the fullest possible propaganda effect from the event.[41] Articles could now tell selected pieces of the story of *U-Deutschland*'s origins, the founding of the shipping line "Deutsche Ozean-Rhederei," and the "epic" of German technology and courage in the face of uncountable odds. The Bremen Stock Exchange opened next day with speeches extolling the voyage's economic significance; Kaiser Wilhelm himself sent the Bremen Senate an effusive congratulatory telegram. The Deutscher Flotten-Verein, roughly equivalent to Britain's Navy League, issued commemorative coloured prints of her arrival.[42] The home-coming had all the trappings of a national celebration: flags and bunting, ships' sirens, and bands in pubs and restaurants playing the uplifting strains of "Deutschland, Deutschland über Alles." As the submarine slipped alongside the quays lined by throngs of onlookers, she was welcomed home by a bevy of representatives from business and state: Alfred Lohmann, who had launched the concept, the Grand Duke of Oldenburg, and the aging Graf Zeppelin whose hopes of flying his own dirigibles to America had been dashed by the outbreak of war. Hotel Hillmann treated the crew to breakfast, while the press were treated to luncheon and stories; and the Bremen Senate gave a formal reception to the crew and prominent guests in the Hansa city's famous City Hall. The program's founder and director, Lohmann, received an honourary doctorate in political science from the University of Kiel, and Captain König an honourary doctorate of medicine from Salle. In the words of the medical faculty's testimonial, König, "as bold captain of the first mercantile submarine [had] broken the enemy blockade and enabled science and the medical-chemical industry to regain its world position in times of duress."

U-Deutschland reportedly paid for herself from the proceeds of this first transatlantic trip, and had supplied the German army's requirement of raw rubber for six months. In just seven weeks' time, on 10 October 1916, *U-Deutschland* slipped secretly out of Bremerhaven for her second voyage to the United States. This trip, too, subsequently became a public-relations coup. In the words of the *New York Times* – repeated in the German and the Austrian press – the submarine immediately became "the talk of the town."[43] American businessmen applauded her as a fitting augury of steadily improving trade relations with Germany. Captain König wrote an account of his exploits for the Ullstein War Book series in 1917 entitled *Die Fahrt der Deutschland* [The Voyage of the Deutschland], which had sold over half a million copies by the end of the year. Other accounts followed. One book in the series, Ernst Lassen's *Handels-Uboot "Deutschland"* [Merchant Submarine "Deutschland"] was a collage of press clippings, fact, and fancy, and marketed the idea that the freight boats *U-Deutschland* and *U-Bremen* had been on missions of peace. In fact, it argued, even Germany's combat submarines had been on missions of peace in their defence of the homeland.

Whatever public-relations points *U-Deutschland* had scored in the United States were soon forfeited when the combat submarine U-53 completed its work off the American coast. It had been deployed to escort the second freighter *U-Bremen* and to pay a ceremonial visit to Newport. On its return, it was to attack merchant shipping beyond the United States' three-mile limit. Although *U-Bremen* was mysteriously lost on this her maiden voyage, U-53 nonetheless conducted the visit to Newport and, within hours of departing the American port, sank five Allied merchantmen off Nantuckett Island on 8 October 1916. American sailors who had so recently paid social calls to the U-boat now had to stand helplessly by while the submarine coolly dispatched the steamers to the bottom of the sea. As neutrals, they could do little else. News of the polite protocol of U-53's visit and her "piracy" hit the American press almost simultaneously. Blaring headlines, large photographs, eye-witness reports, and "official" leaks, the pages of commentary told all there was to tell.[44] According to the press reports, Newport had been "aroused by [the] U-boat's raid." In the words of the *New York Times*: "No one had thought of the long gray visitor as a destroyer of shipping and perhaps of lives."[45]

U-53 arrived home to a hero's welcome on 28 October 1916 after a forty-two-day mission. The harbour echoed with ships' sirens and whistles; two bands, officials, and throngs of citizens met them at the lock entrance; Admiral Scheer himself addressed the crew and pinned the Iron Cross on each man. The Imperial Cabinet sent a letter extolling the "consummate achievement," and Captain Hans Rose was honoured by an audience with the kaiser himself, in order to render his verbal report.[46] Like the exploits of *U-Deutschland*, those of U-53 became staples of Germany's naval lore. Touted in books, songs, poems, and postcards, they came to symbolize Germany's extraordinary technical achievements and maritime panache. In newspaper articles in October 1926 marking the tenth anniversary of U-53's exploits, and again in his *Auftauchen! Kriegsfahrten von U-53* [Surface! The Missions of U-53, 1931], the submarine's captain would remind a peacetime Germany of the great traditions in which he had played such a prominent role.

Reports about U-53 that reached Berlin via New York, Boston, Bern, and London fuelled long and enthusiastic commentary in the German press. Her arrival and subsequent operations off Newport seem to have taken the German reporters by surprise and led them to surmise that many more U-boats were now operating off the American coast." The sheer technical achievement of deploying an independent combat U-boat on such a long-range mission was gratifying enough. The voyage of U-53 meant that Germany had therefore "breached the wall of England's concept of sovereignty on the seas."[47] On 11 October 1916 Berlin newspapers reproduced sensational cables from Washington and other US cities about submarine operations in the western Atlantic. In one important respect at least, the German perspective was as clear as it was correct: U-53 had complied meticulously with the rules of detention and search governing cruiser warfare. This was crucial, for the German Reichstag in Berlin, as widely reported at the time, had been addressing a subject that was causing much agitation: unrestricted U-boat warfare. This extreme measure seemed to offer the only means of bringing about a swift and victorious peace with Great Britain.

German submarines had by this time been fighting in the major theatres of operation from the North Sea to the Mediterranean. Press reports and books promoted their exploits and defended the German cause. The merchant U-boats and U-53 were by no means the only ones to press into remote regions. In 1916 the anonymously written *U-Boote im Eismeer* [U-boats in the Polar Sea] focused on a new and largely unknown area. As an advertisement explained, this tale of the exploits of U-195 told of "the cruiser warfare of our submarines in the high north with its superhuman efforts and magnificent results." Its operational orders, which the book claimed to include, were daunting: "The execution of this operation demands of you and your crew commitment to the extreme limit of your resources; demands will be made of you such as our U-Boat Arm has scarcely faced before." The point was well taken. Stalking Allied ships carrying "American" munitions along a route of some 3000 kilometers over the top of Norway to Alexandrovsk on the Kola Peninsula and on into the White Sea was indeed a new venture. Reflections on the nature of war and on German success punctuate the adventures. On crossing the scene of the great Battle of Jutland of 31 May 1916 – after which, in fact, Germany's High Seas Fleet would never venture out to sea again – the narrator ruminates on the devastating results of Germany's superb gunnery against Britain's Grand Fleet: "Below us, over 60 meters deep, lie the victims of 31 May – *Queen Mary, Invincible, Indefatigable,* and the like. Even many a fair comrade from the German side sleeps his last seaman's sleep. [This was the] day when England's Trafalgar fame was shattered by the tumultuous bursting of German shells." The author was at pains to explain that although submarine warfare might lack the roar and glamour of the big guns, it was no less dramatic. "The character of our [undersea] weapon demands of the submariner even tougher things. Dangers surround him on all sides, not a moment of rest or release from tension. A hunter silently stalking his game, but in the next moment is hounded and hunted himself." These terms became the leitmotifs of u-boat literature: hunter and hunted, stealth and destruction, heroism in isolated silence, and the inevitable twist of fate.

"U-boats in the Polar Sea" recounted tales of the hunt in the freezing weather and of German humanity towards survivors of Norwegian vessels; it castigated the nominally neutral United States for profiting from human suffering by supplying the warring nations with war *matériel*; it rejected the American's "hypocritical" protests against Germany's u-boat warfare. As might be expected, the book denounced Allied propaganda – particularly British propaganda – for distorting both the reality and the moral substance of the German war effort. "U-boats in the Polar Sea" was but one of many in the paperback trade that year. Its covers advertised others: seven volumes of "German deeds at sea," nine titles in the series Books from the Front (including one on Gallipoli), and a deluxe edition on Kaiser Wilhelm and the navy "magnificently illustrated" by marine artist Willy Stöwer.[48] U-boat ace Freiherr von Spiegel's *Kriegstagebuch U-202* [War Diary U-202] was typical in taking his readers into the heart of the u-boat experience: artillery attacks against small vessels, torpedo attacks against men-of-war, thrusts into enemy minefields, raging storms, hounding pursuit by the enemy, and finally the happy home-coming. Advertisements in 1917 touted the book as a "true-to-life scintillating description of our secret undersea weapon in its dangerous actions against the enemy."[49]

By now many Allied observers were persuaded that German submarines had undermined the unwritten laws of humanity by fighting with stealth and subterfuge. In the words of a British propagandist working in the United States, the "brotherhood of the sea was a fine, manly freemasonry, and demanded from its members those qualities of courage, honour, and chivalry which are the true seaman's heritage." The rules had now changed: "Not until the coming of the German submarine commander was the Brotherhood of the Sea destroyed."[50]

The kaiser had issued battle orders on 31 January 1917: unrestricted u-boat warfare was to begin next day. Accordingly, Admiral Scheer retransmitted the order with a rallying call to his still inactive High Seas Fleet. With "devotion, commitment, and the full might of attack and defence *every* unit of the navy [was to] put itself at the service of the U-Boat Arm." Yet in relaying the kaiser's words, he embellished them to embody his own dreams of big-ship superiority, the only form of national grandeur that Mahanian theory promised.[51] "The peace which we want to force through by means of u-boats," he concluded, "must become the second birth of the German High Seas Fleet."

German submarine attacks in this bold new phase began inflicting severe losses on Allied shipping in European waters. U-boat ace Otto Hersing's operations are a case in point. An instant hero on sinking the light cruiser HMS *Pathfinder* on 5 September 1914, he later achieved even greater fame as "the saviour of the Dardanelles" in April 1915, where his bold ventures claimed a dazzling array of warships and merchantmen. Once again in home waters after exploits in the Mediterranean, the Irish Sea, and the Atlantic, he destroyed during the night of 23–24 February 1917 six Dutch merchantmen totalling more than 30,000 tons. Books and poetry would ring with acclaim. In the words of Admiral Henning von Holtzendorff, Britain's "war of starvation, this fantastic crime against humanity, had been turned against its originator."[52] Germans were convinced that "England" was now getting its own back. Germany's minister for the interior informed the nation in April 1917 "that the technical results of u-boat warfare [had] exceeded the navy's expectations."[53]

Two popular technical books of that year, one of them an official admiralty publication, delivered the same message. In the words of the admiralty's book, the u-boat was now the primary weapon in the German arsenal; "in u-boat warfare we possess and are applying the right means to incline England to peace."[54] In fact, however, u-boat strategy had virtually overreached its grasp, for now the very thing that German politicians had feared the most actually happened. On 6 April 1917 the United States entered the war on the side of Britain. American belligerency coincided with the most severe crisis of the war, when u-boats were sinking one in four of all ships leaving British ports.

German analysts predicted a u-boat victory by August 1917, a date not far off British estimates that anticipated a critical curtailment of supplies from overseas by October. Nowhere was the magnitude of the disaster clearer, nor the bankruptcy of Allied antisubmarine methods more striking, than on the southwestern approaches to Britain. Here converged the routes for most of Britain's vital overseas trade. Losses in this area jumped from twenty-eight merchantmen in March to fifty-eight in April; many of them were large ocean-going vessels, the most

desperately needed ships in the Allied inventory. In this critical area
not a single German submarine was sunk.[55]

Nine major pulp-trade books marked the year 1917. In January
Admiral Carl Hollweg completed the manuscript of his *Unser Recht auf
den U-Bootskrieg* [Our Right to Submarine Warfare]. The purpose of
his quasi-legal treatise was "to trigger the reader's conviction that our
German philosophy regarding U-boat warfare is firmly rooted in
formal law [but that] an appeal to that sense for natural law so
indwelling in Germans has now become necessary" because of the
Allies' distortions of truth.[56] Hollweg's book is a pot-pourri of chapters
on such topics as "Maritime Law, the U-boat and the War," "The U-boat
War and Victory," "On Faith and Confidence," and an exhortation "To
the U-boat Crews." It ends with a curious chapter entitled "Vision."
"Let it run like water off a duck's back when they call you Pirate,
Barbarians, Huns und Child-murderers," he counsels his U-boat men.[57]
It's all lies, he asserts, for in fact the German submariner has been
meticulously ethical and legal. His point was well taken and found
widespread support.

In "Vision," Hollweg meditated on a spiritual experience that he
claimed to have had on Memorial Day (Totensonntag) a year earlier
in Berlin when he was reciting the Lord's Prayer. The chapter's rather
fuzzy-minded reflections on the war (and quasi-theological ruminations on naval duty) climax in the final affirmation of the "Power and
the Glory" of God as expressed in the closing words of that prayer. At
this point the admiral had found himself especially inspired, and
therefore concluded his account in bold-face type: "The word 'Power'
punched deeply into my memory. Yes, give us the power for the will
to victory, Thou Governor of Battles!" His book would be well reviewed
for its high-minded patriotism, and would be touted as "destined to
be the 'Book of the Hour.'"

Following Hollweg by a month, German submariner Iwan Crompton published his book on the exploits of U-41 and on Britain's use
of Q-ship U-boat traps. His purpose was to dispel any residual support
in Germany for "Old England's" claims of being the grand purveyor
of "chivalrous" and "noble" action in war. Entitled *U-41: der zweite
Baralong-Fall*, his book drove home the point that U-41's confrontation
with a murderous British U-boat trap had constituted "the second
Baralong case." Britain's *Baralong*, as German readers would have
remembered, had captured German submariners and hung them as
pirates. (These assertions were not far from the facts in this documented case of a war crime at sea.) The real paladins in the war, he
wrote, were not "English" sailors, but German submariners. (The book
would once again invoke this theme when it was revised for the 1940s;

this time, however, the English sailor would be replaced by a menda-
cious Churchill in the German's catalogue of scorn.)

Even technical books had a political message. In 1917 Johann
Kirchner's illustrated *Das U-Boot bei der Arbeit* [The U-boat at Work],
for example, celebrated the fact that "not a day goes by without happy
news reaching us about the brilliant successes of our u-boats." Indeed,
his comments suggest that the German naval press and intelligence
had done its public-relations job well. "Like scarcely any other weapon,
u-boats have become the common property of all Germans, and their
successes are on everyone's lips. In the broadest circles of our Volk,
u-boat stories and accounts have found acceptance." A submarine
engineering officer, Kirchner had written in non-technical language
to inform both the stay-at-homes and the soldiers at the front just how
a u-boat worked and what it meant to be a submariner. He sought
broad appeal; with the navy's recruiting campaign in his sights, he
wrote especially "to awaken in the hearts of German youth joy and
delight in the U-Boat Arm."

Berlin's new publishing house Press for U-boat Literature, under
the editorship of Professor Franz Schulze, had by now launched its
first volume in the series U-boat Books for the general reader. Revealing that the submarine had by 1917 replaced the capital ship as
Germany's major vessel of war, Schulze's *Die Schwarze Waffe* [The Black
Weapon] placed the u-boat in the context of Germany's "grand" naval
tradition.[58] He set out to do so by highlighting the surface fleet's major
achievement in the war, showing that the u-boat was now its successor.
The book therefore began with a rousing paean to the great victory
which Germany's High Seas Fleet had won over Britain's fleet at
Skagerrak (the Battle of Jutland) on 31 May 1916, and which had
made the whole country jubilant at the dominance of German seapower. (Germany had in fact won a tactical victory, but the strategic
victory was Britain's.) He then invited the reader to accompany three
submariners on their adventures on the high seas. Submarining was
now the great heroic adventure of mass-market navy books. Schulze,
an academic hack-writer in the service of *N* since the earliest days, had
already produced two u-boat books in 1915, and later in 1917 produced a sequel to "The Black Weapon." His *Erich Sarnekow der
U-Bootsheld* [Erich Sarnekow, the U-boat Hero, 1917] once more delivered a tale of adventure and camaraderie, set this time in the Baltic
and the Mediterranean. It was standard fare and thus warmly received.

The tone of much of this rousing prose of 1917 is best captured by
a poem published in broadsheet form after Otto Hersing's destruction
of six merchant vessels in a single night in February that year. Like
Weddigen's u-9, Hersing's u-21 is a special icon of submarine history.

The centrality of the Hersing poem for the cult of personality may be inferred from the place of honour it holds in the Hersing Room in the U-Boat Archives in Cuxhaven today. Framed and under glass, the poem provides striking contrast to Hersing's sombre furnishings and memorabilia. As tawdry as it seems, the following translation does justice to the verse.

Through German hearts there flashes a ray
Of high, proud jubilation.
Even wavering souls are uplifted today:
It's a festival for the nation.
And seaward roars from homeland's shore
Thundering hurrahs for our defence in war:
The greatest fame has again been won
By Hersing's U-boat Twenty-One.

The poem idolizes all U-boat commanders, whose combat to the death has by now "drawn Britain into court" to face the long-awaited judgment day. Such skippers are models of valour and duty for the nation under duress. The time for mercy is past, the lilting rhyme runs, and U-boats can no longer offer any quarter. Spiced with occasional hints at Medieval epic and Teutonic lore, the verse heralds the end of Britannia's tyranny.

Awaken, German Spirit of vengeful spite,
Enliven your submarine liegemen.
Let each one rise in heroic might
And fight the British siegemen.
Make warriors' fists as hard as steel
To smash the enemy without appeal.
Plant in all hearts the seed now begun:
The Spirit of submarine U-21.

Despite the rise of the cult of the hero among the various "patriotic publishing houses," some authors still portrayed the submariners as but ordinary citizens who had risen to the grand occasion. Thus Wilhelm Köhler's 1917 anthology of first-hand accounts entitled *Deutsches Heldentum zur See* [German Heroism at Sea] promoted the self-effacing nobility of the common man: "There is no bragging and swaggering with heroic deeds. They are just men quietly and willingly carrying out their duty without superfluous words, without hate. The officers do their tasks with a cool matter-of-factness. They are like cogs in a great machine. Animated by boundless trust in their U-boat, they would certainly rather go to the bottom with it, than ever scuttle it or let themselves be taken prisoner."

In point of fact, however, thirteen U-boats were self-scuttled in October 1918, while one was scuttled the following November and twelve gave themselves up without opposition to internment. But in 1917 Friedrich Sanders-Bremen's *Der Heldenkampf unserer U-Boote* [The Heroic Struggle of Our U-boats] could still endorse Köhler's view. His book describes the tasks and achievements of U-boats in a war that Germany "has been forced to wage." As his opening remarks correctly explain: "At the beginning of the war not even the finest experts on the German fleet scarcely foresaw what paramount significance the diving boats would win for themselves." Having pursued his theme and enunciated the principles of submarine warfare, the author concludes with cameo sketches of Germany's great aces: Arnauld de la Perière, Forstmann, Heimburg, Hersing, Morath, Rose, and Valentiner.

Most of these aces would publish their own memoirs and accounts of adventure and daring before war's end, and some had already done so. Heimburg's *U-Boot gegen U-Boot* [Submarine vs Submarine, 1917], for instance, spoke of his Mediterranean and Black Sea operations in the tiny inshore submarine UC-21, nicknamed *Occarina*; Robert Moraht's *Die Versenkung des Danton* (1917) recounted his experiences with U-164 from the Baltic to the Mediterranean, and his sinking of the French capital ship *Danton*. Printed in the format of the Ullstein War Books and costing only a mark, Moraht's message was typical in its sententious simplicity: "Firm and hard as the steel of which this U-boat is made, so also should be the hearts of the men who want to sail the sea aboard it. Like good comrades, we all must be able to rely upon each other doing his duty at his station, whenever and wherever it may be ... With this goal before us let's begin our daily task with the cry: His Majesty the Kaiser – hurrah, hurrah, hurrah ... With God for Kaiser and Empire!" Moraht had cause for celebrating his victory in this show-piece tale, for to judge by contemporary French newspaper reports the *Danton* represented one-twelfth of the French fleet tonnage; her loss was equivalent to a French defeat in a major sea battle.

U-boat ace Max Valentiner's *300,000 Tonnen Versenkt! Meine Boots-Fahrten* [300,000 Tons Sunk! My Submarines Voyages, 1917] is a typical tale of submarine warfare against Allied maritime commerce. Written for the Ullstein War Books series, its opening paragraphs deliver an impressionistic picture of the ocean floor littered with the hulks of U-boat victims – from the North Sea to the Black Sea. Valentiner sustains the up-tempo immediacy of his first-person narrative of exploits aboard his U-38 by limiting the account to his own personal experiences and by taking "certain liberties" with his material "for military reasons." As a result, his account provides a pocket-book of undersea adventures to entertain the unsophisticated reader. Central to his concerns is the quality of men he commands: "Only the best are selected for the submarine service. But when I see my 30-man crew before me I always think that I have gotten a particularly fine selection. Real nifty chaps ... and I understood the side-long looks of many a pretty girl who would most certainly have wanted to go out with our jolly company." Clearly, joining the submarine service held promise of adventures both afloat and ashore.

In the autumn of 1917 the German admiralty staff published its *Effects of the Submarine War in Official Perspective*.[59] In the light of U-boat successes, the booklet reassessed the well-known and oft-repeated strategic view about Britain's utter dependence on overseas trade; it stressed her need to defend her lifeline of transoceanic trade against enemy attack, and confidently sounded victory. Britain's "most inventive brains and greatest financial resources" have not yet curbed the inroads of what they call the "U-boat pest." England, as the staff report claimed with some credibility, was beginning to crack under the pressure. "No longer does England command the sea, for unhindered by her superior surface fleet, the U-boat undercuts her overseas links." Thus having spurned Germany's peace overtures, Britain had "conjured up her own fate by her own hand."

Just how true this was the German public could read in news reports and journals of the Navy League. In August 1917, for example, the Austrian Navy League's monthly magazine *Die Flagge* had summarized the effects of the first five months of unrestricted U-boat warfare and had assured the public of Germany's obvious success: "The longer the U-boat war lasts, the more numerous, urgent and sometimes impassioned the questions become that are asked in many circles of the population: Does the U-boat really represent the infallible means for forcing the enemy to his knees? After a most earnest examination of all contributory factors both for and against the sharpest U-boat war, it must and shall be answered by an unequivocal *Yes*."[60]

By January 1918 the first purpose-built U-cruisers were nearing completion, and Britain's Admiralty had become increasingly concerned about the Germans' growing capacity to sustain long-range operations. By this time, too, Admiral von Holtzendorff had explained to the foreign office that "the military necessity of splintering the enemy's defence measures" called for drawing new areas into the already declared blockade zones.[61] This ultimately meant attacking in North American waters.

Working conditions aboard U-cruisers during lengthy operations were tough, and reports about them never reached the public.[62] Medical reports from shipboard doctors pointed out the problems arising when seventy-three men spent more than three months in a confined space containing only 500 cubic meters of breathable air.[63] Lack of proper ventilation, and the forced confinement of crew below decks for up to four weeks during stormy weather, led to serious problems of what medical doctors called "practical hygiene": respiratory ailments, digestive complaints, bleeding gums, and insomnia. During one particular mission off Madeira, internal temperatures reached 46 degrees Celsius. The thirty-five men in the junior crew quarters shared but eight bunks – always damp from the weeping of condensation along the unsheathed ship's side. The food was frequently of poor quality or in short supply. A physician's report pleaded the absolute necessity of having a trained cook on board to ensure proper nutrition. Moreover, adequate food supplies could not be carried. This made it all the more necessary for rations to be topped up with stores taken from captured vessels.

The U-cruisers presented problems as fighting machines as well: they wallowed in heavy seas, and were slow and often unstable when pursuing targets. We learn from one medical report that "gunners must be big and powerful people. The muzzle flash is very strong and often blinds the crew; handling the heavy [5.9–inch] gun for hours is fatiguing." As for the crews working the upper deck, they often stood up to their shoulders in water. In the light of such appalling conditions, was it any wonder that when *U-Deutschland* and U-53 entered American ports in 1916 their captains forbade their crew from revealing what conditions aboard were really like? The conflict between reality and fiction was played out in the lives of the crew, who struggled to eke out a grim survival, while propaganda projected images of swashbuckling heroes taking the world by the tail.

A similar tension between reality and fiction existed on the British side as well. Thus Charles Gilson's *Submarine U-93* (1917), as his subtitle proclaimed, offered "A Tale of the Great War, of German Spies, and Submarines, of Naval Warfare, and All Manner of Adventures." Published by The Boy's Own Paper press, a division of London's Religious Tract Society, the book stood among the ranks of The Boy's Library of Adventure and Heroism – rousing, patriotic fare to nourish the Darwinistic fantasies inculcated in young readers. Gilson's *Submarine U-93* was the story of villainous Germans whose "cold-blooded and terrible" plots of sabotage and "treachery" both in the neutral United States and on the high seas are ultimately foiled by a plucky English

lad driven by the single-minded desire to combat Germany's "iniqui-
tous" designs for world domination. Born of "a fighting race" of
Britishers and bred of stout values, he embodied "the spirit of self-
sacrifice and honest heroism."[64] The adult world revealed itself to him
in an unequivocal light. Thus while British ships set about their business of destroying the enemy either like "joyful greyhounds loosed
together from the leash" or else "like a joyful dog on a lawn," German
submarines skulked about and hid beneath the waves in cowardly
fashion.[65] Against the background of British fair play, the U-boat
emerged as an eerie weapon of primordial power: "There rose out of
the water, like some hideous monster of the under-sea ... U-93 ... there
is something about a submarine that is uncanny. The capacity to float
half-submerged, the peculiar shape and the dull slatey colour of this
latest triumph of naval science, remind one of some weird antediluvian
animal – one of those strange, gigantic monsters that are known to
have inhabited the world long before man made his appearance."

We are left in little doubt that such primeval "monsters" were
ultimately inferior to civilized England which (at least as anti-German
fiction would have it) had no need to resort to such fiendish devices.
Weapons at once "fragile, slender and evil-looking," Germany's U-boats
were regarded from the British perspective as "the vipers of the sea –
venomous snakes whose backs may be broken with the lash of a whip,
whose heads can be crushed with a stone."[66] And as might be expected,
the head of Gilson's fictional U-93 is indeed "crushed with a stone" –
destroyed under the bow of our plucky lad's freighter. HMS *Dreadnought*'s ramming of Weddigen's U-29 may well have inspired Gilson's
scenario.

The Ullstein War Book series continued its production even while
German fortunes faltered during the last year of the war. Thus the
engineer of U-35 published a memoir for the series in 1918 entitled
In der Alarmkoje von U-35 [In the Alarm-Bunk of U-35]. Quite properly
showing the engineer in the very nerve-centre of the submarine, Hans
Fechter wrote not only to describe life aboard a U-boat, but to "flesh
out the achievements that now fill the world" with awe. That same year
U-boat ace Kapitänleutnant Walter Forstmann published his *U-39 auf
Jagd im Mittelmeer* [U-39 Hunts in the Mediterranean]. At the behest
of both the Ullstein press and the author, Konteradmiral Carl Hollweg
supplied a fiery preface.

In graphic fashion the reader at home and in the trenches learns how the
submariners live and fight. The book shows both these readers that our
conduct of the war on sea and land is in fact a united front, and that the

combat missions of our U-boats are not only gnawing ceaselessly at the marrow of our enemy's economy, but are also working directly in the service of the land war when their unerring torpedoes dispatch men and material, machines and munitions into the mute depths of the sea.

Yet despite his bravado, the facts were decidedly different. Prospects of success for U-boats were becoming increasingly bleak. Since the early spring of 1918 staff officers had been rehearsing the traditional litany of woe. Strong Allied countermeasures in the German blockade zone around Britain meant that more than a third of all U-boats on patrol between March and July came back empty-handed. Worse was yet to come. By August the monthly tonnage target of 600,000 tons of shipping sunk no longer kept pace with Allied shipbuilding; Germany now required "at least 800,000 tons in order to break even."[67] This was a pipe dream. Yet Hollweg's preface to Forstmann's *U-39 auf Jagd im Mittelmeer* preached that "the powerfully superior English fleet [watches] powerless" as German U-boats sweep the seas clear of all opposition. The war at sea, he wrote, marked "the demise of English maritime superiority." He projected a U-boat image that had been a popular cliché since the earliest days of battle. Germany's submariners were not only the saviours of the Fatherland's power and honour, but bold knights in a war of liberation seeking to help the world's oppressed cast off the yoke of British hegemony:

In town and country we know today that somewhere in the world, at every hour, one of our U-boats has got our worst enemies by the throat. Tenacity and will for victory are the watchwords both within and without ... The U-boats, please God, will liberate us and the whole world, for ever and ever, from English maritime tyranny; they will eradicate the scourge of her starvation warfare, under which not we alone, but the weak of this world have been sighing for centuries.

Casual readers in need of authentication could turn to newspapers where skilful manipulation of war statistics seemed to confirm that claims like Hollweg's were describing actual fact. The *Berliner Lokal-Anzeiger* for 6 June 1918 juxtaposed its front-page headline, "Our U-boats active off USA," with another proclaiming, "Since 27 May over 55,000 prisoners, 650 guns and 2000 machine guns captured."[68] Though the article eventually explained these statistics as the total captures on *all* fronts, it managed to give the initial impression that U-boats off America had swung this mind-boggling success. Indeed, Schultze-Bahlke's book *U-Boote* (1918) proclaimed that German submarines were serving an international cause by forcing the "English" to recognize freedom of the seas for all nations. It followed that Britain's "greedy imperialism" must bend to the U-boat's will.

For obvious reasons, the German press withheld the truth about the failing U-boat war, while the censor blocked all politically harmful news from abroad. On 4 June 1918 the *New York Times* had disparaged the German strategy of sending U-cruisers into North American waters in order to interdict Allied shipping and break morale. As the article noted, "the dispatch of the piratical craft to this country has not accomplished the desired results."[69] This was indeed correct. The report argued that a cynical German Naval High Command was acting wantonly with its human resources. "Submarines are comparatively cheap. The cheapest thing in Germany today is human life, and to sacrifice a submarine or two on the chance of getting one of the large American transports ... would show a handsome profit." In fact, the contrary was true. Germans had always been cautious with their U-boats, and the government had always limited "unrestricted warfare" to specific locally defined zones. Two weeks later in Germany a harried Reichskanzler met with his senior admirals, among them von Holtzendorff, who had long advocated total, unrestricted U-boat warfare. The navy now blamed the government for having had a failure of nerve in not thrusting the U-boats – particularly the large U-cruisers – at the enemy's jugular. In the words of Admiral Koch: "We now have the new weapon that can relieve the pressure and promise success; not to use it as required, and not to create the appropriate conditions for its proper deployment for purely political reasons, that is something for which the Naval War Office cannot accept responsibility. The failure of the U-boat cannot be laid to the charge of the navy."[70]

In these words, German naval leadership had washed its hands of all stigma for its apparent ineffectiveness, and upheld the selfless valour of the naval service. The fault, we are told, lay with ignorant politicians. In taking this position, naval leaders had implied that the U-Boat Arm was an end in itself. The theme of the government's political incompetence to decide in naval matters runs throughout U-boat literature. Admiral von Holtzendorff's struggle with the kaiser and the chancellor epitomized this cleft. In fact, the very claim that there were such things as "purely naval questions" – questions devoid of political ramifications – laid a moral trap; it ultimately played into the hands of those who took comfort in having been "only a soldier" doing his duty. This theoretical separation between political responsibility and military capability was fraught with ethical and moral problems. Less acute in reflections on the First World War, such problems would become particularly contentious when re-evaluating the record of military service under National Socialism in the Second World War.

Meanwhile the German navy was struggling with quite a different problem in the long-inactive surface fleet: revolution was in the air. Failure to resolve growing dissatisfaction in the lower decks would not only cripple the navy's ability to fight, but also severely tarnish its public image. The Sailors' Strike of August 1917 led to the naval court martial and summary execution of two seamen implicated in the Enlisted Mens' Movement. Widely perceived by sailors as judicial murder, this tragedy stoked the fires of revolutionary forces in the surface fleet and eventually helped topple the German naval command in the November Revolution of 1918. As an astute historian has recently explained, by debating the strike in public session on 9 October 1917 the Reichstag laid bare one of the nastiest wounds in the body politic and caused "irreparable harm to Germany and the navy."[71] These events of such national and international importance could no longer be kept under wraps. Public disclosure of the navy's severe internal crisis of leadership followed upon the debates. The British press quickly sensed the destructive undercurrents of dissolution in Germany. In the words of the *Manchester Guardian* of 11 October 1917: "Without a doubt this mutiny is the most serious political event in Germany since the outbreak of the war, and indeed, since [the revolution of] 1848."

In fact, however, the strike of August 1917 was no mutiny at all, but a disorganized appeal by frustrated, angry, and neglected surface sailors for urgently needed social reform. The German navy's leadership responded with repression. A judicious assessment first published in 1969 has come down on the sailors' side. "What the navy so effectively hid was the simple fact that its own officers through their bungling, incompetence, and abdication of responsibility were to blame for the navy's inglorious end and that there was virtually no Bolshevik influence in the rebellion that overthrew them and spread revolution in Germany."[72] Movements for reform would only be held in check for a year until the autumn of 1918, when surface-fleet sailors mutinied against their superiors and when the superiors themselves rebelled against their government by trying to order the High Seas Fleet to sea. Firmly engaged in battle against the enemy, the U-Boat Arm stood aloof from this domestic turmoil.

Significantly, the only serious historical novel ever written about the High Seas Fleet, Theodor Plievier's *Des Kaisers Kulis* [The Kaiser's Coolies, 1930] took the side of the sailors, thus anticipating this judgment of history by almost forty years. In attributing the surface fleet's low morale to inactivity and to the cynical indifference of officers to their men, the novelist endorsed the pre-eminence of the U-Boat Arm.[73] In U-boats one found not only purposeful action, he observed, but a real sense of community and brotherhood that cut across the ranks. Completely dependent on confidence in each others' judgment and skill, the crew shared the same feelings, food, and fate. U-boats, Plievier wrote, were an elite service that had siphoned some of the best junior officers from the surface fleet, thus leaving the capital ships with the old crones. Sailors, too, took every opportunity to transfer to submarines.

By 1918 the U-boat had indeed become Germany's pre-eminent weapon. On the one hand, the U-Boat Arm was not troubled by the strains that were tearing the High Seas Fleet apart; on the other, since the U-boat was one of the last cards remaining in German hands, the leadership had no choice but to pour resources into it, not the least because strengthened Allied antisubmarine defences were having their effect. A memorandum from General Ludendorff to his head-quarters staff on 10 February 1918 makes the point from an industrial perspective: the movement of U-boat parts from manufacturers to assembly yards was to be granted "a higher priority than aircraft, motorized vehicles, and [even] rolling stock containing powder and munitions."[74]

During the final weeks of the Great War, Vizeadmiral Carl Hollweg had been drawing up plans for the "further development of the navy after the war"; he prepared a document entitled "First Estimates after the Conclusion of Peace."[75] "The radius of action of a submarine navy is limited," he argued. "For this reason we cannot do away entirely with large numbers of ships-of-the-line, and our ability to conclude alliances after the war will play a great political role." He had none-theless replaced the Tirpitz Risk Principle, based on a powerful sur-face fleet, with a new Risk Principle of his own. It rested on the energetic pursuit of submarine warfare. He therefore foresaw a sub-stantial peacetime fleet: twelve capital ships, forty small ships, twelve torpedo-boat flotillas, twenty airships – and two hundred submarines. Significantly, "a considerable part of these U-boats must be useful in long-range operations."

The Great War, of course, did not end as the Imperial German Navy had hoped. Suffering an ignominious defeat, its fleet was interned by the British. Only by scuttling its own ships in the Royal Navy's fleet anchorage in Scapa Flow did it find any hope of rescuing its forfeited honour. In an ironic twist of fate, the Allies would exploit Germany's submarine technology, especially the U-cruisers, as prototypes for their own future submarine development.

U-boat literature would continue to be written during the inter-regnum of an uneasy peace. It would support the dreams of Admiral Hollweg's postwar fleet – particularly the pressing need for large flotillas of submarines. U-boat action never died in the pulps. Retold by naval writers in the 1920s and 1930s, submarine exploits were promoted as models for the kind of national spirit that would redeem Germany from the shadows and restore her place in the sun.

2 In the Wake of Versailles, 1919–38

Reichskanzler Theobald von Bethmann Hollweg published his reflections on the Great War within a year of war's end. He had been deposed in 1917 for failing to support unrestricted submarine warfare; for failing, that is, to use Germany's "ultimate weapon" out of fear that it would provoke the United States to cast off its precarious belligerent neutrality and join in the battle against Germany. Amidst the ashes of defeat, Bethmann, like Tirpitz in his memoirs of the same year, sought meaning by examining the past. At the time that the peace conditions were being announced in May 1919, Bethmann was tidying up his page-proofs for his publisher. This timing lent a tone of urgency and currency to his preface, in which he asserted that the current political reality had vindicated his historical study "beyond measure." Bethmann's view of Versailles was uncompromising: "a more dreadful instrument for subjugating the defeated the world has never seen."[1]

The German and Austrian Navy Leagues were by this time lamenting the demise of both their imperial fleets. "With but a heavy heart," exclaimed Austria's *Die Flagge*, "we ponder the events, under the pressure of which our battle fleet met its tragic end after its glorious history. We are still too close to the impressions of the crushing conclusion of the war ... to be able to assess the profound tragedy of the loss of our Imperial fleet."[2] It was "an unspeakable misfortune," another sailor wrote in his journal. Naval memoirs would continue to dramatize the dishonour of defeat until the eve of the next war.[3]

A first step in reassessing the past lay in marshalling the "facts" about what had happened. This was the object of Konteradmiral Albert

Gayer's four-volume series *Die deutschen U-Boote* (1920) on U-boats and their conduct of war.[4] Gayer had been chief of the Third U-boat Flotilla and subsequently served in the Imperial Naval Office. His books became standard works and were republished in 1930. They represent an earnest effort at critical assessment in order to see things in their proper context. No less circumspect was Korvettenkapitän Friedrich Lützow's *Unterseebootskrieg und Hungerblockade* [U-boat War and Starvation Blockade] in 1921. During the Great War Lützow had been a staff officer with the Commander, U-boats, Vizeadmiral Andreas Michelsen. Drawing on international law, Lützow attempted to reach an "objective judgment" of what had transpired. His position was that Germany had strictly observed international accords, whereas "England" had conducted her blockade in contravention of all international and humane convention. In 1925 Michelsen himself followed suit with his history of submarine warfare from 1914 to 1918. His preface explained his reason for writing: "… not only to show the German people (Volk) just what the U-boat war meant in reality, but because I have the need to set the deeds of the U-boat crews in the proper light and to protect the U-Boat Arm against undeserved disparagement."[5] His approach was analytical because, as he explained, a "purely military description of U-boat deeds would necessarily consist of heroic deeds whose profusion would soon tire the reader." Significantly, however, literature narrating "heroic deeds" was precisely the type that would dominate the market for decades to come. Action rather than reflection prevailed.

The navy had meanwhile mobilized its intellectual talent to produce the multi-volumed *The War at Sea, 1914–1918*. Edited by the Naval Archives, the work would appear in instalments from 1922 to 1934. Major writers included the archives' chairman, Vizeadmiral Eberhard von Mantey, who before the turn of the century had drafted naval war plans against North America; Konteradmiral Arno Spindler, who would produce the official history of U-boat warfare; and Erich Raeder, who was destined to become Grossadmiral in the Third Reich. The official historians, no less than authors who published privately, aimed at rescuing the German sailor from the malignant epithets of "pirate," "criminal," and "war-monger" which the Allied press had so readily marketed; they strove to create a memorial to heroism and to provide the youth of the day with role models as a means for rescuing Germany's lost naval honour. Raeder's introduction to his first volume of 1922 on the exploits of the light cruisers *Emden*, *Königsberg*, and *Karlsruhe* makes his objectives clear. "A monument of homage to the valiant German cruiser crews on the one hand, a book of experiences of cruiser warfare on the other, this work fulfils yet another purpose.

The actions of German cruisers on the oceans are rich in examples of wartime chivalry by commanders and officers, in examples of discipline and humanity by the German crews."[6] What Raeder accomplished for surface ships, Admiral Arno Spindler would achieve for u-boats in his five-volume *Der Handelskrieg mit U-Booten* [Trade War with Submarines].[7] Of the two, Spindler was the better historian. Spindler's final volume was suppressed for having shown that u-boats had in fact been responsible for drawing the United States into the war.

Much less carefully crafted was retired Vizeadmiral Hermann Kirchhoff's *Seekriegsgeschichte* [Naval History in Its Most Important Phases, with Special Consideration of Tactics at Sea, 1921].[8] It is a spiteful and unhistorical work. Lamenting that British authors and memoirists were intentionally falsifying their accounts, and that even the press of nations that had been neutral during the war continued to share the British view, he set to work despite lack of access to official documents. His perspective was uncompromising:

In the final analysis, proclaiming the valiant deeds of our national navy [der vaterländischen Marine] ashore, afloat and in the air was a vital heartfelt need; one indeed closely allied to the need to lay bare the brutal despotism of Great Britain's seapower. May the German people learn from this account and others, that it can never carry out its high cultural duties without maritime prestige [Seegeltung], and that a strong fleet is more than simply a case of *navigare necesse est*; it is imperative.

Here he hearkened back to the Tirpitz's dictum of the great battleship race before the turn of the century: without naval prestige, Germany could never seize its rightful place. Many other navalist works would reiterate the claim.[9]

In visceral support of this thesis, retired Vizeadmiral Carl Hollweg contributed a frothy political sermon as a contribution to Admiral Scheer's book *Die deutsche Flotte in grosser Zeit* [The German Fleet in Great Times, 1926].[10] Hollweg lambasted not only the "infamous" Treaty of Versailles, but also the Dawes Plan (1924) covering Germany's payment of war reparations and the Locarno Treaties (1925) on European security; he railed against those who blamed Germany for the past war. Germany, he asserted, had been motivated by her "just and righteous" claims for naval power. Nor did he take kindly to civilians who were then beginning to examine Germany's naval record: "Like mushrooms after a rain storm, numerous self-appointed pundits have arisen in Germany who, on the basis of files and the memoirs of both our own and the [former] enemy's statesmen, as well as on the basis of doctored-up statistics, claim to be able to prove that German fleet construction was a cardinal error." These self-styled experts, Hollweg reported, now had the temerity to pillory Germany's rightful ambitions as "a sin against the Holy Spirit of international fraternity, and a culpable venture against 'just and generous' England." Such posturing, he declared, was a clear challenge to the older, war-experienced generation. The old boys must now correct this distorted image so that the new generation could recognize the legitimacy of Germany's claims, and – in a phrase echoing Tirpitz – help her take her place in the sun: "*Youth of Germany*, for whom this book is written, hold firm to this truth despite everything: that we – a Germany once rich and powerful through hard work, achievement, and concentrated exertion of our energies – were the envy of all, and that we had the inalienable right, and were indeed exercising a moral duty towards the as yet unborn generations of our overpopulated country by striving to assure and keep open our future possibilities by creating power on the seas."

The admiral's appeal to the concept of "Lebensraum" is unmistakable; his feeling of having been cheated, unequivocal. Germany, he argued, had once had everything in its favour. Firm resolve, moral ideals, and a healthy society, he asserted, had entirely justified, even demanded, competition with every other people in the world. But he was persuaded that Germany had always gotten the short end of the stick when the world was being divided up. As a result, the exploiting nations – Britain and France – had forced Germany to resort to U-boat warfare. "The Anglo-Saxons reviled us with having pursued an inhuman and immoral U-boat war." Yet the real cause behind Germany's having to pursue such measures, he would have us believe, was not German desire, but Britain's "illegal and inhuman" blockade of the years 1915– 19. Still not satisfied, Britain had further dishonoured the German fleet by interning it in Scapa Flow, thereby leaving the Germans little choice but to scuttle their own ships. Only by self-destruction, Hollweg's explanation continued, were the ships saved from utter ignominy. He exhorted German youth to prepare for a rebirth of "Germanic" valour in a new maritime destiny. "That proud German oak which our fleet once was [has] sunk to the bottom of the sea. But already it is sprouting new roots and branches. Germany too will have a new spring. Youth of Germany, persevere and hope, educating your natural leaders [Führernaturen] and training those who are willingly led for the time of Germany's valorous [tatenfroh] reascendency."

Kapitänleutnant Johannes Spieß brought special experience to bear in support of the call for rebirth. He was the only front-line submariner to have served from October 1912 through to the delivery of the U-boats into British hands in November 1918. His *Sechs Jahre U-Boot-*

Fahrten [Six Years of Submarine Voyages] first appeared in 1925 and was reprinted in 1932 by the nationalist Tradition Press of Berlin. Hardbound and well-illustrated, this key volume in the Stahlhelm Series entitled Monographs from the World War offered a rousing, upbeat read after the manner of the pulps: it rang with cacophonous battle-sound. Spieß was not particularly interested in dwelling on the horrors of war at sea; he passes lightly over the drowning of torpedoed enemy sailors to focus on the real point of his narrative:

In narrating my U-boat missions I do not intend to write a formal "history of naval war," much less a complete description of all my U-boat experiences. Rather, I want to show in a series of characteristic events the pace with which the submarine has developed from the stage of uncertain experiments to a wide-ranging weapon; to offer the layman a concentrated insight into the worries and concerns of the skippers of this covert weapon, and an overview of the profusion of continually changing tasks and dangers imposed on U-boats by the war situation and the extraordinarily intensifying enemy countermeasures.

His central message was the failure of German naval leadership to grasp the potential of submarines. At the highest levels, leaders had been slow to cast the U-boats into the breach; they had fussed with merely political considerations when early recourse to unrestricted U-boat warfare would have won the day; they had skimped on funding and had held the U-boats back from attacking prime targets that were there for the asking. Spieß recites a litany of neglect and short-sighted indifference: budgetary restraint that prevented even the installation of an electric alarm bell to signal emergency dives; diesel engines that could not reverse; navigation charts that were inadequate even for Baltic operations. "Trust the [surface] navy to do a thing like that!" Spieß recalled bitterly. But despite material shortcomings, submariners spiritually were "Ready, Aye Ready." On hearing the mobilization order on 1 August 1914 the submariners had burst forth with "a three cheers for the Kaiser ... proud to stand in the very front line at the onset of this gigantic battle."[11] And so, "silently and secretively, as is the style of our branch of the Service, we embarked on the World War." The sum of Spieß's experience pointed to the future: the U-boat was for him and others "the only means of maritime warfare of decisive importance in a battle between Germany and England."

Whether Spieß had been an anglophobe during the war or had become one in consequence of Versailles is not clear. The tone of his book in any event anticipates Germany of the 1930s. In this stridently anti-British light he vividly recounts his service from 1912 to 1914 with the legendary Weddigen aboard U-9. He gives eyewitness accounts of the sinking of the three Bacchanti-class cruisers HMS *Aboukir, Cressy,* and *Hogue* and the cruiser *Hawke,* narrates the further missions of U-9 and U-19 under his own command; recounts operations in the North, Irish, and Baltic Seas and in Finnish waters; explains tonnage warfare and covert operations; dishes up tales of heroism and chivalry, bravado and "heroic death." "Yearning for action, we U-boat captains went to sea; for we had the greatest independence of action there can ever be in war."[12] These qualities of derring-do and single-minded independence would underpin the submariners' cult.

Spieß's tone of disdain for a surface fleet that had done nothing to win the war became particularly bitter as he recounted his final mission, this time not against England but against Germany's own "mutinous and cowardly" ships *Thüringen* and *Helgoland* in October and November 1918. That autumn, Admiral Scheer and his admirals had planned one final thrust into the North Sea to engage Britain's Grand Fleet in a death-before-dishonour charge. (Spieß did not tell his readers that Scheer's plan ran counter to the government's wishes; nor that this "Admirals' Revolt," as it has since been called, was triggered by officers out of touch with political and strategic reality.) In accordance with traditional fleet tactics, he wrote, U-boats had been deployed at sea in advance of Germany's capital ships in order to pick off the advancing British Grand Fleet. The U-boats had been expecting the German High Seas Fleet to come out to do its job; it never came. "The U-boats," Spieß declaimed, "were disgracefully left in the lurch by the crews of the capital ships." German submarines, he argued, had carried the war to Britain on the high seas while the High Seas Fleet had lain idle; now the submarines replaced that fleet as the defenders of German shores. Disdainful of the surface fleet, Spieß underscored the submariners' achievement as the preserver of national honour and order: U-boats had in fact been "the navy" throughout the war, and the capital ships could not even pull off a final piece of bravado after a long war of idleness. Submariners knew that the intransigent surface sailors had to be brought to heel. Thus it was that Spieß, in command of the 1800-ton U-cruiser U-135, took up position off his rebellious targets *Thüringen* and *Helgoland* now held by the mutineers and waited for the order to shoot. To his dismay, conciliators managed to defuse the tense confrontation before he could strike a punishing blow. This kid-glove approach he found just as treasonous as the work of the mutineers themselves. Rebellion and insubordination deserved tough justice.

The senior staffs [of the German navy] had been mentally unprepared for
mutiny and had not learned from English naval history. During the Napole-
onic Wars whole squadrons had mutinied many times. The English antidote
had been: go alongside, fire a broadside into the rebellious ship, board, keel-
haul and hang all ring-leaders to a man. A Nelson would have rounded up
the ships with the arrested mutineers still aboard them and anchored them
in the middle of the High Seas Fleet, transferred the others from *Thüringen*
and *Helgoland,* and have had the lot gunned to bits.[13]

As Spieß would have it, mutineers and slackers of the surface fleet
had prevented peace with honour; they had in fact laid the ground-
work for the humiliation of Versailles from which Germany was only
now beginning to recover. "Our four-year struggle against a world of
enemies would have earned an honourable end" if only the High Seas
Fleet had behaved according to naval tradition. The u-boats alone had
kept the faith; and they alone, he insisted, would continue to bear the
grand tradition. Arnauld de la Perière would reiterate precisely this
point when writing in 1937: "The red rags of revolt were flying over
Kiel" as he entered harbour in u-cruiser U-139 on 14 November 1918.
"That was the bitter end."[14] It was the surface fleet that had capitulated, both spiritually as well as physically; submariners had been
"kaisertreu," faithful to imperial Germany's highest person and purpose. That same year Admiral Scheer's memoir about the High Seas
Fleet confirmed that the u-boat crews had been "thoroughly reliable."[15] Such views were also shared by a lower-deck submarine mem-
oirist: "*We* weren't the ones who had lost the war; we had done our
duty."[16]
A pride of such charismatic "German naval heroes" contributed in
1926 to *Die deutsche Flotte in grosser Zeit* [The German Fleet in Great
Times] edited by Admiral Reinhard Scheer. They included Kapitän
zur See Friedrich Lützow, chief of staff to the commander (u-boats)
during the First World War; Konteradmiral Curt Graßhoff of the
Submarine War Office; and Korvettenkapitän Lothar von Arnauld de
la Perière, wartime skipper of U-35 and the u-cruiser U-139. Vizeadmiral
Carl Hollweg's political homily, as we have seen, had also formed part
of the volume. Nor did the book lack visual impact, for marine-artist
Willy Stöwer, renowned in prewar days for his graphic oils of ships and
battles, provided an excellent romantic portrayal of de la Perière's
U-cruiser in Surface Combat on 10 October 1918. The tales told in this
collection echo similar British heroics published in the British popular
press. For example, the dashing Arnauld de la Perière described how,
having let the ships of a massive convoy roll over his huge submerged

U-cruiser, he then burst to the surface to take on the lot single-handed. In the gutsy style and manner of Ullstein's War Books, Scheer's anthology of derring-do assumed a key role in the propaganda market.

At about this time, in July 1926, the newly formed nationalist movie studio Deutsche Volksfilm GmbH announced that it was launching its production series with "the powerful naval feature film *U-9*, [revealing] the tragic fate of our unforgettable von Weddigen."[17] This was perhaps not surprising, for the Great War was enjoying a renaissance as a subject for popular entertainment in Germany, both in home-grown films and those imported from Hollywood.[18] In the summer of 1926 alone, film companies were advertising no fewer than four other navy features: *Die versunkene Flotte* [The Scuttled Fleet], *Skagerrakschlacht* [The Battle of Jutland], *Versenkung von UC-48* [The Sinking of Submarine UC-48), and *U-Boot in Gefahr* [U-boat in Danger].[19] Typically, the popularity and market appeal of these and others depended on the twin pillars of American cinema: romance and adventure. As Canadian historian Tom Saunders has explained, between 1925 and 1929 feature films about war were "a blend of romance, sentiment, and adventure on the one hand, and quasi-documentaries on the other."[20]

The film *U-9* was no exception. Highlighting the propagandistically valuable story of the sinking of the three British cruisers, it offered the basic narrative of Weddigen's exploits, interwove it with a family drama of an English mother and a German father whose sons fought on opposite sides (thus turning the conflict between Germany and Britain into a "sibling war" (Brüderkrieg), and finally saw Weddigen die as the victim of circumstance. As the advance notice read in part: "Isn't it the tragedy of a human fate that the German peoples' most celebrated hero had to struggle with death in his U-boat at the bottom of the sea on his first mission after his wedding?" There was some historical truth in that, for, as we may recall, Weddigen had just taken command of the more modern U-29 and had been rammed and sunk by the British battleship HMS *Dreadnought*. As in all else, the film-makers fantasized about the German crew's final hours after the battleship's fatal attack. So too did a film critic in his plot summary published just after the film's premier in April 1927. "Locked in the cold iron of their boat deep on the ocean floor," the heroes longed for home while their stalwart captain strode through his vessel to bid farewell to all his comrades who had done their duty even unto death. Then came the sailor's apotheosis as "the waves of the ocean sing their melody over U-29 that sleeps its eternal sleep deep in the ocean's bosom."[21]

Ultimately, the film *U-9: Weddigen, ein Heldenschicksal* [Fate of Heroes], as it was known by its full-blown title, was about heroism and the performance of one's patriotic duty. With this and other films, as Saunders has demonstrated, viewers would have responded along partisan lines. Those wanting to rescue Germany from the shame of Versailles would have recognized a clarion call to arms and patriotic deeds; pacifists would have found confirmation of their position in the subplot of a symbolic family divided against itself. By the late 1920s movie-making was an entirely politicized enterprise. It involved the remilitarization of public opinion. Indeed, radicals in the Nazi party saw a special purpose in war movies, one that went beyond questions of historical authenticity and objectivity. "A war movie was supposed to divide the nation to purify it, that is, separate pacifist weaklings from the strong-willed and heroic."[22] Reviews of the film *U-9* split along just such lines.

When a well-known critic of the *Berliner Tageblatt* debunked *U-9* "with its patriotic trarara-music" as but one more paltry example of militaristic jingoism, the film company bought a two-page spread in the leading movie magazine *Der Film* in order to marshall its supporters for the counter-attack. One full page amassed the endorsements of some seven Berlin newspapers and three cultural magazines, while the facing page pilloried the now excommunicate critic. Where the *Berliner Tageblatt* had seen cheap stylistic tricks delivering "hoopla" and "family soaps" (Familientratsch), the company's supporters – from the liberal *Vossische Zeitung* to the *Berliner Morgenpost* and the *Filmkurier* – saw tactful, realistic, untendentious, and ultimately heroic drama. Supportive critics reported enthusiastic audiences, many of whom seemed sensitive to the inherent tragedy of the story. The movie magazine *Lichtbildbühne* took particular satisfaction in the inclusion of original film footage from the war at sea, and concluded from the applause at the première that *U-9* would be a smash hit.[23] In hindsight, a remarkable chemistry was at work here. By stirring up grand emotions about Germany's heroic past, the film hinted at national destiny and a return of that spirit which had almost been crushed by Versailles. Many popular documents of the period reveal the past as a signpost to the future.

Thus in October 1926, the tenth anniversary of U-53's sensational attacks against civilian shipping off New York under the silent guns of sixteen neutral American destroyers, her captain published a syndicated newspaper story.[24] He would republish much of it five years later in his book *Auftauchen! Kriegsfahrten von U-53* [Surface! Combat Patrols of U-53]. In both cases, Rose wrote out of a sense of obligation to his comrades, whose spirit he regarded as a model for the new age.

My crew readily took all hardships in their stride, maintained in all dangers such placidity and in all storms such a sense of humour that I find them all the more heroic the greater the time-span that separates us from those events. Even if their names are scarcely mentioned, yet I believe that the deeds of my crew and the spirit that animated them should wrest them from oblivion. For it is meet that memory give us courage and hope for the future of our Volk and Fatherland.

This was the very stuff of a variety of swashbucklers: books such as U-boat ace Johannes Spieß's *Sechs Jahre U-Boot-Fahrten* [Six Years of Submarine Voyages, 1925] – reissued six years later under a different title; Kapitän Herbert Sauer's *Die Höllenmaschine im U-Boot* [The Hell-Machine, 1928]; Freiherr von Spiegel's *U-Boot im Fegefeuer* [U-boat in Hell-Fire, 1930]; and Karl Neureuther's anthology *Wir Leben Noch! Deutsche Seehelden im U-Bootkampf* [We're Still Alive! German Naval Heroes in the U-boat War, 1930]. All aimed to correct the distortions of Allied propaganda. They confirmed the chivalrous nature of U-boat warfare and appealed to the youth of the country to keep the faith. Neureuther, a former submarine officer and at the time president of the veterans' organization U-Boot-Kameradschaft München, spoke for his two dozen and more contributors: "Note this, all of you; we front-line fighters are still alive and want to be and remain front-line fighters; not for greed, money politics, and false prophets, but only for concepts so lofty that one can once again experience what we experienced."

A symbol of this national sacrifice was the now famous U-boat Memorial on the 5.7 hectare site at Möltenort at the outskirts of Kiel Harbour. On 8 August 1927 some 3000 naval veterans and visitors witnessed the laying of its foundation stone. Conceived and promoted by Wilhelm Lammetz, a former killick in Germany's Imperial Navy, it would be the only common memorial site for the fallen comrades of both world wars; in 1969 a concourse would be added, bearing bronze tablets containing the names of submariners lost to the enemy in the Second World War. When officially opened on 8 June 1930 it would be a towering structure overlooking the harbour exit – a saluting base for passing warships, a mecca for veterans, a gathering place for the German people on national occasions. When laying the stone in 1927, the former Commander-in-Chief, Submarines, Admiral Andreas Michelsen, uttered words widely reported in the German press. His sentiments would echo throughout the coming years.

This is the memorial of the U-boat fallen whose graves are graced by neither stone nor flower. From the Baltic to the Black Sea and the most northern Arctic, they rest in unknown places in their battle-tried boats at the bottom of the sea. In vain does the hand of those left behind seek on charts and in atlases the spot where the beloved one rests to awake no more. Surely that is the very thing that obliges us to erect on their own home soil a monument to those fallen, that it might be to us comrades and to others left behind a symbol of their graves.

Not all the veterans-turned-author were from the submarine fleet. Korvettenkapitän Witschetzky's *Das schwarze Schiff* [The Black Ship], which underwent nineteen printings in 1930, contributed to this ethos from the perspective of the surface fleet. Published in the series Union Press Patriotic Books for Youth and Adults, it offered bugle-and-drum yarns about the "privateer" auxiliary cruiser SMS *Wolf* which were livelier than many salty dips of the day. Bewailing "the unfortunate conclusion of the Great War" which had "soiled German esteem, German fame and German honour," Witschetzky boldly proclaimed the German sailors' hope for another chance to avenge the defeat – and to rally fresh recruits to the cause. "Thus burns brightest in us German navy men the wish for a prompt end to this condition of profoundest humiliation into which our Fatherland has fallen. Like the great majority of us who volunteered for service aboard the mysterious black ship [SMS *Wolf*] in 1916, all the 'Wolves' will step forth at the next call 'Volunteers! Step forward!'" Yet it soon became apparent that those "wolves" who would in fact make the difference in the next war at sea would be wolves of quite another kind: the stealthy "wolf packs" of the submarine fleet.

Other voices countered such bravado by decrying Germany's failure to grasp what naval warfare was really all about. Perhaps the most important example was Vizeadmiral Wolfgang Wegener's nationalistic study *Die Seestrategie des Weltkrieges* (1929). For Wegener, a salient question of crucial importance for Germany's naval future was why the Great War had produced only one major sea battle. He argued vehemently that German leaders had had little notion of the sea, and knew even less about strategic offence. Focusing on continental defence, they had built capital ships for long-since outdated fleet battles. Continentalism, Wegener rightly argued, had been Germany's downfall. "Today we are the heirs of this powerful struggle [for a European victory]; we are conquered and yet must make our way into the future. If we consciously and clearly place our people under the spirit of the Atlantic, then those whom the 'Great Mother Sea' rocks in eternal sleep will not have fallen in vain. The words of the Flensburg [sic] naval memorial take on symbolic meaning: we must go to sea – *Seefahrt ist not!*"[25]

Wegener's second major thesis recognized the U-boat as the neglected weapon of war. As soon as Germany had grasped the new reality and had excluded the High Seas Fleet from the naval formula, the U-boat had become the sole weapon against Britain.[26] "The second part of the Great War stood under the sign of the U-boat, which, despite all political impediments, might almost have given us peace."[27]

British observers concurred; they acknowledged the U-boats' superb achievements in almost bringing about British defeat.[28] Nonetheless, many non-military observers in Britain had been shaken by the impact of German submarines on naval warfare. The submarine was "this most terrible weapon of warfare"; it was a "skulking" weapon that triggered "murder" and "piracy."[29] It had transformed naval warfare for ever. One German writer argued with prescient conviction that submarining had changed not only warfare, but our whole world and world-view. Hanns Günther's *Die Eroberung der Tiefe* [The Conquest of the Depths, 1928] urged that Germany's U-boat success had set her well on the road to exploiting undersea resources, the greatest "Lebensraum" known to mankind.

Although most foreign writers centred their attention on the pernicious undersea weapon itself, one perceptive observer focused on the crew that manned it. Indeed, in the preface for William Guy Carr's account of British submarines in the Great War, *By Guess – and by God* (1930), Admiral S.S. Hall, commander of the Royal Navy's submarine forces for most of the Great War, highlighted the character of the German U-boat ace.[30] The character of the commanding officer, he argued, was far more crucial in submarines than in surface ships; the submarine skipper himself was the very nerve centre of his vessel. "Germany had some four hundred submarine captains during the war but over sixty per cent of the damage they did was accomplished by but twenty-two [of them]. The inference is obvious ... Fortunately, not every nation can produce such men, and if they cannot [produce them] we can safely let them have as many and as large submarines as they like." In offering such fulsome praise to the Germans, Hall encouraged international negotiators not to worry about allowing Germany her full share of U-boats; for she would never again have the expertise to man them all.

Yet despite the overwhelming success of U-boats in the Great War, one German engineering officer provided a curiously negative judgment in his official study of naval technology. Submarines, air-dropped mines, and torpedoes could not, he argued, replace the battleship as the principal weapon at sea.[31] This was precisely the official attitude that Wegener had been trying to combat. In the years that followed, other naval veterans of the Great War marshalled their experiences and lore for the counter-attack against the pro-battleship view. Significantly, the first of these revisionists was neither a German nor even a submariner, but an American war correspondent.

Lowell Thomas loved to write true-life adventures. His *Raiders of the Deep* (1928), published in German three years later under the more chivalric and less predatory title *Ritter der Tiefe* [Knights of the Deep], played directly into the hands of German naval officers seeking foreign affirmation of their deeds. Its translator was no less than U-boat ace Freiherr von Spiegel, who made no effort to conceal his enthusiasm in the preface to the German edition. "The chronicle of the German submarine war – the epic of the German U-boat – written by an American? Is it possible? By a foreigner, a former enemy? Had we [Germans] no interest at all in the submarine deeds of our heroes – no writer of our own to take them up? Oh yes, we might have had them – but the American beat us to it." Spiegel found Thomas's book remarkable for its tenacity and honesty in clearing the air of insidious rumours about "the inhumanity of German U-boat piracy." Written by a foreigner, the revealing account had finally brought "truth into the light of day" in a more credible fashion than any German writer could have done. Thomas's views therefore had special meaning for post-Versailles Germany. As Spiegel's preface concludes: "And when you read the monument which an American has erected to German heroes, think of those who in times of greatest German need took the heaviest fate upon their shoulders and willingly died for you."

In fact, U-boat ace Spiegel did more than render Thomas's text into German. He had also reshaped and edited it. In doing so he translated values into the text that were specifically his own. A case in point is the passage where Thomas has been commenting on his earlier book about Count Felix von Luckner's adventures as captain of a raider under sail. Turning now to his new theme of submarines, Thomas writes:

And so after a sailor's yarn of scudding the waves with a fair breeze at your back and all sails set, why then [here's] a tale of the tight iron shells that ranged the underwater – spectral, fearsome, and deadly.[32]

This becomes in German:

Now, after the experiences of the romantic sailing ship that slipped through the oceans with canvas set and light breeze, I want to tell you about the fates of that iron, tiny band of heroes who, surrounded by a thousand deaths, furrowed through the depths of the seas – spectral, fearsome, and deadly.[33]

In the passage just quoted – albeit now translated back into English – the translator has the narrator speak to his readers directly and confidentially ("So will ich Euch erzählen"). The intimate form of address (Euch), instead of the formal form (Ihnen), suggests the conventional narrative technique of drawing the "dear reader" aside for a private chat. Then, too, the translator has shifted the adjective "iron" from the submarine to the men: Thomas's "iron shells that range the underwater" (the submarines) have become "the iron, small band of heroes," the submariners themselves. What in Thomas's hands was merely their "tale," though to be sure a rousing one, has become their "fates," their "destinies." The translator's shift in tone and meaning matched the tone of the times. For in typical National-Socialist jargon, "iron" heroes would be "welded together" in the "tough struggle" for "German freedom." Gathering momentum at the beginning of his book, Thomas exudes:

The campaign of the U-boats held the world spellbound. One of the latest marvels of modern technology, striking a sweeping, fearful blow that threatened to decide the issue of the conflict of the nations – that surely was a thing to clutch the imagination with an iron grasp. And then there were the weird perils of the men who navigated beneath the surface of the sea, who struck their blows from the recesses of the ocean's bosom. The ever-threatening fate of the submerged coffin stands eerie and supremely terrifying. Ah, what stories waited to be told! Not merely stories of mad adventure, but history, important and of intense interest to all men. Surely no chapter of the history of our time needed telling quite so much as this.[34]

This passage, at least, was translated with reasonable accuracy.

Raiders of the Deep was the result of a style of investigative reporting for which Thomas later became famous in radio and TV. He had tracked down U-boat veterans and recorded their yarns and experiences; he had fleshed out the background and the characters with glitzy flair and guided their narratives to provocative and sometimes sensational insights. His "raiders" – the "knights" of the German translation – were indeed the big names of the First World War of whom later German narratives would speak. Indeed, some of these aces would themselves publish memoirs during the 1930s where they would include virtually verbatim some of the stirring tales they had already seen published in Thomas's account: Johann Spieß's recollections of submarining with Otto Weddigen, who sank three British cruisers in September 1914; Walther von Schwieger's account of sinking the *Lusitania* in U-20; Lothar Arnauld de la Perière's adventures in U-35 at Cattaro, and in the U-cruiser U-139; Richard Feldt's raids off the US coast in the U-cruiser U-156; Otto Hersing's combat exploits when sinking HMS *Pathfinder, Triumph,* and *Majestic;* Waldemar von Kophamel's voyages, including his journey with the U-cruiser U-140;

the adventures of Robert Wilhelm Moraht, Baron Adolph von Spiegel, Johann Spieß, Otto Steinbrinck, Max Valentiner, Otto Weddigen, and a host of others. In all, it was a superb slate of performers, assembled to dispel the British "myths" about the depravity of the German sailor. Thus Thomas recounts the fateful encounter of the redoubtable Reinhold Salzwedel with the "infamous" Gordon Campbell, RN; Campbell had been skipper of the Q-ship that had flouted international law by murdering members of a U-boat's crew who had fallen into his trap. Thomas's description of Salzwedel is a propagandist's delight: "He was an outstanding chap, blond and blue-eyed, with a fine wide brow, a firm chin ... a proud carriage of head – a gallant, laughing, frank-eyed boy, as far as possible from the popular conception of the barbarous Hun."[35] This style itself would become a convention of propaganda art, as other writers followed suit. In the German edition, the translator appended a Roll of Honour listing the names of the fallen. Among them were many famous names that had long since assumed a patina of martyrdom: Weddigen, Hartmann, Schwieger, Salzwedel, and Valentiner. Their stories would continue to be told by the "iron band" of faithfuls who looked forward to the new age.[36]

U-boat ace Max Valentiner's *Der Schrecken der Meere* [The Terror of the Seas, 1931] was a *tour de force* of its kind. (It would be released the following year with a slightly modified title – and more adventures.) In the words of Admiral Arno Spindler's preface to the first edition, Valentiner had conjured up the "romanticism of U-boat navigation that ranged the distant seas" and had woven "a chain of gripping, adventuresome submarine missions." In the preface to the second expanded edition that same year, the president of the Vienna branch of the German Navy League attacked the prevailing literary style and tastes in German culture. Indeed, since 1919, intellectual circles in both Germany and France had been waging a press battle against militarism and nationalism, and in support of a new European patriotism.[37] Then, too, three provocative revisionist novels had been debunking the supposed heroism of service to the national cause: Ludwig Renn's *Krieg* [War, 1928] and Erich Maria Remarque's widely acclaimed *Im Westen Nichts Neues* [All Quiet on the Western Front, 1929], both of which laid bare the senseless horror of the war and became immediate bestsellers, and Theodor Plievier's *Des Kaiser Kulis* [The Kaiser's Coolies, 1930], which unmasked the moral hypocrisy of the High Seas Fleet's leadership. Remarque's novel had been serialized in Ullstein Verlag's flag-staff newspaper *Die Vossische Zeitung.*[38] They would have rejected Renn more because of his leftist leanings than because of what he had actually written. Faced with such apparent opposition, the president of the Vienna branch recommended

Valentiner's "unaffected and hence all the more dramatic" approach to honest narrative. The result was a book that "must be read in a single sitting," and one that would motivate the new generation. As the Austrian veteran wrote:

Young people should take this book to heart. May they be uplifted by the narratives of a man who did his best under the most difficult circumstances, and whose will for victory, whose zest for action and patriotic optimism never faded. In contrast to those shoddy literary works [Machwerke] which aim to kill the military-mindedness [Wehrhaftigkeit] of future generations, may our youth here look upward to an instinctive leader to whom the Fatherland means everything.

The instinctive leader (Führernatur) of which Valentiner is here deemed a prototype was by this time already looming large in German politics.

Thus firmly launched, Valentiner's narrative whisks the reader off into the toughest combat zones and ends with the revolution that destroyed not only the country, but the old navy as well. Valentiner's closing lines summarize the contents of his work: "a slice of sailors' fate, a slice of soldiers' fate, a slice of German life lies in this book; and much German love for the Volk and German suffering and sorrow. But from this seed Germany's greatness has already begun to arise once again."[39]

Another expert account was provided by Admiral Hermann Bauer's historical and political survey *Das Unterseeboot* [The Submarine as Fleet Component, in International Law, in War and in the Future, 1931]. In prewar days Bauer had been chief of the First U-Boat Flotilla; he had served as Commander, Submarines, until he was succeeded by Michelsen in the summer of 1917. Published by one of the major naval presses, his book echoes the conclusions of a line of apologists from Bethmann Hollweg to Max Valentiner. "Today in Germany, external pressures have condemned the submarine to death. It shares this proud fate with other branches of the service which were particularly dangerous to the Allies in the Great War. But the German people know that the pick of German manhood fought and died aboard [U-boats]; not for long will they be deprived by force of this weapon which has grown so close to their heart."[40]

Former U-boat skipper Ernst Hashagen seems to have been the sole voice of reconciliation among this clamour for national prestige. While placing his hopes in the League of Nations, he also recognized that there are times when one must fight for one's country. For that reason he chose to narrate the U-boat experience as a benchmark for coming generations who no longer seemed to understand the concepts of duty and sacrifice. In the final analysis, he pointed out, the war had been about Germany's legitimate struggle for nationhood and national grandeur. His *U-Boote Westwärts!* [U-boats Westwards, 1931] would provide the title for a popular war film in 1941. Hashagen ventured onto the current literary scene fully recognizing its "wealth of war novels, stage plays from the trenches and other such war literature."[41] Those that sell best, he continued, are unfortunately not those that speak of the "heroism ... courage and patriotism of those who faced death out of patriotic duty; the bestsellers are those books which paint the business of war as provocative and humiliating for those who were forced to take part in it no matter what had motivated them."[42] The "successful" books he had in mind were doubtless Renn's *Krieg*, Remarque's *Im Westen Nichts Neues*, and Plievier's *Des Kaisers Kulis*. "We submariners are not poets, but we have really experienced something [vital] and we do have something to tell – from a different, rather foreign undersea world in which we, too, lay in the 'trenches.' May the new generation achieve that for which we fought in vain." A fellow navalist reviewed Hashagen's account as the book of the hour.

At a time in which war literature is flooded by the hack-work of the uninitiated, it is sheer deliverance [geradezu erlösend] when a front-line combat officer takes up the pen and recounts his experiences. Whoever wants to breathe salt air, to feel the sea breeze, to experience manly adventures, should take this book to hand. It is the best that has yet been written about such things.[43]

While Hashagen may well have been alone in wanting to reconcile, he was still one of a crowd of memoir-vendors who propagated the u-boat ethos. Most of them were former war heroes.

Korvettenkapitän Otto Hersing's *U-21 rettet die Dardanellen* [U-21 Saves the Dardanelles] appeared in 1932 as a pulp-trade hardback, complete with photographs of submarines and of his victims HMS *Pathfinder* and *Majestic*. Hersing described firing the first "live torpedo in world history" and how "the world trembled" when he sunk the cruiser HMS *Majestic* on 5 September 1914. He began with "the once so proud, powerful, and undefeated German fleet" being ultimately interned in Scapa Flow; he ended with a romantic lament for a bygone age: "There lies the most successful u-boat, u-21, on the ocean floor; rest softly in the peace of the infinite sea." He was not alone in expressing such sentiments.

Valentiner's whip-cracking memoir *Der Schrecken der Meere: Meine U-Boot-Abenteuer als 'Kaiserlich-deutscher Pirat'* (1932), a further revised version of the similar titles of 1931, indulged in more "adventures" that celebrated the superiority of the German sailor and his extraordinary weapon. The book's title projected the dashing self-image of Valentiner as The Terror of the Seas, while flouting the British propaganda view of him as an "Imperial German Pirate." German newspapers extolled the book. The newspaper *Augsburger Neueste Nachrichten* called Valentiner's work an "odyssey of German seamen, a breathtaking, striking, sometimes frightening book filled with the bursting of shells, the diabolical whishing of torpedoes, with the stifling air in sinking U-boats." The *Breisgauer Zeitung* found it "a book filled with love for the German people and Fatherland which must once again rise from its misery to its former greatness." The *Generalanzeiger* of Stettin recommended it as a work that might help "keep the spirit of heroism alive in our youth." The Nazi party's *Völkischer Beobachter* regarded this "very true book" as "a good shot-in-the-arm" that triggers the right emotions and ideals.

This was precisely the goal of Korvettenkapitän Robert Moraht's book *Werwolf der Meere: 'U-64' Jagt den Feind* [Werewolf of the Seas: U-64 Hunts the Enemy, 1933]. It rejected all those "horror tales about the deeds of our U-boat people" spread by Allied propaganda, and showed "what we really did and thought." It ran through thirteen printings with the nationalist Vanguard Press between 1933 and 1938. Submarine warfare using U-boats, Moraht explained, was significantly different from the general conduct of war by armies on land: alone and cast back upon their own resourcefulness and ingenuity, U-boats carried the fight to the very heart of the enemy's territory "according to the adventurous ideals of earlier centuries." It was a chivalrous war. "Today after fourteen dark years it can finally be expressed: this tradition must never ever be lost if Germany is to assert its rightful place in the world." On this point even some surface sailors agreed, though they doggedly insisted that capital ships alone could assert maritime prestige and power.

On 3 May 1933, the year in which Adolf Hitler came to power, the German navy launched the three-mast training bark *Gorch Fock*; she was to replace the *Niobe*, which had been lost in a storm the previous July. *Gorch Fock* was a magnificent ship. She had been named after the poet laureate of German seafaring whose stories and verse had captured a generation of German readers. He had lost his life "for Kaiser and Empire" when the cruiser *Wiesbaden* was sunk at the Battle of Jutland on 31 May 1916. Yet his writings, many of them published posthumously, continued to spread the gospel of naval prestige among a largely continentally minded people. His diaries appeared in 1917 as *Sterne überm Meer* [Stars over the Ocean] and in 1934 as *Ein Schiff!*

Ein Schwert! Ein Segel! [One Ship, One Sword, One Sail]. For Germany's naval tradition, the launching of his namesake in the spring of 1933 was a critical turning point. In the keynote address of this national event, Grossadmiral Erich Raeder mixed the vitalist rhetoric of his day with poet Gorch Fock's often jingoistic sentimentality:

Happy, hopeful confidence fills us all at the sight of this proud sailing training vessel. For German youth from every German stock shall receive aboard her the basic principles of education and training that will make them leaders at sea ... *Gorch Fock* embodies the struggle of manly German youth with the sea, and that almost instinctively arising, wonderful, profound love for the sea that lays hold of everyone that comes to know it with all its beauty, its enormous power, but also its dangers and terrors.

The adventure of sail, as we have seen, figured largely in the iconography of adventurers beneath the sea in submarines. Freiherr von Spiegel's autobiography of 1934 would specifically link the tall-ship sailors' "wide world" and "hurricane-struck" adventures with the underseas exploits of the u-boat.[44]

Like the launching and commissioning of the *Gorch Fock*, the publishing of books of the period evoked the rich naval tradition that many German veterans felt needed to be fostered. Korvettenkapitän Fritz Otto Busch published his *U-Bootsfahrten* [U-boat Voyages, 1934] but regretted in his preface that young people found "the sad history of the u-boat war uninteresting and incomprehensible." He, however, would offer a pocket-panacea for Germany's apparent disinterest in the navy. After providing a simple overview of the u-boat war from 1914 to 1918 and a sketch of u-boat technology, his booklet highlights the old canon: u-9 under Weddigen, Schwieger's sinking of the *Lusitania* with u-20, Otto Hersing's u-21 in the Dardanelles, and u-boats off the Murmansk coast. An appendix provides the battle record of "the most successful u-boat commanders" and a "list of u-boat losses, types, and flotillas." The publication concludes with a vocabulary of nautical expressions. Dedicated to his fallen comrades of the class of 1912, it was a tidy package with a clarion call. "These are colourful pages from the u-boat war to show the layman, especially young people, how dutifully, unflaggingly, and radiant with hope our u-boat crews – the truest of the true – did their best to win the war for Germany. Here is shown how they went to sea, fought and lived, how they spoke and thought, and how their supreme law was loyalty to the Homeland, gallantry, indefatigableness and the will to victory."[45] Most of the u-boat crews who had died, he recognized, had died in combat. His preface therefore ends with a lament taken from an old u-boat song: "Viking, you bold one, where is your grave, / Where did your laurels slip 'neath the wave?" The book was reissued four years later, for these tales needed retelling to those most needing the gospel of the U-boat spirit: "to our young people, who are our hope and our pride in the Third Reich."[46]

U-boat ace Max Valentiner published once more in 1934 in the Ullstein War Book series. His *U-38: Wikingerfahrten eines deutschen U-Bootes* [Viking Voyages of a German U-boat] made what had now become conventional political pronouncements. The "Viking Voyages of a German U-boat" which his subtitle proclaimed linked the rugged Teutonic manhood of Viking explorers with the dangers of sea battles. After the grand adventures and successes, and despite the submariners' sense of purpose and duty, Germany had to his mind met its abysmal end through revolution and internal collapse: "Fate drew back for one final blow [and] robbed us of everything that until then had been both our creed and homeland – our great, struggling Germany."

With Hitler's rise to power in 1933, national recovery became a major theme in both fact and fiction. Kapitänleutnant Werner Fürbringer's *Alarm! Tauchen! U-Boot in Kampf und Sturm* [Alarm! Dive! U-boat in Combat and Storm, 1933] was one of many vehicles for the message. Fürbringer, a former commanding officer in the Flanders Flotilla of the First World War, served up a good tale without political diatribe or innuendo. It remained to his former flotilla commander to read between the lines and to write a preface interpreting "U-boat spirit" for the new age.

Unspoken among ourselves during the war, it was the lofty song of unconditional trust in the commander and in one's own capabilities, of selfless commitment of the individual self to the greater whole, of the defiant manly pride that prefers to cast its own life into the breach rather than stand weak and incompetent before one's comrades, of profound inner conviction that one's utmost strength was most bitterly required. This spirit gave the young U-boat commanders the strength to set forth again and again into the enemy mine fields, into the convoys ... into the hail of depth charges.

This is the very spirit and image that *Das Boot* novelist Lothar-Günther Buchheim would pillory in the 1980s as the "rambo-zambo" style. But the commander's language was typical of the day. In concluding his autobiographical account *Alarm! Tauchen!* U-boat skipper Fürbringer spoke of his 1932 lecture tour of Germany when he awakened the avid interest of young people in his exploits. The more he told them "how our U-boat people fought for the highest good even when the battle seemed most hopeless," the more they were stirred by the submariners' self-sacrifice for love for the Fatherland. There was no doubt in his mind that their heartening response boded well for the future. "So much may as yet be uncertain in Germany, and many a difficult hour may still face us, yet one thing is clear: these young people have the right stuff to lead Germany toward freedom and happier times."

The theme of national recovery was not restricted to writers who had been officers in the navy. Former members of the lower deck also raised an occasional voice. Ludwig Freiwald's *U-Boots-Maschinist Fritz Kasten* (1933) portrayed submariners as a fearless lot; their bearing epitomized the "breakthrough of the racial ideal" [der Durchbruch des völkischen Gedankens] which National-Socialism now promised to make real. His book concluded with the tumultuous scenes of masses of citizens spontaneously gathering to hail troops parading in torch-light procession through the Brandenburg Gate in Berlin; it exuded his pride in German sailors marching in columns with Nazi "brown shirts who were ready to sacrifice their lives for this hour." This last sentence underscored more than its appearance in this slim piece of pulp-literature might suggest. As emphasized elsewhere, the tightly bonded brotherhood once deemed the sole preserve of the the u-boat crew has now been transformed into a paradigm of the whole nation. The new cachet of patriotism is the u-boat spirit. Karl Wiebicke's *Die Männer von U-96* [The Men of U-96, 1934] provided another of the rare lower-deck views of submarine life. Picking up where Valentiner's "Viking Voyages" had left off, he laboriously explained his aim: "to make known to the younger generation that in the bond between leader and followers [Führer und Gefolgschaft], in pulling together on the same rope, great things can be achieved and adversities with-stood, a fact which finds its most striking confirmation today. Just as today, so then we acted according to these words: Everything for Germany."[47]

By this time there was no dearth of u-boat literature. In fact, there was so much of it that Fritz Otto Busch introduced his *U-Boots-Taten* [U-boat Deeds, 1934] by commenting on the glut of "both good and bad u-boat books" on the market. His sole reason for adding his own contribution to the growing genre was his own authentic experience. He felt it uniquely qualified him to initiate the layman by "reproducing the battle-shattered, sea-tossed, wind-torn atmosphere, the magnifi-cent never-failing comradeship of the crews, the cheerful intrepid spirit which prevailed aboard u-boats."[48] Like many others, Busch deplored "our unfortunate geopolitical situation." From the navy's point of view it was in fact serious, for Germany's naval aspirations were still contrained by the terms of Versailles and had been further limited by international treaties that prohibited her development of submarines. At the moment she had no submarines at all – although she was secretly designing and building them and their components abroad. (She would unilaterally repudiate the restrictive regulations in 1935 and launch her first submarine.) Adding his voice to those of other naval veterans, Busch aimed to show "every German just what we have lost because of being prohibited from having submarines." Regulations limiting the small fleet, he argued, had now made a mockery of Germany's rightful "will for defence." He therefore asserted what other writers had only implied: the German navy must demand submarines again. Here his turgid prose appealed not to any sense of grievance or aggression, but to claims of naval tradition with its old iconography.

Admonishingly and defiantly stands the mighty ship's bow of the Navy Memorial Monument at Laboe; broadly it reaches outward over the blue Baltic, over the former exercise area of our U-boats. When will it again look down onto the outbound grey U-boats, whose slim narrow bodies with battle standard and with white wake astern set forth on the tough work of peace?

Whether the general public shared this vision with Busch and other veterans is an open question. Certainly, the counter-culture of intellectual pan-Europeans and pacifists, together with popular anti-war novels, gave Busch ample cause to lash out against all the "pacifist babble" that envisioned a nation without armed forces. His anthology included tales by well-known officers (from Korvettenkapitän Forstner's "Starvation Blockade and U-boat War," to Admiral Arno Spindler's "U-boat Decoys") and contributions by obscure writers from the lower deck.

With his book *U-bootsgeist: Abenteuer und Fahrten im Mittelmeer* [U-boat Spirit: Adventures and Voyages in the Mediterranean, 1935], machinist's mate Gerd Bock also took up the cudgel against those "pacifist hack-writers." In the simplistic style of the War Books, Bock extolled the life of duty and sacrifice. He explained the commitment of those who, like himself, had "fought for Volk and Fatherland out of simple, pure, good love, out of sure instinct, and out of duty and devotion to the homeland." This, of course, was the vocabulary of the 1930s, but his sincerity should not be doubted. Hearkening back to horrors of an unwanted war that had "burst forth like a natural catastrophe," and to the "shameful" behaviour of the armed forces during the revolution of November 1918, the lower-deck author proclaimed a truth to which all submariner's adhered: "The German U-boats did *not* participate in the so-called revolution! They did *not* strike their flags." National Socialism, he confidently asserted, had now taken the nation on to greatness; and German submariners, who to his mind had always kept the faith, could now reclaim the laurels that were rightly theirs.

The loathsome time of the disintegration of all stout values, the haggling, cowardly time of hucksters and petty shopkeeper minds – that is all past. At last heroism is among us in order to make history. Our creed in the u-boat war was Germany, nothing but Germany! And that is today our call to the future. At long last, without being mocked and ridiculed we can fasten the u-boat badge onto the honourable brown [Nazi] shirt of an awakened Germany.

Whatever their wartime rank or experience, all attested to the fact that naval strength was now more necessary than ever before, and that the u-boat was the best means to assert German sovereignty and honour.

One submariner took quite a different path by becoming a pastor and social activist. Thus u-boat officer Martin Niemöller, as the title of his famous autobiography reveals, had moved "from u-boat to pulpit" (*Vom U-Boot zur Kanzel*, 1935). Niemöller had won the Iron Cross, was subsequently ordained after studying theology, and came to welcome the rise of National Socialism only as a means of restoring the position and prestige of the national churches that had been eroded during the Weimar Republic. He joined other pastors in signing a declaration of fealty to Adolf Hitler. Urged by friends and associates to write about his experiences as First World War submariner, he regarded his memoirs "as a much belated piece of Great War literature." War had been a rite of passage for all participants, British as well as German, and for this reason he hoped his book would focus readers' attention on some central truths. "It will, perhaps, perform a humble service to those who, like myself, unconsciously found their true selves during the Great War and who, in that Mighty Furnace of God, reverted back to the elementary and simple basic truths of humanity which, after the end of the war, impelled them to seek a new life."[49]

In Niemöller's case the "new life" ultimately meant opposing Hitler. His sea-change came about when he sided with resistance theologian Dietrich Bonhoeffer to attack the Nazis' infamous Aryan Paragraphs which, among other things, enshrined a number of anti-Jewish prohibitions. The resultant 1934 Barmer Declaration of the Confessing Church flew in the face of Nazism by assaulting the so-called German Christians who had easily accommodated themselves to Nazi politics.[50] As reflected in the title of a British edition of his autobiography in January 1939, his journey would lead *From U-boat to Concentration Camp*.

For his "treason," Niemöller would spend a total of almost eight years in prison, the last four of them in Dachau. A leader in the Confessing Church, he would survive the war and help inspire the church's declaration of the doctrine of Germany's collective guilt for both the war and the Holocaust.[51] Many in U-boat circles regarded him as a loose cannon until his death in 1984. Throughout the 1930s he was a lone voice, for the tide of U-boat supporters was turning to full flood.

Typical of the trend were Fregattenkapitän Jacob Rehder's *U-Bootsfallen* [U-boat Decoys] and Freiherr von Spiegel's translation of Admiral Gordon Campbell's *Wir jagen deutsche U-Boote* [We Hunt German U-boats], which had originally appeared as *My Mystery Ships* (1937). Spiegel's introduction brought with it a warning that if the "lads" of the new U-Boat Arm weren't up to snuff, the result would once again be British hegemony on the high seas. The submarine – particularly the German submarine – was one of the "wonders" of the war. As Karl Grosse also argued that year, no nation would want to be without them.[52] U-boats, another author intoned, are a fundamental part of German tradition. And German tradition, Paul König concluded in his 1937 revision of his "Voyages of U-Deutschland" (1917) was once again being fostered – by the National Socialist movement.

Austrian veterans, as we have seen, had also joined the campaign. In 1935 Korvettenkapitän Georg von Trapp turned his hand to tendentious memoir as well. Ironically, his fame as a U-boat ace would be outstripped by the "Trapp family" myth in the musical *The Sound of Music*. His *Bis zum letzten Flaggenschuß: Erinnerungen eines österreichischen U-Bootkommandanten* [Until the Last Round – Memories of an Austrian U-boat Commander] was published in Salzburg and Leipzig; it regaled its readers with salty yarns and blamed inept politics for Germany's defeat. By this time his platform had become the catechism of veterans' sermonizing: Reichskanzler Bethmann Hollweg had tried to "wrest Germany's most effective weapon out of her hand" because of his unholy fear of provoking the then neutral United States. President Wilson, von Trapp argued, had been well aware of the overwhelming underwater threat and had exploited international politics to "exclude [from the equation] the Central Powers' most dangerous weapon, the U-boat." Bold political leaders, he insisted, would have attacked and exploited the U-boat's advantage. That, surely, would have caused Britain's early defeat. But Germany had had no bold leaders, he argued. Prevented from waging unrestricted warfare in the Atlantic and around Britain, U-boats had been forced since 1916 to confine themselves to tonnage warfare in the Mediterranean and Adriatic Seas. When Germany finally did get its act together and declare unrestricted submarine warfare on 12 February 1917, "Austro-Hungarian and

German officers in the officers' mess in Pola greeted [the news] with a sense of deliverance." Just how good the submarine actually was emerges from his account of Max Valentiner in UC-20. It was Valentiner who carried out "the first underwater night attack against a dark ship" ever recorded: "it had never been attempted in the U-Boat Arm, neither in peacetime nor in war – but the skipper dares it, he knows it's safer" than a daylight surface attack. In this he was right. For in this attack, UC-20 sank the 12,550-ton armoured cruiser *Léon Gambetta* with the loss of 771 lives. What emerges is the U-boat skipper as paladin; the commander as mystical, intuitive leader whose sang-froid inspires his crew to victories against overwhelming odds. It is an image that Nazi propagandists would exploit.

Werner von Langsdorff was at the beginning of this new wave. His anthology *U-Boote am Feind: 45 U-Boot-Fahrer erzählen* [U-boats against the Enemy: 45 Submariners Tell Their Tale] gathered narratives from most of the "great names" of the Great War, four of whom had already joined the Nazi party. Published in 1937 and introduced by former ace Konteradmiral (Retired) Lothar von Arnauld de la Perière, it sought "to pass on to the growing generation" what Arnauld called "the submariners' matter-of-fact fighting morale and spirit of comradeship." Of 800 U-boats constructed, he pointed out with lean dramatic effect, 343 had reached the front and 199 had been lost to the enemy. Werner von Langsdorff was becoming adept at this business of propaganda writing. His earlier anthologies of patriotic fare had served similar markets: "Pilots against the Enemy – 71 Fliers Tell Their Tale" and "German Flag over Sand and Palm – 53 Colonial Soldiers Tell Their Tale." The thirty-eight-year-old von Langsdorff was an ex-Luftwaffe pilot; he had won the Iron Cross First Class and had joined the Nazi party; he had become a "Führer" (leader) in the National-Socialist Flying Corps and was an active public speaker on party and racial [völkisch] affairs. Another contributor to Langsdorff's anthology was Hans Rose, former commandant of the famous U-53 that had crossed the Atlantic to attack shipping off Newport in 1916; he was now an ss-Sturmführer. Yet another was Otto Steinbrinck, U-boat skipper during the years 1914–19. Steinbrinck had been the most successful skipper of the Flanders command, and had won both the Iron Cross and Pour le mérite, with 216 ships and 230,000 tons to his credit. He was now an ss-Standartenführer.

Von Langsdorff offered a veritable smorgasbord of adventure and heroics: the oft-rehearsed theatrics of "U-9's great hour" when Otto Weddigen sank the three Bacchanti-class cruisers in September 1914; the adventures of Walter Forstmann (U-12), who had sunk some 400,000 tons and won the Prussian medal Pour le mérite; Karl

Dönitz's sophomoric account of sea duty under the command of Forstmann, and anecdotes of his own command of UC-25 and UC-68 in Atlantic and Mediterranean waters; the exploits of Arnauld de la Perière; Paul König's account of training under Rose and his own subsequent command of the submarine freighter *U-Deutschland* to the United States; Hans Rose's exploits with U-53 off Newport; and contributions by lower-deck personnel as well. The officers were aces all, names that still echo, however faintly, among U-boat buffs at Kameradschaft beer-table smokers.

Duty, heroism, patriotism, and apologetics rang throughout the book. Walter Schwieger rendered a first-hand account of how he had sunk the *Lusitania* with U-20: his well-aimed torpedo had struck "a four-stack steamer with many masts [that burst with an] unusually powerful detonation followed by a gigantic cloud of smoke. Masses of wreckage flew as high as the funnels. A second explosion followed as though munitions had gone up."[54] That was how he saw it some years after the event. Only in these final moments of the victim's agony could he identify her as the *Lusitania*: she "sank quickly, as utmost panic broke out on the decks, and overfilled life-boats tumbled into the sea and splintered among the drowning." A lower-deck account of life aboard "a modern 800-ton boat" simply prickled with vocabulary that was fast becoming the hall-mark of Nazi ideology: the crew was "welded together" (zu einer Einheit zusammengeschweißt) and was "utterly committed" to its tasks (seinen Posten restlos ausfüllen). Hans Rose plumbed the psyche of the German submariner. In his prose converged the language of the philosopher Kant and that of the National Socialists: "we were driven by the categorical imperative of duty and unbending will [in the struggle for] freedom of the seas."[55] He had first published these lines in 1926, then again in 1931, and now once more in 1937. Here as elsewhere, "iron" resolve and "tough" endurance "steeled" the U-boat crews for the ultimate sacrifice. Thus Dönitz's contribution to the anthology delivered an apotheosis of seering sentimentality; he recounted his postwar return in a Hapag Lloyd steamer to the very spot where his First World War submarine UB-68 lay in 3500 meters of surging sea. This set-piece offered a vision of his lost crew ascending into U-boat heaven; it was a piece of purple prose understandably not resurrected in his later memoirs.

In my dreams I saw you, little band, led onward by you [chief engineer] Jeschen, mounting the steep path to the gate of heaven. A wet strip of sea water was your track – the salt flood dripping from your hair and weather gear. All of you were leading our youngest sailor, little Thalman – the memory of that sudden plunge out of life still stood in his frighteningly wide-eyed gaze.

Your pale, taut faces looked upward, elevated, towards the longed-for goal. Then you saw in the distance in the radiant rosy morning light the high and mighty heavenly castle with its cloud-wards striving towers and battlements. Yea, the gates of heaven were opened wide unto you, for you men could not give your people (Volk) any more than you had already given.[56]

Keeping this spirit of sacrifice to Volk and Vaterland alive remained the submariners' commission in the interwar years. The surface fleet had failed. "U-boat loyalty" to comrades and the elite undersea service (to take an epithet from submariner Carl-Siegfried Ritter von Georg) nurtured both the spirit and the faith.[57] In a reconstructed scene in this anthology of 1937, Ritter von Georg takes us back to 1918, the revolution year when the old order was disintegrating; a submarine crew that has rescued the U-boat's colours from the ignominy of surrender to the British returns them to the U-boat's former skipper. Again, the ideological clichés of the new political era underscore the fervour of commitment and dedication.

Iron earnestness lies on the weather-tanned faces of the submariners; yet the eyes gleam as once before when we used to face the enemy in pitiless artillery battle. I lead my trusty comrades into the room; they form single rank before me – icy stillness – my heart begins its aching beat – with a crackle a sheathing slips to the floor – and notwithstanding a revolution now raging in all of Germany, the trusty crew presents its commanding officer with the proud, victorious flag: black, white, red ... From eyes that had fearlessly faced the enemy for years, tears flowed.

That was the spirit that prevailed on all our U-boats. That front-line spirit from which deeds were fulfilled, deeds of which even today [1937] our former opponent reports with esteem. That is the spirit which, newly awakened, has once more brought Germany to equality of rights among the nations, and to economic recovery.

Nurtured "in the years of our defencelessness," as another witness in the anthology put it, the U-boat spirit that had "stood alone against the enemy" was now preparing the way for Germany's future under a new leader: "The Führer gave us back our honour and weapon. Thus German U-boats once again stand guard in order to protect the peaceful work of the people (Volk)."[58] The thirty-eight-year-old writer of this passage, a U-boat captain from the 1916–19 era, had joined the SS by 1930; at the time of publication he was an SS-Sturmbann-führer.

By this time other naval writers too had extolled Adolf Hitler as the paladin who had restored the U-boat to a grateful nation. As the former commanding officer of U-90 expressed it in a book published in 1937: "Today we U-boat men know better than any what we owe our revered Führer and Chancellor Adolf Hitler."[59] The skipper complained that "the influence of German politics on German naval warfare was a dark page" in the 1914–18 era; if submariners had had their own way they would have won the war – without the half-measures of the politicians. "Those times of half measures are now past, and a Germany under the leadership of Adolf Hitler will in future do the whole job," U-boat ace Freiherr von Forstner concurred in his pulp *U-Boot ahoi!* (1938). Now living in a reawakened Germany with a new fleet, he surveyed the exploits of "German U-boats in war and peace" as his subtitle had announced. Indeed, his book was a proclamation of the new age of naval supremacy.

The hour of our salvation [had] finally tolled. An awakened Germany breathed in relief, when Führer and Reichs Chancellor announced on 16 March 1935 that after the final collapse of our former enemy's disarmament charade we had taken our own military sovereignty into our own hands. The announcement of the introduction of general military service triggered great jubilation throughout Germany. Everyone will know that we former U-boat men welcomed it with particular joy when our government announced a few weeks later: "the first U-boat U-1 entered service today, and has hoisted its flag and pennant."

That year German submarines U-33 and U-34 would undertake illegal covert operations in Spanish waters, committing what many years later was deemed an act of piracy by sinking Spanish submarine C-3 on 12 December 1935.

On 30 May 1936, after nine years under construction, the Navy Monument in Kiel (Marine-Ehrenmal-Möltenort) was officially dedicated. The huge monument even today dominates the shores at the town of Heikendorf on the Kieler Förde. Since the 1920s a significantly smaller memorial had stood on the site, erected by the survivors of the U-Boat Arm in memory of the fallen submariners of the Great War. Rising eighty-five meters above sea-level, the austere and imposing fin-shaped brick tower stood like a sentinel over the maritime traffic that coursed in and out of Kiel harbour. Its reopening in 1938, presided over by Adolf Hitler, was a national event.

The solemn ceremonial inspired at least one major book of U-boat rhetoric. The author of *U-Boot-Fahrer und Kamelsreiter: Kriegsfahrten eines deutschen Unterseebootes* [Submariners and Camel Riders: Combat Missions of a German U-boat] had attended the opening of the Kiel

Memorial; the event had set him wondering whether the younger generation really had any idea of what its forebears had achieved. More especially, did it have any appreciation of U-boat missions to Tripoli and Morocco? Apparently unaware of the amount of U-boat literature available to inspire the young, he expressed his aim in the spring of 1939: "With this book I would like to erect a monument to the men of UC-20. May their courage and deeds live on in our German youth!"[60] Some of the stories, of course, were already well-known yarns. Not unjustly, the author extols the technical achievements of UC-20 and its crew for coping, among other things, with enormous challenges during a single independent mission when covering "a run about as long as from Plymouth to Buenos Aires without stopovers or refueling." His authority for such claims is Admiral Arno Spindler's official history of the submarine war. "As a military and technical achievement the journey of UC-20 is worthy of esteem. Even the greatest endurance of a submarine at sea, that of U-53 during its operations off the American coast, was surpassed by 13 days by the smaller, 300-ton UC-20. That's new proof of the demands to which U-boats and their crews are equal when the chips were down."[61] Despite the sensationalism and the popular style of so much that was written during this period, certain hard facts – like the one quoted above – remain. Many years later when reflecting on the opening deployments of the Second World War, Admiral Karl Dönitz would address the question of why neither German nor Allied leaders had recognized the obvious: operating over great ranges and against superior surface forces, U-boats had been an effective weapon of attack.

Dinklage's *U-Boot-Fahrer und Kamelsreiter* went through two printings in 1939, and in doing so joined a pride of navalist memoirs. Each book-jacket carried advertising blurbs for others and shared one major thrust.[62] As a review in the *Deutsche Allgemeine Zeitung* said of Hermann Jung's *Die letzten Korsaren: Kriegsfahrten deutscher Hilfskreuzer* [The Last Corsairs: Combat Missions of German Auxiliary Cruisers], these narratives had proven that "the old male virtues were still alive! And over their adventures stood that which was even greater – faith in Germany." As Admiral Wilhelm Marschall had put it in his *Torpedo Achtung! Los!* [Torpedo Away! 1938], the new era had now begun in earnest: "The seed is sown! We, the war-generation, see it rise with our own eyes; it's a magnificent feeling to be here and to be able to help it happen. Heil to our Führer!"[63]

On the eve of the Second World War, former U-boat commander Hermann Jung published his memoirs of underwater combat in 1914–18 entitled *Krieg unter Wasser: Der Opfertod der Fünftausend* (1939). Subtitled "The Sacrifice of the Five Thousand," it eulogized those

German submariners lost to the enemy – 50 per cent of the total submarine force. Jung included not only his own experiences, but selected exploits of the submarine service he loved: U-9's sinking of the three Bacchanti-class cruisers in 1914, action in the Dardanelles, combat with Q-ships, and trade warfare. Written in the popular style of the Ullstein War Book series, it strove for immediacy, atmosphere, and "a good read." But it had an eye to the future, and to those naval virtues that his country would once more have to muster. His preface invoked the words of Frederick the Great: "It is not necessary that I *live*, but rather that I do my duty, and that I fight to save Germany."[64] The U-Boat Arm, Jung argued, had at first been underestimated; for a long time it had been relegated to merely defensive service against an aggressive enemy in home waters.[65] Faced with the inadequacy of the High Seas Fleet, Germany had then overestimated the capacities of U-boats and had cast them into the breech by setting them tasks with which they could scarcely cope. But once the true "offensive spirit" had been found, U-boats had come into their own.

Why had U-boat warfare ultimately failed? Not because of the German submariners, Jung argues in concert with other veterans since the earliest days. Germany – and with it the U-Boat Arm – had collapsed because of inept political leadership. "Despite the difficult tasks they had been given, and despite their heavy losses, German submariners, even at the end, still felt strong enough to fight on. They knew that considerable reinforcements in hundreds of new U-boats would shortly reach the front."[66] As we now know, this was more vision than reality. But the vision was strong. For Jung, the German submarine service had gathered its own momentum; it had become an end in itself, a mystical body sacrificed on the altar of patriotism. To his mind, the tragic nobility of its final hours was best evoked in the words of the war poet Ferdinand Freiligrath (1810–1876), whom he quoted in part:

Doch ein Blutritt war es, ein Todesritt;
Wohl wichen sie unseren Hieben,
Doch von zwei Regimentern, was ritt und was stritt,
Unser zweiter Mann ist geblieben.

Und nun kam die Nacht, und wir ritten hindann,
Rundum die Wachtfeuer lohten;
Die Rosse schnoben, der Regen rann –
Und wir dachten der Toten, der Toten.

These verses from Freiligrath's stirring ballad "Die Trompete von Gravelotte" (1870) – the German equivalent of "The Charge of the

Light Brigade" – conjured up the fearful glory of battle. They spoke of a "blood-ride," a "death-ride"; they mourned the loss of 50 per cent of their cavalry; they invoked the hallowed memory of the dead. But they communicated more than a merely noble gesture. They picked up the patriotic theme of "Die Wacht am Rhein" made famous by Max Schneckenburger's poem of that title. Written much earlier in 1841, the poem "The Watch on the Rhine" had embodied the sharp emotional tones of nineteenth-century strife. Political conflicts between France and Germany had at that time turned the Rhine into both a national and a spiritual symbol. Schneckenburger had captured the jingoism of 1841; almost thirty years later Freiligrath had rejuvenated it by evoking the double victory of the Germans over the French at Gravelotte in August 1870, at which time half the German soldiers were killed. Now in 1939, U-boat commandant Jung made "the navy connection." In quoting the two verses from Freiligrath's ballad, Jung had conjured up a world of religious and metaphysical proportions; he had underscored a proud lineage from which his "U-boat Knights" had descended, and to which their successors would owe allegiance. By forcing Germany to deliver up all its U-boats in 1919 and by forbidding it from ever building any again, Britain had erected to German submariners what Jung called "the most sublime monument a soldier can wish." That monument was nothing less than Britain's dread of German U-boat power. As Jung's memoir concludes: "With all the greater satisfaction do we survivors see what is happening [now] after twenty years: how bold hands have shredded the Dictate of Versailles which had been extorted from us by threats and with brutal might – how a new second German U-Boat Arm is now developing, based on the spirit and on the traditions of the glorious first!"[67]

1934: Weddigen Day, 22 September 1934. ss-Führer Heinrich Himmler greets the veterans of Weddigen's crew of 1914.

1935: U-Flotille Weddigen (from top, clockwise: Kurt Fehl, Hermann Voll, ? Hagedorn, Gerhard Kar)

1936: Captain Karl Dönitz, Commander, Submarines (left), inspecting the flotilla with his guest, his First World War U-boat captain, retired ace Otto Hersing of U-21.

1937: Germany's most-decorated U-boat ace of the First World War, Lothar von Arnauld de la Perière, visits the U-boat flotille.

Preis **20** Pfg.
12. Oktober 1939
Nummer 41 / 14. Jahrg.
Druck und Verlag von M.
Du.Mont Schauberg, Köln

Kölnische
Illustrierte Zeitung

In diesem Heft: Die letzten Stunden vor Warschau

Sie haben die Courageous versenkt

1939: "They sunk the Courageous." Cover of the Cologne illustrated magazine for
12 October 1939 celebrating U-29's (Schuhart) sinking of the British aircraft carrier
on 17 September.

1939: tower of U-48 (Schultze) painted with the names of the eight ships sunk between 5 September and 17 October, a total of 52,668 tons. The last named, *City of Mandely,* was actually the *City of Mandalay.* Note the U-boat's "black cat" insignia.

1939: Günther Prien salutes Hitler on being received in the Imperial Chancellery after his daring success in the British fleet anchorage of Scapa Flow.

DAS DEUTSCHE U=BOOTLIED

Worte: Ob.-Masch.-Mt. Gottfried Wittich, Mt. W. Fichner.   Weise: Ob.-Masch.-Mt. G. Wittich u. Masch.

Was schleicht da durch das Meer
gespenstig grau daher?
Was furcht die grüne See
in Luv und auch in Lee?

Refrain:
Ein U-Boot ist's mit schlankem Leib,
gewiß fährt's nicht zum Zeitvertreib.
Es fährt gerüstet und gewandt
gen Feindesland, gen England!

Ein Auge nur es hat,
doch das genügt ihm glatt,
zu sehn das feindlich Ziel
und Tod zu bringen viel.

Der Kommandant befiehlt,
die Männer es nicht hielt:
Torpedo klar und los,
bohrt sich in Feindes Schoß.

Verderben speit das Rohr,
der Schuß den Feind erkor.
Er trifft ihn hart und wund,
schon liegt er auf dem Grund.

Wes Geist beherrscht das Meer?
Wes Wille gilt daher?
Es herrschet auf der See:
Deutschland in Luv und Lee!

1940s: postcard, "The German U-boat Song," trumpeting that Germany rules the waves.

Liebes, blondes Seemannskind

Worte und Weise von Masch.-Obergefr. Oskar Linke-Lohbrück

1. Liebes, blondes Seemannskind,
   Gib mir einen Kuß geschwind.
   Heute noch muß ich an Bord,
   Weine nicht, heute muß ich von dir fort.
   Seemannsliebe, Seemannslust
   Wecktest du in meiner Brust.
   Darum, blondes Mägdelein,
   Sollst auch du nicht traurig sein.

   Kehrreim:

   Wer ein rechter Seemann ist,
   Gern die kleinen Mädchen küßt.
   Alle Mädchen sind ihm gut,
   Denn er küßt sie voller Glut,
   Und das tut und das tut
   Allen Mädchenherzen gut.

2. Fährt mein Schiff aufs Meer hinaus,
   Bleibt mein Herz bei dir zuhaus.
   Und ich denke stets zurück
   Nur an dich, nur an dich mein blondes
   Glück.
   Jede Stunde, jeden Tag
   Spür' ich deinen Herzenschlag.
   Dir allein nur bleib ich treu.
   Lebe wohl, mein Schatz, ahoi, ahoi!

   Kehrreim: Wer ein rechter . . .

3. Sterbe ich den Seemannstod,
   Wein dir nicht die Augen rot.
   Denk, mein Seemannslieb, daran,
   Unser Feind, unser Feind heißt
   Engländer.
   Und trotz Bomben und Gefahr
   Bleiben wir zum Angriff klar.
   Hüte dich, o Engländer,
   Blaue Jungen greifen an.

   Kehrreim: Wer ein rechter . . .

1940s: postcard, "Sweet, blond sailor's girl." Sentimental love-em-and-leave-em song, for you know what sailors are.

1940: inspection of U-33 by (l to r) Adolf Hitler and Karl Dönitz. The skipper (von Dresky) never returned from this mission. The boat was sunk by British minesweeper HMS *Gleaner* while it was laying mines in the Clyde estuary on 12 February 1940.

1941: U-boat skipper Hardegen celebrates Christmas in the bow compartment of his U-123 on patrol. Note Christmas tree and portrait of Hitler.

1942: U-123 (Hardegen) sinks the 6768-ton ss *Coimbra* by gunfire on 15 January during Operation Drumbeat.

1942: crew of Teddy Suhren's U-564 on bridge, with Canadian Red Ensign and photo of British prime minister Winston Churchill taken from Canadian tanker ss *Victolite* on 11 February.

1942: Erich Topp's "Red Devil" U-boat which tangled with HMCS *Sackville*

1943: "Thetis and the skipper enjoying a tender moment." U-172 (Emmermann) crossing the equator with traditional nautical highjinks.

1943: U-172 covered in ice on northern patrol.

1940: tower of U-25 (Schütze) decorated with heraldic shark's jaws and death's head.

1945: U-1009 surrenders to HMS *Byron* on 7 May 1945, when Germany announced her capitulation. Note the black flag flying at the periscope.

1945: prisoners' dock of the British Military Court Martial in Hamburg in October. These crew of U-852 (l to r: Skipper Heinz Eck, Second Officer August Hoffmann, Medical Officer Walter Weisspfennig, Engineering Officer Richard Lenz, and Bosn Wolfgang Schweder) were found guilty of war crimes for having murdered victims of the ss *Peleus* they had sunk. The officers were executed by firing-squad.

3 Dönitz's Men: U-boats in the Third Reich, 1939–45

Unabated since the early 1930s, U-boat literature had been looking forward to, even forecasting, the new age of Germany's maritime offensive against Great Britain. Scarcely had war begun in 1939 when two mass-produced booklets on the subject appeared: Otto F. Schütte's illustrated *Deutschlands U-Boote: Der Schrecken Englands* [Germany's U-boats: England's Terror] and Fritz Otto Busch's *U-Boote gegen England* [U-boats against England]. With an introduction written by a submarine engineer, Schütte's work bridged the gulf between the grand theme of the 1914–18 war "against England" and the theme of the new age. In doing so it gathered together all the pent-up rancour that had been nurtured during the 1920s and 1930s. Alluding to Hashagen's famous book *U-Boote Westwärts!* [U-boats Westwards, 1931] – which he described as "one of the best and most interesting books" to have emerged from the First World War – Schütte capitalized on the implicit "command" that the title contained: "For that's just what the title is – a command; it points out the enemy who both then and now wanted to destroy Germany, and against whom both then and now the counterstroke must be directed." Ever true to the imperial claims, the submariners would sally forth with the nation's blessing: "In this war which has been forced upon us we wish our U-boats further success; they have an historical task to fulfil, fundamental to the very existence of our nation."[1] As in the First World War, it was the submarine, not the blue-water surface fleet, that bore what was repeatedly referred to as Germany's "historically legitimate" destiny. The submarine's very appearance bespoke fore-ordination, tradition, and iron will: "... lean, beautiful U-boats. Brightly gleams the sun upon the decks from a clear blue autumn sky, reflecting itself in the oily harbour water, and painting small trembling curls on the grey flanks of the steel bodies which, with the broad hump of their conning towers, are moored to their base like primeval sea-monsters, sinister hunters of the sea."[2]

Busch's "U-boats against England," completed in November 1939, drew upon a mixture of sources: news releases and radio reports of the propaganda ministry, newspaper articles, and his own notes from the first days of the war. It provided popular sketches of Germany's initial submarine successes. Some of these had indeed been major.

Germany's opening moves in the U-boat war had at first been tentative. But some spectacular successes set the stage for a series of media events that the propaganda ministry would exploit. On 17 September 1939 Kapitänleutnant Otto Schuhart (U-29) sank the aircraft carrier HMS *Courageous* in the Western Approaches, with the loss of 518 British lives. The BBC announced the loss the next day, and the news, as a German submariner later recalled, "spread like wildfire throughout Germany."[3] It allegedly galvanized the public, whose long-dormant faith in this weapon was suddenly reawakened. Schuhart's attack on the *Courageous* had "struck a chord in the memory of the German people."

Within a month, during the night of 14 October, Günther Prien's U-47 struck the Royal Navy's fleet anchorage at Scapa Flow. Just as Versailles and Compiègne had epitomized the nation's abject defeat, so Scapa Flow, where in 1919 German sailors had scuttled their captured fleet, had up to now symbolized the navy's humiliation and shame. Prien's brazen and calculating attack was therefore charged with propaganda value. Not only had he penetrated Britain's seemingly impregnable fleet haven, but he had sunk the 29,000-ton battleship HMS *Royal Oak*, with the loss of 830 British lives. The mission became the very stuff of legend, with a stalwart German submariner bearding the imperial British lion in his den. As Winston Churchill put it: "This episode, which must be regarded as a feat of arms on the part of the German U-boat commander, gave a shock to [British] public opinion [and] might have been politically fatal to any Minister responsible for pre-war precautions."[4] German propaganda made use of the attack and immediately broadcast details. In a German submariner's retrospective: "For the first time the name of Prien was heard by the German people. Prien in Scapa Flow – where twenty years before, the German High Seas Fleet had gone to the bottom!"[5]

Shocking to the British and exhilarating to the Germans, this extraordinary mission made Prien the first charismatic hero of the new U-boat war and launched the new phase of submarine iconography.

Acclaimed in newsreels, newspapers, radio, and public parades, Prien lost little time in writing his memoir under the imprimature of Berlin's nationalist publishing house The German Press. U-boat skippers Günther Prien and Joachim Schepke had little time to produce reflective memoirs. Thrust into submarine combat at the outbreak of war in 1939, they were too preoccupied commanding their submarines to ponder the meaning of history, and too much in the hands of the propagandists to see much further than the present. In their brief but enormously successful service from 1939 until 1941 they became the legendary "tonnage kings" for which naval history remembers them. Together with Otto Kretschmer they constituted the holy trinity of the early u-boat war. Each one left a literary legacy: Prien and Schepke prior to 1941, when they met their death, and Kretschmer after his release from a prisoner-of-war camp in Canada once the war was over.

Günther Prien's *Mein Weg nach Scapa Flow* [My Road to Scapa Flow] appeared in the autumn of 1940 as a survey of "the most interesting episodes" of his career both before and after his attack on Scapa Flow. He too recognized this pivotal point in naval warfare "as a mile-stone" both in his own life and in "the constant flow of events." He therefore recast the chronological sequence of his experiences in order to treat his major success last. "That seemed quite correct in a book narrated right from life." One officer on the mission to Scapa, who himself would become a submarine commander of note, hinted at the character behind the tale: "He is of quick-silver vivaciousness, like a boy about to play a prank."[6] Such, at any rate, was his mind-set just prior to the epic attack.

Prien's eye-witness account of destroying the *Royal Oak* captured the visceral elements of undersea warfare that had already dominated the genre since 1915. His graphic images implicitly restated the conviction of German invincibility. Having slipped through the anchorage and fired his lethal torpedoes, Prien and the sailors on the bridge were struck by the vulnerability of British sea power.

But now something occurs that nobody expected, and which nobody who has seen will ever forget in his life. A wall of water rears up. Its as though the sea were suddenly standing on end. Dull blows resound one after another like the artillery barrage of a battle until they merge into a single ear-splitting burst. Cones of flame shoot upward – blue, yellow, red.

The sky disappears behind these hellish fireworks. Black shadows fly through the flames like huge birds, falling into the water with a splash, causing meter-tall fountains to shoot up. They're huge fragments of mast, of the bridge and the funnels. We must have hit the magazine, and the death-dealing cargo has ripped the ship's body apart ... Its as though the gates of hell had suddenly torn open, and I were staring into the midst of the blazing inferno.[7]

Having destroyed his target, nothing remained but to escape: "get out of here safely, out of this witches' cauldron." The description almost echoed Spieß's account of Weddigen's destruction of HMS *Cressy* in 1915, and thus linked with a pattern of popular literary leitmotifs.

In highlighting his already famous penetration of Scapa Flow, Prien exploited the derivative and stereotyped formula of U-boat literature that would continue throughout the war, trying to show what it was like to command a submarine on such a dangerous mission. "At such times all feeling ceases. You think with the Boat, you are the brain of this steel beast that's now creeping up to the much more powerful foe. At such times one must think in iron and steel – or perish."[8] The dehumanized industrial language of iron and steel, of welding and burnishing, was the stock-in-trade of National Socialist propaganda. Nine years after the war, a British translator of Prien's book would complain with some justification "that a literal translation would be obscene and often ridiculous [and had] forced some toning down of the picturesque language."[9] In trying to find an unrepentant Nazi to present to the British public, the translator had overstated the case, for in fact the book is really not as colourful as he led his postwar readers to expect. As he had explained, it is but "a breezy yarn told with no pretensions to a literary style."

Prien sweeps his reader through the euphoria of a grateful nation's accolades. The public adulation had begun with his entering harbour, with ships manning the side to greet him (just like Weddigen in U-9 some twenty-seven years earlier). His tumultuous reception amid martial music and flowers at dockside was dominated by the presence of Admiral Dönitz; it reached a climax when both he and his crew flew to Berlin in Hitler's personal aircraft, and when Hitler presented Prien with the Knight's Cross of the Iron Cross. Photographs captured exquisite moments of the national celebration: Prien's triumphal entry in an open staff car through Berlin's Brandenburg Gate; the arrival of the folk-hero and his crew to the Reich chancellery surrounded by tumultuous crowds, and their grand reception in the large private office of their radiant Führer with all the Nazi party's high functionaries. Of meeting the Führer himself, Prien wrote, "the dream of my youth had become reality, and perhaps the greatest and best thing in life is when we actually do realize the dreams of our youth." In this light, National Socialism was more than a political philosophy; it was a grand movement of self-realization whose guru, seen in his great loneliness of command, was Adolf Hitler. "His dream becomes deed ...

his faith gains life," Prien had written of the Führer. Such lines accorded with the recruiting thrust of much U-boat literature: German youth too could fulfil its own dreams by coming aboard.

For a story of such potentially high propaganda value, it is told with striking restraint. As Prien's postscript notes, he had stuck to the truth. Yet the media compensated in full measure for his modesty. The Nazi party's photo tabloid *Illustrierter Beobachter* provided full-page coverage of the events: photos showed Hitler shaking Prien's hand and presenting the Knight's Cross, Prien and his crew dining with Hitler, Prien shaking hands with propaganda minister Dr Goebbels. Bold headlines proclaimed "Naval Hero Prien and His U-boat Men – England's Naval Supremacy Shaken," and "The Führer and Nation Offer Thanks." These were followed by full-blown speculations about the U-boat having shattered British self-confidence. The *Berliner Illustrierte Nacht-ausgabe* and others picked up the themes and spread them across the country. Prien's achievements would continue to provide copy for months. Almost a year later to the day, the *Hessische Landes-Zeitung* and others proclaimed sinkings of 327,000 tons of Allied shipping in two days, as our "U-Boat Arm delivers crushing blows" – accompanied by the now almost obligatory photo of Prien, or some other ace, on his U-boat bridge looking casual and self-assured. As the illustrated magazine *Elegante Welt* put it, "there is such a thing as a U-boat face: [it's that] steely, wistful expression" caused by "the tough, primitive living conditions aboard, the tension, [and] the skipper having to live by his instinct." Braced by iron-bound discipline, and interwoven by constrained apprehensions, "this life would etch deep lines in the faces of these young men."[10] In 1943 another writer would evoke the submariner's "sharp, prematurely aging, yet cheerful face."[11] The battleworn and confident visage of the rugged, idealistic submariner became a standard icon of U-boat culture.

Traditions thrived and were consciously fostered by such practices as naming new submarines after renowned predecessors from 1914–18. Thus when the new U-53 was launched, officials invited the former crew of her famous First World War namesake to attend the ceremonies. Hans Rose, the captain of the first U-53, described the portentous scene in an updated version of his *Auftauchen! Kriegsfahrten von U-53* [Surface! Combat Patrols of U-53, 1939]: "When we then lay our hands on the new boat and transfer our spirit and loyalty to it, it can mean only this: there's a comradeship unto death for our beloved Fatherland and for our Führer Adolf Hitler."[12] Rose had been in the National Socialist movement since 1930 and had written elsewhere that the navy had matured him: under naval tutelage he had grown from a petit-bourgeois lad to a member of a great nation. His sense of cohesion and continuity had found expression among other veterans on Weddigen Day in 1934; the former crew of the famous u-9 had gathered at the grave of their captain to commemorate the twentieth anniversary of his masterful attack against three British cruisers. On this occasion, the inspecting officer had been none other than Gestapo chief and ss head Heinrich Himmler.

Public interest in the u-boat war was controlled and nurtured by the propaganda ministry, which urged its war reporters to provide more drama and colour. The German Naval War Office had long inclined towards more sober, factual accounts, but it eventually bent to the pressure from the party-driven ministry.[13] The result was a controlled mixture of truth and fabrication, of news and manipulation. The public's understanding of u-boats was therefore in large measure a fiction; it was a contrived fantasy which the survivors of the war would carry into the postwar years as the "truth" against which they would measure the veracity of reconstuctionist history.

Like Prien's account, Joachim Schepke's *U-Bootfahrer von heute: Erzählt und gezeichnet von einem U-Boot-Kommandanten* [Submariners of Today: Narrated by a U-boat Commander] also appeared in the Berlin publishing house German Press in 1940. One of his principal purposes was proclamation of the Tirpitz doctrine of naval supremacy. As he wrote in the preface: "A people that doesn't understand the sea will always remain a second-rate nation; the key to world power is that we Germans must go to sea on the world's oceans." Apart from this attempt at addressing the broad issues of maritime policy, Schepke indulged in the most primitive humbug ever put at the service of German recruiters and propagandists:

Dear German reader, know when you take this little book to hand, that it has been written just for you, whether you be man, woman, old or young, more or less well-to-do or educated, whether you be a seaman or not a seaman.

And know this too: a people that doesn't understand the sea will always remain a second-class nation. If you who live deep in the interior of the country don't believe this, then read this little book right to the end; then you'll believe it ... and then you will know that we Germans must go to sea, and that the key to world power is on the sea.

Schepke's assurances to the reader that he was not writing a piece of propaganda would have fooled no adult of even modest wit. The book was a blatant piece of recruiting pamphleteering, with his invitation to "come aboard my u-boat and breathe in the air." Conning his reader with the intimate form of address, Schepke scarcely masked his tone of militant paternalism: "You've already read many books about the submariners of the last war; thrilled by it all, you now want to know of their heroic deeds ... and of how things are going with us U-boat men today."[14] The authority for promoting the splendid life to be led beneath the waves went beyond that of the combat U-boat skipper himself. Adding weight to his own experiences, Schepke cited his "Führer," Adolf Hitler, who had "addressed the submariners at Wilhelmshaven at the beginning of this war and said that he could not imagine a finer community of fighting men than a U-boat crew."

Taking his German reader on a tour of his U-boat, Schepke took care to introduce each trade so that the reader might get the feel of what this band of brothers was really all about. Nazi ideology is never far away. Unlike Prien, Schepke was a National Socialist, and his account was sometimes stridently polemical. In one passage, for instance, he introduced the youngest member of the crew, traditionally called "Moses" in the German navy: "Now, quite contrary to what you, a conscientious Aryan, might think, [the term] Moses doesn't mean that we have a Jew on board. No, my dear friend. In the first place you don't find any Jews at sea at all; and secondly, the seamen would hardly share their space with such an aberration of nature [Schöpfungsprodukt]." Schepke also railed against Britain's "race for sea supremacy," and appealed both for personal sacrifice – and for recruits: "Germany needs many submariners. The more U-boats there are to sail against England, and the more German men who resolve to face their vilest enemy on the high seas, then all the worse it is for him. And all the better for Germany!"

Schepke's book is noteworthy for its exploitative style and for the often mindless commitment to political ideology. His image of the U-Boat Arm was nonetheless conventional – dash and bravado, and a nobility of mind. Touted in public as "the most successful U-boat crew" (similar accolades had regularly fallen upon Prien and Kretschmer), Schepke and his shipmates made many public appearances. Thus the notes for an official visit in January 1941 to München, "the capital city of the [Nazi] Movement," as the printed program described it, gave them maximum exposure to both populace and press and stressed the links between U-boats, national culture, and the Nazi party.[15] The visit included a city tour and a visit to "the Brown House," from which Hitler had operated in the days of the famous Beer Hall putsch; it scheduled a visit to the "House of German Art," in which party-driven aesthetics were extolled and where the propaganda-writer Lothar-Günther Buchheim, later famous as the author of the novel *Das Boot* (1973), displayed his politically correct work. The tour ended with an evening reception given by the "mayor of the capital city of the movement."

In the same year that Prien and Schepke produced their popular works, Vizeadmiral Otto Groos published "What Everyone Must Know about Maritime Warfare" (1940) under the imprint of Berlin's People and Empire Press.[16] The introduction by Großadmiral Raeder harped on the grand old themes of maritime prestige that Tirpitz had first orchestrated in the *Dreadnought* days before the First World War. Groos himself marched out traditional naval wisdom by charging leaders of the First World War era with having initiated only "half-hearted" measures against "English encirclement." Times had now changed, he explained, and Germany could finally be bold. "Thanks to the inspired leadership of Adolf Hitler, there now stands opposite British sea power a Großdeutschland unified in all its lineages, and firmly welded together in its philosophy."[17] Here his linguistic mix of biology and metallurgy is telling, for he described the organic unity of all Germanic races in a vibrant new nation [in allen Stämmen geeint] firmly forged together in a single philosophy [in seiner Weltanschauung fest zusammengeschmiedet]. Wilhelm Reinhard's *Wir an den Maschinen* [We Engine-room Men, 1940] saw similar vitalism in the u-boat's organic integration of man and machine: "… a remarkable and miraculous synthesis of spirit and heart-blood of comrades, of steel body and cable-nerves in the machine, of the will for combat and life, of torpedo and gun: comradeship between man and machine! They bear the homeland over water, under water. In the heart, in the machines … God bless this little, several hundred-ton-large German world."[18]

Vizeadmiral Karl Dönitz, Commander-in-Chief, Submarines, also published in 1940. He released his extended essay "The U-Boat Arm" in order to reach as wide a readership as possible, "even those in the interior of the country and laymen."[19] It underwent three printings in the first year of publication. Significantly, he had signed off the manuscript in January 1939, some eight months before the war began. Drawing upon historical precedents from the First World War, and also looking into the future, Dönitz encapsulated the nature of what he and other writers called the u-boat spirit. "The U-Boat Arm is a special weapon and branch of the service, which requires technically highly developed boat material [and] which above all needs tough, combat-ready and devoted crews, with the best training and skill. The u-boat man loves his weapon. It has proven its bold spirit in the Great War, and even today's U-Boat Arm is nurturing this plucky desire for one's best endeavour."[20]

Fritz Otto Busch had used similar language in "U-boats against England," which appeared in 1939: tonnage warfare offered "the surest and most powerful weapon against England's illegal hunger blockade" of Germany and required of German crews a "readiness to commit themselves unto the ultimate sacrifice." Of course, the "ultimate sacrifice" would increase the need for recruits to replace the dead, and many books, like Korvettenkapitän Max Bartsch's forty-page pamphlet *Was jeder vom deutschen U-Boot wissen muß* [What Everyone Must Know about the German Submarine, 1940] specifically targeted this requirement. Bartsch's booklet opened with a schoolboy conversation: "Heil Hitler, Hans! How's everything in West End school?" Hans replies that things have been going very well indeed. The new teacher has been explaining "the world situation" and awakening the young to the great cause. He has even told them of the grand life in the U-Boat Arm: submarine service makes a man out of you; learning in the navy means learning for life. This enthusiastic schoolboy banter is followed by a series of typical U-boat yarns from 1914–18, and the book ends with two pages designed to answer the rhetorical question: "And how do we get into the navy?" Gerhard Wiedemayer's *Waffe unter Wasser* [Weapon Underwater, 1940] built similarly on the U-boat legacy of the First World War. In "sending forth [his] little book to teach the reader unshakable faith in Germany and in its victory," he had felt inspired by one of the major musical icons of German submarine history: Hermann Löns's popular song about setting off against Britain, "... denn wir fahren gegen Engeland."

Löns had himself been a casualty of war in 1914. But as Wiedemayer rightly noted, his song had already "enthused a whole generation and a whole German world." Ever popular, it was played and replayed in pubs, newsreels, and feature films during the war, and in reconstructionist films after 1945; it was a main-stay of military songbooks and gave its name to the navy's fleet newspaper '... *gegen Engeland': Marine Frontzeitung*. A song on the age-old theme of the warrior taking leave of his beloved in order to fight for home and country, it nonetheless singles out "Engeland" as the bitter, hereditary foe:

Comes the news that I have fallen,
That I sleep in the ocean's flood;
Weep not for me, o my darling
Think, for Fatherland I've spent my blood.

There our flag unfurled at the masthead
Showing forth our Empire's might;
For we will no longer suffer
That the Englishman scorns its sight.

The fourth and final verse culminates in the painful farewell – "Give me your hand, your little white hand" – and legitimizes the parting as necessary for the national cause: we are setting forth against England – "denn wir fahren gegen Engeland, Engeland!"

Another resurrection from the Great War was Iwan Crompton's book *Englands Verbrechen an U 41* [England's Crimes against U-41], first published in 1917 under a slightly different title. Reissued in 1940, it had been revised to fit the new mood. Fulminating against "Churchill's methods" and "British skullduggery" in the Great War, and railing against Britain's "most base calumnies [and] repulsive hate orgies against Germany," it claimed to reveal the "dastardly" use of submarine decoy ships. Such a Q-ship was the famous British vessel *Baralong*, which had committed "the crimes against U-41" not merely by sinking the U-boat, but by shooting her survivors in the water. (British sources subsequently admitted the atrocity was true.) That the British commander had subsequently been decorated by the king was simply too much for the author of "England's Crimes" to suffer silently. Crompton noted bitterly that "in 1939 the same Englishman [who had committed the crime] is once again summoned by the same Mr. Churchill [who had been First Lord of the Admiralty in the Great War] to exercise his 'proven methods' against the German U-boats."

It was now abundantly clear to Germany's officials in their secret enclaves, and indeed to all who read the daily press, that the Battle of the Atlantic would be the scene of the great "decisive battle" that German strategy had always envisaged.[21] Yet it would turn out to be a vastly different clash of naval forces from that which most people expected. Instead of a confrontation of massed fleets like the battles of Trafalgar or Jutland, it became a drawn-out six-year struggle marked by sudden, frequent, and violent encounters across the whole breadth of the ocean. The turning point would come in 1943 when, by all analysis, Germany had lost any hope of victory against the massed maritime resources of the British Commonwealth and the United States. However, as a result of a series of decisions, Germany would keep on fighting desperately until her unconditional surrender on 8 May 1945.

When Germany lost her three greatest tonnage kings in the month of March 1941, the propaganda ministry lost its most marketable knights of the deep. In the night of 8 March 1941 the British destroyer HMS *Wolverine* sunk Prien's famous U-47.[22] Just over a week later, in the night of 16/17 March, the British destroyer HMS *Vanoc* detected Schepke's U-100 on the surface. In the first successful encounter with the new type 286 radar, she rammed the U-boat, slicing through Schepke himself and destroying the submarine. That same night the British destroyer HMS *Walker* detected Kretschmer's U-99 by asdic (sonar) and shattered it with a pattern of six depth-charges. Bursting to the surface in its death throes, U-99 disgorged thirty-nine of her crew including Kretschmer, who spent the rest of the war as a prisoner in Canada. A former submariner subsequently observed that the loss of Prien and Kretschmer was regarded at the time as a "double tragedy that confused the German population," who had come to regard them as "invincible heroes."[23] Conscious of the demoralizing void, it would be months before German authorities could bring themselves to admit the loss of Prien, the adulated "Bull of Scapa Flow." British propaganda, by contrast, quickly exploited the situation. In radio broadcasts to Germany, and with air-dropped handbills it jibed:

Schepke – Kretschmer – Prien. What has become of these three officers, the most famous German U-boat commanders, the only ones on whom Hitler has bestowed the Oak Leave Cluster to the Knight's Cross?

Schepke is dead. German High Command had to admit it. Kretschmer is captured. German High Command had to admit it. AND PRIEN? Who has heard anything of Prien recently? What does German High Command have to say about Prien? WHERE IS PRIEN?

The handbill from which these lines are taken included a photograph showing a captured German submarine officer disembarking from a Royal Navy destroyer; as the handbill exclaimed, he "had gone to sea as a wolf of the Atlantic and is now arriving in England as a prisoner of war." Picking up the familiar theme of the Hermann Löns song "… denn wir fahren gegen Engeland," the flyer taunted: "They did indeed set out against 'Engeland'; but they're not returning home!"[24] In a Germany still clinging to her heroes for hope, Prien's fate continued to tantalize the public mind. Speculation remained rife until the 1950s that Prien was somehow still alive – either in Britain, in a Russian prison camp, or in a "ghost U-boat" that refused to give up. Principal among the works that helped keep the hero in the national memory was Wolfgang Frank's book *Prien greift an* [Prien Attacks, 1941]. Allegedly based on official documents, this historical novel about the life of Prien was dedicated "to the Living as a model, to the following generation as solemn admonition, and in memory of Günther Prien and his men." The title page quotes lines made famous in Prien's own war book *Mein Weg nach Scapa Flow* (1940): "What is success? You can call it luck or grace. But the main thing for us men is just this: to have the heart of a fighter, and to be able to forget oneself for the sake of the cause one is serving."

Frank's book took his readers through the usual adventures and concluded with Prien's setting forth on his last voyage. He ended with a classical U-boat theme of youth spiritually matured beyond their years, and spared the melancholy fate of having to face old age: "You [Prien] were favoured with being able to perfect your life early, something which is granted to few – the full life of a great clear soldier through Becoming, Renown and Death ... No Boat will sail without your standing invisibly on the bridge." Frank would publish another life of Prien in 1958, but the different cultural climate would prevent him from indulging in such maudlin passages.[25] Certainly, his 1941 version, full of Prien's sayings and insights, reflected the temper of the times. Prien's description of the U-boat is a case in point: "A boat is a living creature. If everyone does not become one of its organs, if everyone doesn't understand that we must function together like a beautiful, elegant, supple beast of prey, then its nothing ... And that's the magnificent part about our weapon: the individual by himself is nothing, all are everything."[26] The word "weapon" (German, *Waffe*) in the above quotation is the same word for *arm* in the expression "U-Boat Arm." Thus the submarine is the microcosm of the whole submarine service from which it takes its higher meaning, and with which it shares its societal values. These values were not subjected to searching criticism in the public domain. Writers of the day indulged primarily in myth-making.

A saliant example was the feature film *U-Boote Westwärts!* [U-boats Westwards], which drew its title from Hashagen's well-known novel about German submarines in the First World War.[27] Launched during a gala premiere in Berlin on 9 May 1941 attended by senior members of both the military and the Nazi party, the immensely attractive production (according to then prevailing tastes) was by all accounts the hit of the year. The production by Ufa studios in Berlin had had the full backing not only of Naval High Command, but of the Commander-in-Chief, Submarines, Admiral Karl Dönitz, his officers and crews. With the U-Boat Arm and its leaders receiving such credits in advertisements, the public could accept the stirring account of "U-boats in combat against the English battle-fleet" as entirely authentic. Only one of the actors would remain associated with the U-boat image. Jochen Brennecke, who portrayed an idealistic naval lieutenant, would, as a gunner's mate in the naval reserve, publish his first book of submarine lore in 1943. Between 1956 and 1984 he would publish four more works of popular U-boat history.

With its mixed background of rousing martial music, romantic serenades, sentimentality, and visceral action, the film *U-Boote Westwärts!* delivered a propaganda punch. Indeed, the propaganda ministry found that it not only promoted national policies ("staatspolitisch wertvoll"), but was aesthetically worthwhile. For both these reasons it was deemed valuable for educating the German Volk (volksbildend). It portrays the Germans as chivalrous and gallant, and impeccably correct in their pursuit of merchant shipping according to the Prize Rules of detention and search. Individually sailed ships, we learn, were invariably afforded the courtesies of international law. Indeed, only when the Allies run ships in convoys do the film-Germans attack without warning. Dramatic tension was of the essence. In one such scenario the U-boat skipper stops a Dutch merchantman on the high seas. His four-man Prize crew scour the vessel and discover it attempting to smuggle aircraft propellers to Britain in contravention of international law. But just as the four Germans are setting their scuttling charges and the Dutch crew escapes into life-boats, British warships arrive. The U-boat skipper has no choice but to torpedo the Dutchman, leaving his own sailors to be picked up by a British destroyer – a cruiser, according to advertisements – as prisoners of war. Always with an eye to the dramatization of that inner struggle between a soldier's heart and his sense of duty, the script captures a poignant moment exploited in a great many works of this genre: the moment of crucial decision. Here as elsewhere, the higher calling of duty wins out. Knowing his men safe aboard the very British destroyer he now holds in his sights, the U-boat skipper masters his pangs of conscience and fires his lethal torpedoes. The contemporary movie magazine *Illustrierter Film-Kurier* captured the essence of selfless and rugged dauntlessness that the film-makers wanted to portray.

The U-boat escapes [the counterattack] submerged. Only at dusk does he surface again, his men hoping to find their [captured] comrades have escaped the sunken Englishman unscathed. And they really do manage to discover warrent officer Warmbusch and the seriously wounded Lieutenant von Benedikt [played by Jochen Brennecke] drifting on a raft ... Von Benedikt dies with the proud smile of victorious youth on his lips.

In fact, the young officer's last words – "It is sweet and honourable to die for the Fatherland" – expressed sentiments long since debunked in the First World War poetry of Wilfred Owen. For Owen, "Dulce et decorum est" had been "the old Lie" told to "children ardent for some desperate glory." But for the film *U-Boote Westwärts* it was still coin of the realm.

After a successful mission of many months, the U-boat returns home to be received and welcomed by Admiral Dönitz – played by Dönitz himself – who lauds their heroic achievements. Addressing his movie-set submariners, he utters slogans that he would deliver in real life off the set: "Struggle, sacrifice and victory; the fight goes on." And in the words of the movie magazine: "They will set forth once again, fight once again, be victorious once again just as long as the order is issued: 'U-boats Westward!'" Dönitz would send his men to sea until Germany's capitulation on 8 May 1945. By that time all that would remain of the film's bravado would be the haunting strains of the movie's hit songs "Warte mein Mädel, dort in der Heimat" and "Irgendwo in weiter Ferne." As these titles imply, by that time many a sweetheart was waiting "back at home" for the hero who now lay "somewhere in distant reaches" and would never come back. The Allied Military Government banned the film after the war.

But in the 1940s even historical works supported the national bandstanding about the cult of heroism. For example, Hans Arthur Thies's *Der Eiserne Seehund: Wilhelm Bauer, der Erfinder des U-Boots* [The Iron Seal, 1941] examined the origins of the u-boat and focused on its inventor Wilhelm Bauer and the "Iron Seal" with which he had experimented in 1850. This was the second book on Bauer since Hauff's treatise of 1859, but it was far less scientific. The subtitle promised the reader "action, fate and adventure," where in fact Thies himself had exercised restraint by merely calling the book a biographical novel. Prien had written the cover blurb.

By awakening his readers to the cultural background of the halcyon days of u-boat warfare, Thies clearly intended to ride the wave of u-boat euphoria. His introduction promoted the view that Bauer had moved in a mystical sphere of primal instinct and intuition, that somehow he had emerged from the Volk and returned to the Volk, and that he had been endowed with "the wisdom of the possessed." Such fuzzy-minded, pseudo-mystical palaver was typical of National Socialist philosophers. The final flourish of the turgid introduction set Bauer's work in its cultural context.

One and the same will, one and the same goal-oriented power stand in the damp, dark, hulking space of the Iron Seal of 1850 and in the machine-pounding technosaur of 1940 which the Dreadnought [battleship] so fears: both are peering and waiting into [sic] the future. They are struggling for the morrow. And thus one and the same line [of tradition] across a whole century runs through both of them: through the crew that today sails off into the rising dawn of the Germans, and through Corporal Wilhelm Bauer, the first man who dove into the twilight.

Thies salted such fare with excerpts from the famous poem "Prometheus" (1777) by Germany's classical poet Johann Wolfgang von Goethe. Thies has bent to his ill-defined political purpose this magnificent work from the writer's revolutionary "Storm and Stress" years. With the intent of raising a clarion call against Britain, Thies transposed the classical Titans of Goethe's poem into the arch enemy England. "Who helped me against the insolence of the Titans?" Goethe's chained Prometheus cries out in indignation. "Who saved me from death, and from slavery? Hast thou not done this thyself, holy, glowing heart?" And of course the reader must conclude that the "holy, glowing heart" – of Wilhelm Bauer, Prien, Schepke, Kretschmer, and Hitler – has indeed fulfilled national destiny. In 1942 Thies produced another edition.[28] This time he ended with visionary presentiments of music, mists, and memories, thereby fusing contemporary reality with some saccharine hints at Bauer's mystical involvement in the outbound "iron swarms" of u-boats heading into battle.

Bauer's development of the submarine was dramatized in 1942 in the feature film *Geheimakte WB1* [Secret File wB1], directed by Herbert Selpin and starring Alexander Golling. In his battles against imperial bureaucracy and myopic military leadership, Wilhelm Bauer (the wB of the film's title) emerged here as a clairvoyant harbinger of Germany's technical mastery of a new and unprecedented weapon. Once again, the viewer was reminded of continuity in change, of the historical traditions of a submarine superiority that bore its own seeds of destiny.

Yet another important link in the u-boat's organic Chain of Being was formed that same year by Kapitänleutnant Wolfgang Kaden's book *Auf Ubootjagd gegen England* [U-boat Hunt against England]. Kaden too underscored the historical continuity of submarine service and self-sacrifice since the First World War. He claimed to have "read many books about the [First] World War" and to have been "awed by the blue and grey lads," the sailors and soldiers who prefigured his own experience of war. Only now could he "work his way into what they had felt" and understand the tradition of which he himself was now part. For Kaden, war at sea was an existential matter, cutting through all that was superfluous in human culture. Far from recognizing the fact that the first victim of war is truth, he argued the view that war had actually made phrase-mongering and sloganeering unnecessary and had revealed the sailor as the repository of all honesty. War showed, in words echoing Dönitz, the sailor's commitment to deeds: "In the eyes of the sea and of death, everything that is false, petty, ungenuine and untrue passes away; all empty phrases, all ringing words are extinguished; every human vanity, every human covetousness sinks away. In the face of the sea and of death only the simple, the unpretentious and the true is of value – and ultimately only the deed!"[29]

Such sentiments were doubtless shared by retired Admiral Hermann Bauer, who in the First World War had been Commander-in-

Chief, Submarines. Bauer dedicated his autobiography *Als Führer der U-Boote im Weltkriege* (1942) "to the memory of fallen comrades in the World War, and in memory of my only son who, faithful to their ideal, fought and fell in the present war as a U-boat captain." In command of U-30, his son Max-Hermann had been sunk with all his crew on 10 April 1940 near the Shetland Islands.[30] Yet the old admiral did not mention his son by name; for, like the fallen comrades of an earlier generation, Max-Hermann too had doubtless merged himself namelessly into the brotherhood of naval tradition. Kaden's phrase lent a catechetic authority to this approach: "In the face of the sea and of death only the simple, the unpretentious and the true is of value – and ultimately only the deed!" Such sentiments were also shared by the official war reporter Harald Busch in his popularly written picturebook *U-Boot auf Feindfahrt: Bildberichte vom Einsatz im Atlantik* [U-boat on Patrol, 1942]. "Millions of German and foreign radio listeners," he explained, and "millions of newspaper readers" have thrilled second-hand to the crushing exploits of German U-boats against Britain's lifelines. Now his book promised to offer a first-hand look. With all the stock-in-trade of battle narratives – "tough, tireless chase" and "bold decisions" – he commented on his photographs. (Left without his rhetoric, his excellent pictures would have spoken even more eloquently for themselves.) The last shot showed the naval flag flying from a U-boat's stern – black Swastika in a white circle against a black cross on a red background. The caption linked the earliest days of Teutonic exploits with the new-world mission of National Socialism. "Like the vikings who once wore their red battle shield at the mast, pursuing their feudal rights at sea [Herrenrecht], so they too set forth today across the broad Atlantic, the German U-boats, wearing the blazing red battle flag which the Führer gave them: in the battle for the future."[31] Werner Hartmann's richly illustrated account *Feind im Fadenkreuz* [Enemy in My Sights, 1942] provided a commander's view of battle.[32] As Admiral Dönitz wrote in the perfunctory preface to the book, "mental dash is the essential thing in life, and Hartmann, you've got it!" He thanked Hartmann for "the magnificent descriptions" that were bound to show the reader what U-boats are all about. While Dönitz admired such visceral traits as "mental dash" and "spiritual verve" [seelischer Schwung], he never disguised his anti-intellectualism when commanding his boats. Thus, when concluding the preface, he fired off some of his now famous "whip crack" action words: "seizing the moment is better than subtle pondering." Certainly, the book is a lively read, vivid and entertaining. In launching the book, both Hartmann and Dönitz had the practical aim of recruiting for the submarine service. In the words of the preface, Dönitz had hoped the book would "attract the right young talent – tough, hardy lads with steadfast hearts." In Dönitz's words, U-boat skipper Hartmann would have found it the "finest success if young men who love seafaring and soldiering would be moved by the [U-boat] experience to join the fleet along with us."

The adventures of one such fresh recruit authenticated the very U-boat spirit such books promoted. His story *Dem Tommy entwischt* [Escape from the Tommies, 1942] was a shallow yarn published by the propaganda ministry's German Press in Berlin. Not surprisingly, it marketed all the clichés about "stupid Brits" and "naive Amis," and extolled the "resourceful German" as the Allies' superior foe.[33] Torpedoed by a British ship, the untrained recruit was taken prisoner and sent by ship to Canada, where he jumped ship and crossed the border into the United States. Here he spent many months until he was finally deported. His journey took him by ship to Japan, then across Asia to Moscow, and finally to his parents' house in Berlin. "The very next day I reported to Naval High Command, back from English POW camp. The C-in-C U-boats [Dönitz] presented me with the Iron Cross First Class and the [coveted] U-boat badge." Although he doubtless deserved the Iron Cross, in actual fact only qualified submariners could wear the badge and, technically speaking, the returned recruit was still untrained. But the story served a moral purpose, for his "U-boat spirit" of self-reliance had demonstrated his qualification for the elite corps. Such stalwart men were indeed sorely needed, for U-boat losses were higher than the general public knew. According to one former submariner's memoirs, the crews themselves "were not told the official figures of German losses, but were well aware of the heavy risks they ran, and on each return to harbor they could not fail to notice the gaps among their comrades. Very few of those who had sailed forth in 1939 were still with them."[34]

Meanwhile, the imperial security service continued to monitor the national mood, excerpting newspapers and radio programs and assessing public opinion on the war. Its secret "Reports from the Reich" is a rich source of officialdom's perceptions.[35] From the earliest "Happy Time" of Germany's successful U-boat war against British shipping in 1939, through the second "Happy Time" of virtually unopposed submarine attacks off the North American coast from January to April 1942, the security service reported a consistent image of invincibility. In January 1942 the prevalent mood was of "joy and surprise" at U-boat successes.[36] People reportedly admired "the grand bravado of the German U-boats." Radio audiences had apparently been deeply impressed by the broadcast series "From the Diary of a U-Boat Commandant," during which famous skippers recounted their exploits, among them Kapitänleutnant Freiherr von Tiesen-hausen who had sunk the British battleship HMS *Barham* in November 1941 with the loss of 862 lives. At the same time, security reports noted the public's conviction that "a new U-boat type is at work," and its belief, based on "the Führer's announcement, that massive deployment has now begun."[37] This "loss of prestige for America" was widely considered on a par with its defeat at Pearl Harbor. The report concluded that the German populace was "grateful for every hint about this branch of the service," for the U-Boat Arm now seemed to embody Germany's national destiny and purpose.

As one might expect, the Nazi party newspaper *Völkischer Beobachter* was central in propagating this trust in the supposedly infallible weapon. With its bold black Gothic print and tabloid-style red under-linings, a typical edition announced in November 1942 that every piece of enemy territory was under U-boat attack – "from Capetown to Canada."[38] Subsequent December editions reported "U-boats tearing huge holes in Roosevelt's supply lines to North Africa," and declared that U-boats were "London's greatest worry."[39] Soon after, the paper published a map strewn with clusters of red dots marking the victims of the U-boats' worldwide "hunting exploits," and announced their "annual bag." The map embraced large areas of the globe: from the Arctic waters around Spitzbergen to south of Argentina, from Canadian inland waters to the Gulf of Mexico, Panama, the Caribbean, and South Pacific, and from the eastern Mediterranean to the Indian Ocean. "Like drops of blood gleam the red spots on the map of the Atlantic, each one designating the spot where an enemy transport or merchantman was sunk."[40] Each sinking "consumes the fighting power of England like a heavy loss of blood." Graphic portrayal of U-boat successes in which "U-boats hunt from the North Atlantic to Madagascar," left the readers little doubt that Germany was winning the war.[41]

The harsh facts of the case were different. Soon the "Happy Time" of 1942 turned into the "Sour-Pickle Time" of 1943, when Germany lost the crucial Battle of the Atlantic that ultimately would determine the outcome of the war. From that time onward, the German submarines had no chance of ultimate success. This, as historical studies now assure us, Admiral Dönitz must have known. Faced with an implacable and distasteful reality, Germany found all the more reason to continue with propaganda publishing. Seven major U-boat books appeared that year. Written by U-boat commanders, propaganda officers, and submarine buffs, the narratives ranged the world's oceans, regaled the reader in the exploits of a self-appointed hero of Operation Drumbeat off the US coast, recounted the history of the German submarine since

Bauer's experiments of 1859, and revived the legends of the long-lost ace Joachim Schepke.

Salient among these publications was Kapitänleutnant Reinhard Hardegen's "true-to-life" account *Auf Gefechtsstationen! U-Boote im Einsatz gegen England und Amerika* [Action Stations: U-boats against England and America] in 1943. As skipper of U-123 he had participated in Operation Drumbeat (January–April 1942), Germany's first strategic advance against the North American coast. Reports by him and others had already provided the media with a wealth of material for public dissemination. Some of it, of course, could not be published for security reasons, but the fanciful claims and high adventure of imaginative propagandists would fill in the gaps. Studio shots and trick photography, for example, supposedly showing periscope views of the lights of New York, fleshed out the weekly newsreels and led audiences to believe that daring German submarines could always operate with impunity. Recognized as the second "Happy Time" of U-boat warfare, Operation Drumbeat had caught an unprepared and unsuspecting North America almost completely by surprise. One German submariner simply called the operation a "duck shoot." Hardegen's war book was a "good read," according to the taste of the times, and promoted the idea that "soft," "degenerate" North American culture could not compete with the German submariners' toughminded professionalism. At one point Hardegen recalled a prewar visit to an American submarine in the United States and compared it with its German counterpart. The American machines were "spacious" and indulged in "luxury," whereas German submarines were cramped. And yet, Hardegen explained with pride, the Germans held the advantage.

The difference lies in the fact that our submarines arose as fully charged attack-weapons for war, and we put everything into them in order to concentrate the greatest fighting power in the smallest space. As far as the German soldier is concerned, private wishes and conveniences quite naturally take a back seat. The American, however, places great value on his so-called comfort – all of which may make a strong impression when viewing on gala occasions. Recent history has shown us just how well they stand up in combat ...

In trailing off this last sentence, Hardegen knew his readers would recognize the great American failures, not the least of which were Pearl Harbor and Operation Drumbeat. But Germans not only had better equipment, his argument continued; they had better role models and leaders, too. Hardegen must have felt close to his Führer, for his boat (U-123) is the only one documented by photographic evidence as carrying a mounted portrait of Adolf Hitler, displayed prominently in the control room; the portrait was hung by the Christmas tree when Hardegen and his crew celebrated in the bow compartment while on patrol. A winner of the coveted Knight's Cross, Hardegen sang the praises of such aces as Kretschmer, Schepke, and Endraß, whose aura had contributed to the cult of his craft.

Like many other works of submarine literature, Hardegen's book was prefaced by one of Grossadmiral Dönitz's whip-crack benedictions that appealed for fresh recruits for the elite service. In fact, Dönitz's one-page pitch was a variation of the one he had written the previous year for Werner Hartmann's war story "Enemy in My Sights." In the preface to Hardegen's book, Dönitz conjured up "the old role model of cool, plucky aggressiveness," and then launched himself into the characteristic Dönitz performance. "Up and at 'em! is better than pondering and long hesitation. Attack – Up and at 'em! – Sink! May this book go out and recruit new blood for us among the youth, ready to fight along with us in this most decisive battle of the war. For only by breaking Anglo-American sea supremacy can we guarantee ourselves a free Europe." Dönitz had signed off this piece of bravado in February 1943 when it was already becoming evident that Germany had lost the war at sea.

On the home front, the propaganda ministry attempted to keep morale high by treating expectant cinema audiences to the weekly newsreels (*Wochenschau*) that highlighted and extolled the u-boat war. According to the secret police, the German populace greeted the u-boat achievement "with joy and satisfaction."[42] A recent German film historian has explained that these newsreels were designed to show "the folks back home" that "with navy desperadoes like u-boat commandant Günther Prien, the Teutonic myth of the hero transfigured in death had once more arisen" in German culture.[43] Indeed an official directive issued at the beginning of the war had ordered newsreel cameramen to photograph German fighting-men in viscerally aesthetic poses showing "the clear, noble image of German soldiers who even in the heat of battle are upright, optimistic and accustomed to victory." Always accompanied by the adrenaline-pumping finale of Franz Liszt's *Les Préludes*, the film clips became the means, in the Reichkanzler's phrase of 1918, of grafting u-boats onto the German heart. Many of these weekly newsreels were actually contrived studio shots. They provide a particularly salient example of the way in which fiction and the popular imagination interact to form national experience.

Newsreels and propaganda in Canada and Britain took similar approaches in promoting feelings of victory against the background of a ruthless enemy's warfare. Indeed, in 1943 the National Film Board of Canada produced *Corvette Port Arthur* which took viewers through a brief odyssey of naval adventure as the douty vessel and her stout-hearted lads protected Britain's lifelines on the high seas. Ever lurking beneath the waves were Nazi submarines, which in this case could not escape the devastating Canadian attacks. One U-boat – actually a "tame" British submarine on training duties and feigning lethal damage – broke the surface after having suffered a depth charge attack. Now the audience could see how cowardly Germans actually were. Portraying the "craven Hun" while tumbling out of hatches in mock panic, the British submariners surrendered their "doomed" sub to a gallant Canadian Prize crew who stormed aboard from their lifeboat. Corvette *Port Arthur* had easily won the day.

The view was different, of course, in Germany. Glodschey's *U-Boote: Deutschlands Scharfe Waffe* [U-boats: Germany's Loaded Weapon, 1943], for example, provided a useful omnibus of U-boat experience. It swept from Wilhelm Bauer's experiments of 1851, through the "glorious test of the U-boats 1914–1918," to Schuhart's sinking of the aircraft carrier HMS *Courageous*, and to Prien's attack on Scapa Flow im 1939. One chapter let the reader in on a conversation with Admiral Dönitz, and another narrated the deeds of captured ace Kretschmer in U-99. Others replayed von Tiesenhausen's sinking of the battleship HMS *Barham* and "Hardegen's Drumbeat off New York," and then traced U-boat exploits "from the Mississippi to the St Lawrence rivers." As proof that old traditions still prevailed, the book ended with a list of the highest award winners in the U-Boat Arm up to 7 July 1943. This was Glodschey's third navy book in as many years.[44] By this time, as he correctly stated, the German people had learned considerably more about the war at sea than had been the case in 1914–18: "through their writings and pictures for press, radio and film, war reporters and propaganda officers have let the hot breath of the frontline of the war at sea waft into the homeland."

At a time when U-boats were being severely pressed by Allied forces, Glodschey's latest account had special meaning: "Especially today it is good for the German people to know with what toughness, courage, and tenacity the glorious victories of our U-boats are being achieved." Yet in speaking thus he afforded a glimpse of the true situation. As propaganda minister Goebbels had said in a recent public address, "people at home hear of their [U-boat] successes so often that they are wont to accept them automatically; nothing is more false." One must take nothing for granted, for German submarines were now facing "the solid resistance of the enemy." Jost Metzler's tale of adventure and courage, *Sehrohr Südwärts* [Periscope Southwards, 1943], stressed this very point. Propaganda nonetheless continued to celebrate the U-boats impunity in striking wherever they wished. As one of the clearest examples of German supremacy, Goebbels singled out the daring attacks in Canada's St Lawrence River which had occurred in the spring and summer of 1942: "They made a sensational stir throughout Canada – Just think, a German submarine in the very mouth of the giant river that bears the waters of the Niagara and the Great Lakes to the Atlantic!"[45]

Recruiting remained a major aim of u-boat war books that stressed the national aspect of the naval service. Fresh blood had always come not only from coastal cities, but also from the larger population centres in the interior of the country. The navy fostered links at the grass-roots level, arranging for cities to "adopt" u-boats in order to identify themselves more closely with their deeds. Judging by a letter from the mayor of Erfurt to the crew of its adopted ship, u-77, the interior city took pride in the navy connection: "The U-Boat Arm is playing a decisive role in the crucial battle of the German people. Every success report triggers resounding joy in the German people. We note with satisfaction that men from inland regions are also proving themselves in submarines. And we are proud of it."[46]

Some of the articles and books were written specifically for juvenile readers. Typical of these was Franz Führen's short picture-book *Kapitänleutnant Schepke erzählt* [Schepke Narrates, 1943], for which Dönitz wrote another of his formula prefaces:

GERMAN LADS! This booklet draws the picture of one of our most battle-proven commanders, Kapitänleutnant Schepke. In his zest and reckless way he was often just a big boy, but as leader, fighter, and soldier he showed that he was all man. His readiness and will [to fight] for Führer and Volk he sealed with the greatest sacrifice by giving of his young life in combat patrol. His youthful spirit, his manly toughness, his bold daring unto utmost commitment [serve] as a model for all who come after him, [and] live on as his legacy. This spirit speaks to you too, lads – and in his own words. May you strive to become "all man" just as he.

[signed] Dönitz, Großadmiral, Commander-in-Chief, U-boats

Another title aimed at the juvenile audience was Edgar Schröder's picture-book *'UX' stand im Mittelmeer* [UX in the Med, 1943]. As a member of a propaganda company, the author had been given the task of photographing the war at sea for home consumption. As might be expected, he marketed submarines as the elite service: "Very few of us will experience submarining, even though the number of u-boats and u-boat men in this war is increasing from day to day, from week to week, from month to month." What he did not explain, of course, was the fact that Germany's increasingly heavy losses had created the need to produce more men and *matériel* to fill the void left by Allied attacks. The author offered his young readers encouraging consolation: if few citzens could actually become submariners, the next best thing was to be an arm-chair traveller with this photographic account by a genuine war reporter. Judging by a presentation copy signed by the principal of the public school in the inland town of Michelstadt (Odenwald), and now held in the U-boat Archives in Cuxhaven, it must have been a prized volume; it is inscribed to a young pupil "for his industrious efforts in the school paper-drive, December 1943."

By now Dönitz was facing unbearable losses and had virtually withdrawn his U-boats from the Atlantic. Clearly, this strategic withdrawal made it more difficult for the press to produce the kind of propaganda impact that the political and naval leadership needed. The press responded inventively by reycling the old heroic names and by publishing outdated or massaged statistics. The myth of the silent service soon provided an alternative ruse; the lack of new success stories could be explained away by extolling the U-Boat Arm's virtue of keeping mum about its great deeds. Thus Schröder could explain in his book *'UX' stand im Mittelmeer* that "quite typical of U-boat warfare, [his] book would contain no sensations," leaving it to army stories to narrate such fare. Sea warfare and land warfare are inherently different, the narrator explained. Army stories always deal in a "dramatic battle event focusing on some individual deed or group action which only comes to light when those who carried it out have sealed their action with death and can no longer talk, but for whom their deed now speaks." Thus battle-field evidence on land was eloquent. But submariners, he claimed, were very different; they took battle to the enemy alone and beneath the sea, thereby executing their deeds of heroism in silence, and leaving no trace of their ultimate sacrifice:

The epic song of the fallen U-boat men is mute and silent. Perhaps wind and storm waft some distant echo back to shore, back to the homeland. But we humans cannot hear it. A profound silence enshrouded Prien, Endraß and the other fallen U-boat heroes. And yet the U-boat men whom I have met are the greatest optimists. Whenever they set forth, and only when once again out on patrol, they burn for one thing: to meet the enemy. In all likelihood they will be the last ones to fall to the enemy – in the last and greatest of all battles, on the seas.[47]

Propagandists who survived the war conveniently forgot their service to such causes. Such a man was Lothar-Günther Buchheim, famous author of the novel *Das Boot* (1973) on which the film of the same name was based. As we will see later, he continues to cause furore among the aging U-boat veterans because of his attacks against their supposed political involvement in the Nazi era. Yet in the 1940s, he too was an apparently willing tool in the hands of the government he served. His booklet *Jäger im Weltmeer* [Hunters on the World's Oceans, 1943], dedicated to "My U-boat Comrades," contains some very fine photographs, albeit highlighted by slanted text:

The U-boat is both weapon and machine raised to the highest power. Its very essence is attack. We are everywhere and nowhere. We harass the enemy on all the seas and force him into continued defensive ... Round about us we have nothing but the sea. The unpredictable, the adventure, awaits us. It is wonderful to have this ship under one's feet, and to live among this crew of stalwart fellows. Up ahead the sky is grey, as though it were brewing something up.[48]

Just how faithfully this passage reflected Buchheim's submarine experience on this his first and only mission might be gathered from the remark of a veteran who knew him: he was "mostly sea-sick, and shaken by claustrophobia; [and is] today merely a pitiful psychopath."[49] (In Wolfgang Petersen's film *Das Boot* the photographer from the Propaganda-Kompanie was modelled in part on this perception of Buchheim.)

However that may be, Admiral Dönitz seems to have been pleased with Buchheim's product of 1943. Dönitz's preface praised Buchheim for having grasped the essence of life aboard a combat submarine with his "beautiful and striking photos" and his perceptive insights gathered on a single typical mission. Thus "in the most felicitous way possible," Dönitz wrote, "he has fulfilled the wish for a documentary portrayal which will serve our U-boat comrades as a memento, our soldiers at the front and our citizens at home as a valid testimony of our life, our work and our combat achievements." This was high praise indeed. (Buchheim would later claim that he had actually written the preface himself, and had arranged for Dönitz's signature.)

Visceral emotions and passionate pleas are characteristic of writers like Buchheim who had been schooled in the Dönitz era. Typically, the he-man, devil-may-care submariner is now a "Kerl," a "ganzer Kerl," and a "Draufgänger," words perhaps unwittingly plucked from the anti-rationalistic Storm and Stress movement of German literature of the 1770s and 1780s. When writing his novel *Das Boot* as a "memento for our comrades" some thirty years later, Buchheim would reject such language – and the old virtues with it. In doing so, he would unleash acrimonious debate in veterans' circles. But in the spring of 1944 he toed the party line without hesitation, and the *Völkischer Beobachter* carried excerpts from his picture-book *Jäger im Weltmeer* and reprinted some of his dramatic photographs.[50] Buchheim, of course, was not the only contributor, for at this time the newspaper had also been publishing Kapitänleutnant Gert Mannesmann's reports about his previous operational mission. Under the title "Air Bombs Struck the U-boat," Mannesmann insisted that submarines could still deliver a punch, and the public should not believe enemy reports that German submarines were "finished."[51] The word *finished* (abgewirtschaftet) suggests as well "ruined by mismanagement." Presumably, astute readers could read between the lines to discover the real meaning of the Mannesmann story – namely, that Allied air power was now dominating the u-boat war. Indeed, by the autumn of 1944 the *Völkischer Beobachter* itself had to admit as much.[52] After all, the civilian population had long since been witnessing Allied air supremacy over its cities, and must by now have come reluctantly to the conclusion that the u-boats were also being subjected to the same crushing, unopposed attacks. In any event, in its attempt to dehumanize the opposition, the newspaper would reduce the enemy to an unholy (and ridiculous) troika consisting of "us generals, British archbishops and Soviet Jews arm in arm."[53]

As supreme commander of the navy, Dönitz had meanwhile been anticipating the Allies' invasion of Normandy, which was launched on 6 June 1944. In deploying his meager resources some two months earlier, he had issued secret preparatory orders. Every sailor, from Varanger Fjord in Norway to the Spanish border, and in units on the southern coast of France, was to oppose the enemy with "unshakeable determination and grit."[54] Dönitz required that "every sailor be mindful of the fateful magnitude of the task, that he commit himself relentlessly in every situation as sailor, warrior, and man." It was clearly a backs-to-the-wall order, "for not a single meter of ground must be surrendered." A prominent former ace insists today that this was a call for suicide missions. The disarmingly transparent bombast of Dönitz's call to glory in the face of death ended with a threat: "I will destroy with contempt and disgrace anyone who does not commit himself to the very last and does not fulfil his duty to the very limit." He concluded with a flourish such as he had used when sending many a u-boat to sea: "I trust in your combative spirit, Men of the Navy, you who have often proven that you can fight. Together with soldiers of the Army, the Air force and Waffen-ss you will press home the victory." The Allies' success or failure in this enterprise would be "decisive for the outcome of the war and for the very existence of the German people." Dönitz's appeal to the Men of the Navy is telling, for, by this

time, the U-Boat Arm *was* the navy. But so great had been the toll of
Allied destruction, there were virtually no available naval forces left
with which to oppose the Allied landings.

This was clearly the period of end-game in which public opinion
and morale had to be rallied against the omens of defeat. Hans
Rehberg's stage play *Die Wölfe* [The Wolves, 1944] was designed to
serve that end. A member of the Nazi party, Rehberg had been
fascinated by u-boats during the First World War when he became
acquainted with Dönitz.[55] Dönitz had subsequently sent him on an
orientation cruise with u-106 on the mission that penetrated Canada's
St Lawrence River in October 1942. It was doubtless good preparation
for "The Wolves," for Rehberg experienced the full range of submarine life, including depth-charge attack by HMCS *Vison* and harassment
by aircraft as severe as anything experienced by u-boats transitting the
dangerous waters of the Bay of Biscay.[56] The dramatic text, according
to the actor who ultimately directed it, was gripping:

I was profoundly shaken by both the situation and the tension. The situation:
the women at home, the waiting families, the young people out there [at sea]
with their more military than Nazi fanaticism. [I was struck by] their readiness
to die, to commit their all ... The women confronted their men with pene-
trating questions [about the purpose of the war] and submariners who had
died emerged ghost-like through the play to pose their own question about
the meaning of their deaths. There was no hoopla or primitive desire for self-
sacrifice [but] an urge for truth ... The Première was a great success.

Recognized now as as a "Durchhaltestück" (a "backs-to-the-wall" or
"hang-in-there" drama), it idealized the commitment of German submariners.[57] Significantly, Germany's leading actor and director at the
time, Gustaf Gründgens, had declined the offer of having it staged at
his Berlin theater. It therefore premiered in the Breslau Schauspiel-
haus on 16 April 1944, with the well-known actor Bernhard Minetti
in the lead role. Minetti, who had gained fame under the National
Socialist regime – perhaps more as a fellow-traveller committed to his
art and his own survival than anything else – now regards his work
with Rehberg as a serious error of judgment. Having also worked with
propagandist film-producer Leni Riefenstahl (notably in the film
Tiefland), he has found himself tarred with the same brush. Even today
he claims to have played in "The Wolves" for artistic reasons: "I liked
the play, the young submariners' idealism beyond all ideology [moti-
vated by] this youthful urge to power which is natural [in young
people], but which can be abused." The theme of the ideologically
abused submariner would not emerge until after the war.

The assassination attempt against Hitler on 20 July 1944 shed special light on the German naval service. The German Resistance had been planning to kill Hitler for many months and had already undertaken a couple of misadventures before. When informing the U-Boat Arm that this most "outrageous" assassination attempt against the Führer had also failed, Dönitz underscored that the cabal had been a "military" plot – that is, it had been largely an army operation. (With the exception of the resistance activity of ex-submariner Admiral Wilhelm Canaris of naval counter-intelligence, this was largely true.) This apparent absence of naval involvement in the plot to assassinate the head of state confirmed the ethos that had once led the submariners of the First World War to resist the Sailors' Mutiny of 1917 and the revolution of 1918. Thus Dönitz managed to strike the old theme of sailors keeping the faith; where the army had rebelled, the navy had remained true to the head of state. Striking down the head of state was considered an affront to military honour and discipline; it undercut the moral code of the Prussian officer corps. The sense of abiding loyalty to the state is still a source of satisfaction to many former submariners today. Not that they had remained loyal to National Socialism, which they now regard as having been a passing phenomenon, but loyal to the higher calling of duty in the national service. One submariner's postwar memoir described the mood of a group of commanding officers at the time as confusion and dismay: "The fact that someone had tried to murder the idol of the nation exceeded our comprehension. Our reactions vacillated between disbelief and profound sorrow ... What was I to tell my crew? ... They accepted my account with stoic quietness."[58]

Meanwhile, the cult of youth that had remained such a part of u-boat culture found new and ironic emphasis in the autumn of 1944 when, for example, the *Völkischer Beobachter* proclaimed that "Young U-boat Crews Face the Enemy."[59] It merely mirrored the fact that the crews were in fact much younger and less experienced than in the halcyon days. But no one admitted publicly that the reason this was so was simply because most of the older, experienced submariners had by then been killed. Yet the press continued to sell the idea of invincibility and to market the idea of youthful crews as a special virtue of the submarine service. Far from being sacrificed in a hopeless cause, young "Knights of the Deep" were seen as being grafted onto a rich seafaring tradition. The final u-boat book of the war, *Boot greift wieder an!* [U-boat Strikes Again, 1944], supported this propaganda thrust. Here Knight's Cross winners Wolfgang Lüth and Claus Korth regaled their readers with the type of adventure, daring, and bravado that left little doubt about Germany's ultimate victory. Like the fictionalized studio shots in the weekly newsreels, the graphic conclusion captured the U-boat spirit as the victorious submarines set out once more against the enemy.

Precisely formed up, the two U-boats are lying in the lock. Flowers decorate the tower, the periscope, machine-guns and deck-gun. Farewell cheers from German girls. Enthusiastically our eyes are fastened on [Flotilla Chief admiral Schniewind's] lips, and hearken intensely to his every [parting] word, that speaks of the meaning of our struggle, of the toughness and decisiveness of German soldiers. [Then] three hurrahs echo across to us as we hasten off to the battlefront, and three hurrahs echo back to those at home ... The band plays a new U-boat song about the grey wolves of the sea: "Comrades, just keep in mind / Attack! Sink 'em! Knock 'em blind!"

These old Dönitz words – "Kameraden, stets dran denken; / Angriff! Ran! Versenken!" – continued to animate his men as they had done since 1939. By 1941 they had been incorporated into the "U-boat Song" that Dönitz had made the official anthem of the U-Boat Arm. His phrase formed part of the cult of chivalry and bravado, of professionalism and romanticism that had been woven together of so many different cloths. Headlines in newspapers like the *Völkischer Beobachter* – "U-boats for the First Time off the Congo Mouth – 16 Ships and a Destroyer Sunk," and "113 Ships with 730,575 Tons Sunk in October" – underscored the burning theme of German sea supremacy and prestige. First popularized by Tirpitz forty years earlier, this sentiment seemed now to have come of age.[60] The whole world had learned of "the illustrious deeds of German U-boats." Yet this world of fiction ran tangent to the world of fact. Of this, few observers on the home front could have been much in doubt.

Yet in November 1944 the newspaper *Völkischer Beobachter* refused to come to grips with the senselessness of U-boat warfare. Instead, it continued to proclaim the Allied convoy system as "the strait-jacket" into which U-boats had thrust the enemy. This had been achieved by "the unbroken spirit of attack which, both now and in the future, animates the German U-boat men." Though once operating aggressively in the very front-line of attack, they now turned to gallant defence by performing a crucial blocking action in this new and critical phase of the war. U-boats directly tied down over a quarter of a million enemy people, not to mention some 50 enemy aircraft carriers, 400 destroyer escorts, and 400 submarine chasers. Were it not for the U-boats, the Allies might otherwise have deployed these ships to bring more troops and material in pursuit of their "terror campaign" against Germany. (These statistics were not far off Allied assessments.) "Those sacrificed in the u-boat war are [thus] bearing their fruit in relieving pressure on the home front."[61] Unknown to the German populace, however, only one submarine in four was returning from patrol. Significantly, Goebbels's traditional Christmas message to the German people extolled the Holy Season as the "Festival of the Strong Hearts," but made no mention whatever of submarines. Where in earlier speeches he had conjured up images of victorious soldiers and sailors leading the march to the future, he now preached that "the dead urge us onward."[62]

Germany's capitulation on 8 May 1945 brought with it the surrender of all u-boats. Grand Admiral Dönitz, whom Hitler had appointed as his successor prior to committing suicide, was now head of state. He ordered all his submarines to surface, signal their position in plain language, and proceed to the nearest German or Allied base. They were to jettison all ammunition and fly a black flag. To many submariners, this black flag seemed the ultimate badge of shame; it seemed that the Allies had once again foisted a forced confession of piracy onto an honourable service, and had once again thrust upon them the ignominy of 1918.

Dönitz had long since prepared contingency plans for the possibility of Germany's defeat. One of these was Operation Rainbow, which called for the scuttling of the u-boat fleet in order to prevent its capture. It was specifically aimed at preventing the possible re-enactment of the "shame" of 1918 when German naval vessels had steamed into captivity in Scapa Flow. U-boat crews anxiously awaited Dönitz's executive signal. But in stalling for time in order to rescue as many German soldiers and refugees from Russian hands in the east, Dönitz had had to assure the Allies that all naval resources would be handed over intact. In the confusion of the closing days, however, many submariners executed the Rainbow orders on their own. Thus by the time northern Germany had capitulated on 5 May 1945, some 215 u-boats had already been scuttled.[63]

The Nürnberg War Crimes Trials followed upon Germany's complete collapse. Grand Admiral Dönitz himself was one of the accused. He had been charged with three counts: first, participation in a common plan of conspiracy to commit crimes against peace, war crimes, and crimes against humanity; second, participation in planning, preparing, and initiating wars of aggression in violation of international treaties, agreements, and assurances; and third, commission of war crimes, including the practice of total war. He had not been burdened with the fourth charge, crimes against humanity, which included murder and persecution. Many former submariners were prepared to come to his defence. One of many letters bore the

signature of sixty-seven former commanding officers – including Erich
Topp, who as an apostate in 1991 would return to the theme of Dönitz.
The commanders' testimonial faithfully reflects the cohesion in the
U-boat "band of brothers" and embodies the fealty and trust on which
Dönitz could draw throughout the submarine fleet: "We, the under-
signed, declare that the German navy was taught by its leaders to
respect the written and unwritten laws of the sea, and we have always
regarded it as a point of honour to uphold these laws and to conduct
the war with chivalry."

Convicted on counts two and three, Admiral Dönitz was sentenced
on 1 October 1946 to ten years in Berlin's Spandau prison.[64] Significantly, he was not found guilty of any breach of international law
concerning submarine warfare. A former submariner would write
about the events at Nürnberg: "Thus the curtain fell on a drama
unparalled in the history of war."[65] Yet, like the revolution of 1918,
Dönitz too would remain one of the great unresolved themes in the
U-boat performance.

4 Redemption of a Myth, 1945–76

Karl Dönitz completed his memoirs in 1958 after having served ten years in prison for war crimes. The path of his brilliant career had led from submariner in the First World War to Commander-in-Chief, Submarines, and then, in the Second World War, Grand Admiral. It had reached its pinnacle in 1945 when he succeeded Adolf Hitler as head of state. In the words of a British journalist, this made Dönitz "The last Führer."[1] His memoir *Zehn Jahre und Zwanzig Tage* [Ten Years and Twenty Days] is one of the more unusual autobiographies of the last war. During his imprisonment, Dönitz had been virtually isolated from postwar media attention to the events he had experienced and in large measure guided. His recollections therefore bore little trace of the accretions of a culture that had undergone the Allies' "denazification" process. They were largely uninfluenced by a society now trying to probe, to rethink, and in some cases even to justify the dark period of Nazi power from 1933 to 1945. Unabetted by conversations with old comrades in these years, Dönitz's memories and reflections had remained very much his own. With access, once released, to all the war diaries of his former command, as well as to those of the U-boats and the Naval War Office, Dönitz had a detailed chronological and technical framework that lent cogent shape to his thoughts.[2] His work is indispensable to our understanding of the period.

Like the other memoirists before him – Tirpitz and Bethmann Hollweg in 1919, for instance – he too began his reflections with the burden of Versailles. The "manacles" of this crushing treaty, as he put it, contributed crucial elements to the iconography of the German submarine. So, too, did the ignominy of having to scuttle the German fleet at Scapa Flow. Dönitz would not have returned to the navy in the 1920s, he explained, if he had not been encouraged to believe that U-boats would once again serve the German cause.

During the war I had been an enthusiastic submariner. I was captivated by this unique submarine *seafaring* which stands the submariner on his own two legs and gives him a task in the grand expanse of the ocean, a task requiring stoutness of heart and professional skill. I was captivated by the unique *comradeship* engendered by sharing the same fate, the very same living conditions, in the community of a U-boat crew in which everyone depended on everyone else and in which we could dispense with no one. Surely every submariner has sensed in his heart this breadth of space and task, and has felt as rich as a king, and would have traded [places] with no one.[3]

Dönitz had thus begun his memoir with major themes: seafaring, comradeship, shared dangers and fate, duty and commitment. He ended it by enhancing this list with values he hoped to see woven into the very fabric of the new Germany. The standard British translation of his memoirs expresses it this way: "In my life I have met with so much unselfishness and loyalty from the men under my command that I am filled with gratitude towards them. Let no man denigrate the fighting men of this last war. To do so is to besmirch the honour of those who gave their lives in the execution of their duty."[4] Here the British translator has not done justice to Dönitz's original. Dönitz did not say "let no man denigrate the fighting men of this last war"; he said, "No one should disparage the military ethos (Soldatentum) of the last war." To do so "does injury to [our] reverence for those who fell in the fulfillment of their duty."[5] Duty is here a metaphysical end in itself to which, in admiral Nelson's phrase, "all private considerations must give way." Writers who took up submarine history and memoir in the postwar period while Dönitz was still in prison also endorsed Nelson's view.

Popular works on the submarine war were not long in coming. Among the very first was Harald Busch's 400–page *So War der U-Boot-Krieg* [That's the Way It Was: The U-boat War, 1952]. It appeared in London in two abbreviated translations in 1955 and 1956 as *U-boats at War*. According to the German reviewer, "one cannot imagine a book that could describe the history and events of the last U-boat war more realistically, more faithfully, and more grippingly; here nothing is glorified, and nothing withheld."[6] Veterans endorsed the view. For perhaps the first time, the public could now read of the massive human losses in the submarine corps; by Busch's reckoning, more than 32,000 deaths in a service of 39,000 men. But the review was quick to point out what lay at the core of this book: "The human dimension, but also the Great and Noble to which a whole generation of enthusiastic German male youth had devoted itself." Busch, who had served in submarines, was already well known as a prolific author of books on German art and architecture. This was his first venture into naval history. His perspective lent a new dimension to the u-boat record: "This book is about the German u-boats and the men who lived, fought and died in them in the tragedy of the greatest war in history." Five years earlier, the word *tragedy* would have been anathema. Now, however, Busch was quite consciously staking out some middle ground between two extremes in submarine history – defamation and hagiography. "Much has been written about the u-boat war, from the officially inspired wartime accounts to the superficial surveys, inaccurate sometimes to the point of deliberate distortion, of the postwar years. All too often, the writers' preconceived ideas have obscured the essential features of their subject ... The truth is, those who fought in the u-boat service were neither heroes nor war criminals."

Written in a forthright style with no trace of strutting or sabre-rattling, the book offered a fair-minded capsule history of the Battle of the Atlantic. Busch interspersed his lean factual accounts (based on what little official information was available at the time) with zestful dramatizations of the "historical" experiences undergone by German submariners. Even at this early stage he honestly admitted German failures and recognized Allied achievements. He confessed, for example, that Dönitz had ordered Fritz Lemp to alter his log book after having sunk the passenger liner *Athenia*; that the German navy had experienced serious torpedo failures; and that Britain's famous "sub-killer," Captain F.J. Walker, had performed "outstanding service" against u-boats. At the same time, however, he was sharply critical of us belligerent neutrality that had enabled Roosevelt to support Britain's war against Germany without having to declare war; and he disparaged the "destroyers-for-bases" deal of 1940 between Roosevelt and Churchill "as a flagrant infringement by the American government of its own Neutrality Act, as well as of the Hague Convention." As was natural for a storyteller, Busch highlighted Germany's u-boat aces whom the populace had known throughout the war years: Günther Prien "of Scapa Flow," the "Red Devil" boat of Erich Topp, and the "Golden Horseshoe" of Otto Kretschmer (including a sketch of the latter's attempted escape by u-boat from a POW camp in Canada).[7] These adventures, together with the exploits of famous aces like Günther Hessler, Joachim Schepke, and Addi Schnee, offered lively entertainment.

Seen in its best light, the submariner's sharply chiselled public image was heroic even when facing death. As Busch put it: "self-confidence and vigorous unconcern characterized experienced U-boat men and was responsible for their astounding achievements."[8] But Busch went further, adding a new dimension which would not have been countenanced during the war. He explored the anguish of the inexperienced submariner, of youngsters living in physical misery and confronting the sheer terror of war. Here is a scene in which he describes the horror encountered by seasick recruits on their first patrol.

But many of these youngsters were still racked with seasickness and lay with-drawn and wretched on their bunks, longing only to die. Steeped in official propaganda, with its fairy tales of lusty, keen-eyed warriors leaping upon their enemies, they had never imagined that war could be like this. There was no escape; they were caught, imprisoned in that pestiferous dungeon, cheek-by-jowl with unfeeling, unpitying men, whose only thought, it seemed, was to press on implacably through the seas, farther and farther from home, instead of making as quickly as they could for the comfort and safety of land.

The poor lads were gripped by an agony of soul. If only they could get out – simply climb overboard and jump into the sea – instead of being shut in, battened down, in this deafening, reeking tube of steel. If only they had never volunteered. Their thoughts groped out toward home, far away, to their friends. They had no friends now. Shamefully they had been deceived, lured from their homes to meet a miserable and useless end.[9]

Such a passage could easily have been written either by Britain's Nicholas Monsarrat (*The Cruel Sea*) or Canada's Alan Easton (*Fifty North*), for it portrays the same numbing inner world experienced by Allied recruits in their inhospitable corvettes. Had Busch written this in wartime, or even spoken in this manner, he would have faced the treasonable charge of defeatism. U-boat commander Oskar-Heinz Kusch was actually executed in 1945 for having done much less. Now in the postwar period, "defeatism" was considered candour, a means for confronting the past as it "really" was.

Yet despite the book's honesty, its American edition, translated as *U-boats at War* (1955), was prefaced by an educator's "Note to Teachers and Parents" warning of what one would find inside. "The enemy wrote this book. It is the war under the sea from the Nazi point of view – and therein lies the fascination and value of this unique account of the minute-by-minute life of men living in a tube under the ocean from which, the statistics show, few ever made it to shore again. The author makes no attempt to please American ears." The American author of the note had been unable (or unwilling) to shake himself free of the stereotype; he feared that the engaging narrative might beguile young readers into dropping their critical guard. It was therefore imperative to remind them just what the Germans were "really" like: "Because stories of the hunt, chase, and sudden death are so exciting, the student may miss the deep insight into the Nazi naval mind at work which this book supplies." Thereupon follows a list of Busch's supposedly more flagrant "errors," namely those views displeasing to American ears. As we will see, such stereotyped images endured for many years after the war. The British translator of Prien's *Mein Weg nach Scapa Flow* [I Sank the Royal Oak], for example, could scarcely contain his indignation towards the German submarine commander: "It is possible to conclude from the sum of his qualities, [namely] blind adherence to his creed, disrespect and arrogance towards his comrades and ruthless treatment of his subordinates and others, that there were three qualities essential to the making of a good Nazi and unquestionably history confirms that Prien was a good Nazi."[10]

British readers, of course, had already met the stereotyped image of the "Nazi u-boat" in Monsarrat's best-selling novel *The Cruel Sea* (1951). Later translated into German as "Großer Atlantik" [Great Atlantic], it was described by the *London Star* as "the finest story of the last war" and by the *Daily Dispatch* as "a sea saga [which] comes only once in a generation." An admiring German reviewer in 1953 wondered just how German authors would ever compete with such an epic.[11] Here is the scene in which the ill-fated HMS *Compass Rose* has attacked a German submarine and finally blasts it to the surface:

The red glowing tracer-shells began to chase each other low across the water towards the u-boat. She had now fallen back on a level keel, and for the moment she rode at her proper trim: it was odd, and infinitely disgusting, suddenly to see this wicked object, the loathsome cause of a hundred nights of fear and disaster, so close to them, so innocently exposed. It was like seeing some criminal, who had outraged honour and society, and had long been shunned, taking his ease at one's own fireside.[12]

Monsarrat evoked the same features a year later in 1952 when introducing the American edition of Heinz Schaeffer's *U-boat 977*. Fiction and historical realities remained indistinguishable according to Monsarrat's prejudices.

If *U-Boat 977* were not two things – a readable book, and an engrossing piece of war history – I would not touch it with a depth charge.

This point is made at the outset, because I do not wish to figure as an apologist for any part of Germany's war effort. There have been far too many postwar books, films and plays written to expound the thesis that the Germans, though misguided and misled, were in the main honest manly types who fought the good fight like any Christian soldier; I do not want to run the risk of seeming to belong to this gang ... This rubbish has proved readily saleable, as does any claptrap done up in a novelty package, gift-wrapped for the Season of Goodwill; but it is rubbish all the same.

...

The book includes also, to make us burst into tears, a sigh for something which other u-boats ... apparently looked for in vain: a "decent respect for the defeated." Ah, Germany!

But read it for yourselves. It is valuable, as I said, for its authentic picture ... It is more valuable still for the inferential story, the crude driving-force behind it all, the reason for which u-boats came into being in the first place. Reading it, absorbing its filthy and violent outlines, we know just how far politics can travel on the road to insanity, and what men can do to other men in their greedy lust for power.

One year after Busch's *So War der U-Boot-Krieg* [That's the Way It Was] had appeared, Wolfgang Frank published his *Die Wölfe und der Admiral: Triumph und Tragik der U-Boote* (1953). "The Wolves and the Admiral" of his title reflect the now traditional iconography of the submariners and Dönitz. Frank introduced his book as an attempt "to describe the life and activities of one important arm of the German fighting services in the Second World War." The English version appeared as *The Sea Wolves* (1955). But his subtitle – "The Triumph and the Tragedy of the U-boats" – gives front stage to an element that Busch's contemporaneous work had expressed in the text itself. Tragedy, as Frank uses the term, reflects the technical sense of dramatic characters meeting an undeserved fate. And the tragic flaw of the drama – though this is not yet explicitly stated – lies in the submariners' readiness to serve their political masters and country at all costs. This self-disciplined obedience nonetheless constituted their triumph; for in submitting themselves to a higher service supposedly beyond politics, their moral integrity remained untarnished despite the fact that they had served what was now recognized as a seriously flawed regime.

The communication of "authentic" experience became increasingly important in the 1950s, for many writers recognized the distortions that had resulted from propaganda and political expediency. Significantly, however, where the writing of submarine lore had once been restricted to the generally more educated former officers and Propaganda-Kompanie hacks, members of the lower deck also took up the pen. But despite renewed interest in history, as a young German veteran lamented in 1954, it was still impossible to get a composite overview of events because neither national nor international sources were yet open to the general public. And yet, he said, one must somehow throw in one's mite in order to set the record straight. For this reason he published his tales of U-69 that year in order to "contribute a small building stone to the complete overview of this final naval war fought between Germany and England which almost brought both countries to the edge of the abyss." The resultant book, *Die lachende Kuh* [The Laughing Cow], offered little more than its upbeat subtitle promised: "the eye-witness exciting adventure of U-69 in the Second World War." It is a harmless, ingenuous yarn of the life and times of the crew in "the oppressive narrowness" of the submarine. Its publication, the author had written, had been motivated by grass-roots interest among former veterans and the people of Würtemberg, where the first commanding officer of U-69 had his home. Less interested in extolling the virtues of warriors, it reflected a need to inform laymen about what underwater seafaring had really been like. A page of "explanations for land-lubbers" was but one of the features to that end. One thing was certain: "What these men experienced in their inner life, that tense, compressed atmosphere, was the same for friend and foe alike." The tale concluded with a didactic thrust: "To all those who only know of the wartime experience of the U-boats by hearsay, this book can give some idea of what was going on in those men who, in the days of [Germany's] collapse, were slandered as being Nazi submariners, [and] whose former commander-in-chief, Grand Admiral Dönitz – from whom no honourable opponent has ever withheld his esteem – is still held in Spandau [Prison]."[13] Three more years would pass before Dönitz would walk free.

Reassessment and exoneration were significant features of the early postwar U-boat story and found expression in the political arena as well. Speaking in the Bundestag on 3 December 1952, the Federal Republic's chancellor, Dr Konrad Adenauer, paid tribute to the honourable traditions of the German armed services. "We are convinced," he said, "that the good reputation and the great achievements of German fighting men are still alive and will remain so despite retrenchments among our people in recent years." This quotation introduced the first postwar edition of the navy's traditional magazine *Marine Rundschau*.[14] Its dramatic cover photo showed a U-boat bursting to the surface bow-skyward in an emergency manœuvre. It seemed to celebrate rebirth. The first article in this edition dealt with the German u-boat war and with the legal judgments of Nuremberg.[15] As the article concluded, Nürnberg had cleared the U-Boat Arm of any blame, and had "documented before the world [both] the justification of submarine warfare and its actual conduct by the German Kriegsmarine." At about this time journalistic pictorial accounts were beginning to emerge in the popular press. One illustrated magazine, for example, advertised a twenty-two-week series on the "Combat and Demise of the Kriegsmarine" with a full front-page icon from the glory days of u-boat warfare: Addi Schnee at the periscope, overlayed by a periscope view of a sinking ship.[16] The articles were up-beat and naive, without the slightest trace of analysis. Significantly, it was Addi Schnee who had taken Germany's first operational Type xxi "complete submersible" to sea in April 1945, a couple of weeks before Germany's unconditional surrender. This radically new type of u-boat, which could sustain high underwater speeds, had pointed the way to the future of submarine warfare. Had it been available in large numbers a few months earlier, it might have brought the u-boat Service dramatic success – and vindication – even as the Third Reich burned.

Under the guise of objective historical reports, magazines and pulps were cautiously hearkening back to the heroism of the past, yet reconciliation too was in the air. Typical of this were the dedications that Dönitz and his former chief of operations, Admiral Eberhard Godt, appended to the 1957 German edition of Frank's *Die Wölfe und der Admiral* [The Sea Wolves]. Writing after his release from prison, Dönitz expressed "reverence and gratitude" for the fallen of his stalwart U-Boat Arm, but also remembered "the opponent's dead who had also given their lives for their country." His warmest accolades were naturally for his own countrymen who had fought in the U-Boat Arm, long since touted in popular parlance as the "Freikorps Dönitz." Resorting to the conventional iconography, Dönitz described the German submariners as "fearless," "daring," and "a small band always ready for battle." He praised "the crews who courageously took upon themselves the most difficult struggle of the final war years, their sacrificial road for the German people." He signed the dedication with the now famous autograph "Dönitz" – followed neither by rank nor other designation. Admiral Godt's preface was reminiscent of the manner in which he had once reviewed mission reports: "This book about the life, struggle and death of the U-Boat Arm, is written by one who was there, whose experience both at the front and at staff headquarters gives him the right to recount what the survivors report." His words are important, for as late as the 1980s some veterans were still rejecting reconstructionist views on Admiral Dönitz and his U-boats by arguing that only those authors with "valid" U-boat experience had any right to speak on the subject.

Three U-boat books appeared in 1956, each one written by men with submarine experience. One of them was turned into a movie whose supposed authenticity many former submariners reject. And authenticity was a quality for which the war-weary veterans longed – although they insisted on the primacy of their own view. Jochen Brennecke's *Jäger – Gejagte* [Hunter – Hunted: German Submarines 1939–1945] was intended to tell the story as it "really" happened. It was fiction as history, information as infotainment; a brief historical sketch gave the background to each rousing yarn. The title projected two major aspects of the Atlantic war: the U-boats first emerged as the hunters who carried the battle to the Allies, but they soon became the hunted who fell in defeat. In Brennecke's words: "This is no heroic epic. It is the gripping and fateful road of a small band whose every mission was overshadowed by the wings of death." Here were men for whom the "sea was their element, and seafaring their true calling." Brennecke, we might recall, had been a propaganda writer during the war and had churned out the usual slanted fare for his political masters. He had also played a lead role in the feature film *U-Boote Westwärts!* (1941) and might still have been remembered for his final lines, "It is sweet and honourable to die for the Fatherland." Now, however, he was bent on exposing the once-suppressed harsh truth; at the same time, he wished to bear witness to the "spirit which animated [submariners] on their constant path of sacrifice." His portrayal of bravery and commitment is graphic. He leaves little doubt that the German sailor was a victim of ill-begotten politics.

Joachim Lehnhoff's historical novel *Die Heimfahrt der U-720* [Homeward Bound with U-720, 1956] took a similar tack. Serialized simultaneously in a popular magazine, it, too, like Brennecke's book, would be reprinted in the late 1970s. Some twenty years after its launching it would be touted on the jacket blurb as "the classical U-boat novel about the last days of World War II." It was considered nothing less than "the dramatic voyage of a U-boat into the hell of naval war." One review dubbed it "a sincere and honest book that neither whitewashes nor glorifies anything." In artistic terms, however, it is considerably less than such grandiose advertisements claimed.

Much more graphic then either of these two novels was Wolfgang Ott's *Haie und kleine Fische* [Sharks and Little Fish, 1956], which pushed criticism even further. Conventional U-boat iconography would long since have led both the reader of the novel, and later the viewer of the film, to interpret the title in a stereotyped way, with the sharks referring to German u-boats in their voracious battle against the "little fish" of the Allied side. Yet such an interpretation would ironically fall wide of the mark. The "sharks" turn out to be, in fact, the rapacious and immoral political masters of Germany who, in their bid for power, consumed the "little fish" – the faithful German submariners. Deep-textured, broad-canvassed, and vivid, Ott's historical fiction was by far the most accomplished navy novel that had yet been written. Ott explored lower-deck life, naval tradition and training, and the crushing experience of war. He portrayed sailors for whom the reality of combat excluded the choreographed heroics so popular in the pulp trade, and for whom death was not apotheosis but sadism. Ott revealed the sailors' preceptions of high strategy and politics, in which they themselves were little more than pawns. He examined a wide range of gnawing ambiguities: the tension between service to country and service to God, between commitment to national ideals and commitment to private morals. He undertook what few works of u-boat literature had attempted by narrating wartime events in their social and intellectual context. Little wonder, then, that when two key protagonists met near the end of the novel – in a scene set near the end of the war – they had gained a harsh insight: "that it was senseless to continue fighting the u-boat war, and that new u-boats would in any case come too late" to change the course of events leading to national self-destruction.[17] The novel's overriding theme, however, is betrayal. The book ends with a gruesome scene of dead and dying submariners bobbing in the sea after having escaped their sunken u-boat. Within reach of home, each sailor drifts inexorably into his own anguished and helpless loneliness, while scavanging seabirds pick out their eyes. The scene is fraught with disturbing symbolism, for the "little fish" who had been blind to the Nazi Reich have become sightless, moribund fodder. There is bitter irony in the final image of swarming birds, for as the book concludes: "Two patrol boats discovered the twenty men in the evening twilight, and pulled nine of them out of the water alive. The gulls had shown them the way."[18]

Writing in the period of denazification, Ott was immediately able to turn his hand from best-selling novel to film script; in doing so he drew upon some of the best actors of the day to sell his theme. Closely following the novel, Ott effected an astute transition from the epic genre to the dramatic. The film *Haie und Kleine Fische* (1957) highlights moments of conflict and crisis. In one of the plot lines, a young submarine officer struggles to make sense of wartime Germany. As a student of philosophy, he is fascinated by the writings of the nineteenth-century pessimist Arthur Schopenhauer who had seriously doubted the reality of man's free will. For Schopenhauer, the will was blind; man was a slave to his nature, to his emotions and sex drives. This being so, human beings would continue to exploit life until death put an end to the whole squalid and painful process. In the film the young officer returns home from his mission to find that his father, a part-Jewish professor who has spoken out against the regime, has been executed in a concentration camp. The returning "hero" receives a letter requiring him to pick up the body and pay the costs. Subsequent scenes probe fundamental questions about the justification for this particular war, and about the implications of fighting it on behalf of such a criminal regime. As the young officer asks his comrade: How can anybody fight to the death while carrying out the orders of those who had murdered one's father? His answer to his own rhetorical question fits the Schopenhauer model: he breaks the chain of his tacit complicity in Hitler's empire by committing suicide with a shot to the head. If the sentiments are overblown and somewhat melodramatic, they nevertheless fit the mood of the 1950s. Denazification was still in the air in many corners of Germany, and pulp-trade writers were involved in laundering the past.

Attacks on national myths continued. One major event was the feature film *U-47 – Kapitänleutnant Prien*, produced in 1958 with big-name movie stars and music by Norbert Schulte, the composer of the hit song "Lili Marlene." The film was a model both of the reconstructionism the victorious Allies had demanded in the 1940s and of the "political correctness" German revisionists now practised of their own accord.[19] Despite soap-opera gimmicks, the film allowed glimpses of a world beyond the dictates of military and political duty, and created an entirely new Prien possessed of something that many postwar critics deemed absent among German submariners during the war: moral conscience.[20]

The film opens with Prien's family listening to Hitler's hypocritical denunciation of the sinking of the liner *Athenia* and his rejection of the notion that a German u-boat had done the deed. Hitler's reasons reflect an important aspect of Germany strategic policy in 1939: "We have no interest in provoking America." In a subsequent scene the u-boat skipper who had sunk the *Athenia* (it had actually been Lemp in u-30) appears before Admiral Dönitz to explain his error; he had mistakenly identified the liner as an auxiliary cruiser. Dönitz angrily retorts that the political impact is so serious it might be necessary to erase the event from the submarine's war diary. (In fact, that is precisely what Dönitz had ordered done.) Prien, meanwhile, is given a tumultuous welcome on entering harbour after a successful combat mission. Here the Prien myth is writ large, for German newsreels and newspapers had already authenticated the truth of these events. The images that follow underscore the comradeship of submarining, of "heroes" as quite ordinary people serving their nation, of family and the simple pleasures of human devotion. German society is seen as "eine heile Welt," a secure and healthy world of moral probity. It is a world without ambiguity.

This apparent balance is shaken when Prien meets a former school chum who is now a pastor involved in human-rights issues. The pastor tries to recruit the great naval hero to his cause: "God has singled you out of the crowd – you have access to the highest places." The pastor sees in Prien a man who has "blown up 2000 human beings" in his missions, a man profiting from a perverse government that "bestows the highest honours on the biggest killer." (The historical Prien had indeed received the highest military honours from the hands of Hitler himself.) A radically different Prien now emerges. He is different from the image in his own and other books of the day, and different from that in the newsreels. Self-abasement had never been one of his publicly confessed qualities. Yet in the movie he defends his militarism as the acts of someone who is "only a soldier" doing his duty. This facile stance the pastor rejects out of hand as an utterly inadequate response to life: "One is never just a soldier." This scene, and indeed the whole role of the pacifist pastor, is scorned by some U-boat veterans even today – evidence enough that the argument still strikes raw nerves.

Drawn into the vortex of events that begin to mould a new character, Prien faces several crises of conscience that force him to reassess his role in German society. He carries out the Scapa Flow mission, destroys ships, and confronts one of his young sailors who has become hysterical at the sight of the enemy's dead in the water; the youngster cannot believe that his own countrymen have wreaked such havoc. Again Prien's leadership is tested to the limit when the same young sailor has to be restrained while begging Prien for a straight answer to a burning question; he needs to know if current stories about the concentration camps are true. The movie-Prien remains silent, for of course the movie-audience of 1958 has long since known the truth.

The leitmotif of moral responsibility emerges again in a scene set in a U-boat base in France. Prien and his second-in-command meet over drinks in Café Dernier Rivage. Lest the audience miss the symbolism of the meeting in this particular "last chance" café, Prien translates its name into German – letztes Ufer (The Last Shore). Still "just a soldier," he finds himself literally on the final shore before sailing into an uncharted sea of doubt and leaving his friend and fellow officer to his own new command – and his own command decisions. By this time Prien has undergone a radical shift of conscience. In a moody conversation, Prien accepts what has now become obvious: "It simply doesn't suffice to be just a soldier." Further scenes of bloody warfare at sea, and in particular of being pounded by enemy depth charges (a striking prefiguration of a similar scene in Petersen's film *Das Boot* of 1981), and of trying to rescue one of his own men who has fallen overboard under enemy gunfire, thrust the message home. On return, a restless Prien visits the now imprisoned pastor who is awaiting execution for treason. Prien makes him a promise he will not be able to keep: "As a soldier I have done my duty. But when I return I will try to make good what I can." Out on his final mission, Prien sends his last signal to Dönitz. Both in historical fact and in public knowledge of the day, this was the last ever heard of Prien.

Drawing on all the elements of full-blown melodrama, the film imagines an ending in response to the probing and taunting question that British propaganda pamphlets had raised about Prien's whereabouts. Prien's U-boat is destroyed (as it had in fact been by the British destroyer HMS *Wolverine*). In the film version, however, Prien and some of his crew are rescued by a battered British merchantman, only to watch aghast as an unidentified periscope approaches the hapless ship. In a flash-back scene designed for its exquisite sentimentality, the audience recognizes at the periscope none other than Prien's former second-in-command. The attack destroys the merchantman, leaving no survivors. Surfacing to scour the wreckage, the U-boat skipper recognizes Prien's cap among the flotsam and fishes it out of the sea as a final reminder of his mentor's grandeur. Overcome with emotion at having killed the nation's hero, he fails to dive in time when British aircraft arrive and is himself destroyed. This final lachrymose scene – played without musical background in stark contrast to the taste of sentimental movies of the day – forms an effective counter-statement to the bugle-and-drum patriotism that had traditionally accompanied such scenes. The film ends, as it had begun, with the families of Prien and his former second-in-command listening to the official military broadcast to the nation: "two famous submarines have failed to return from their mission, and must be considered lost." If the audience had failed to grasp the moral of this provocative version of Prien, the movie magazine *Illustrierte Film-Bühne* provided it: "The change in Prien is complete [on visiting the pastor in prison]. He now wants to help just as [Pastor] Friedrich Kille has helped. But Günther Prien cannot help anymore, he made up his mind too late. He will never again be able to let his heart speak in his homeland, for this mission remains his last."

At about this time, too, criticism emerged in East Germany, the German Democratic Republic. The political boundaries that had been drawn through divided Germany in 1949 had split the former Reich according to two ideologies. The Federal Republic in the west had established Germany's first democracy by its Basic Law. In doing so it ultimately accepted responsibility for the National Socialist past and committed itself to such policies as reparation payments and rapprochement with Israel. Over the course of many years it subjected itself to a thoroughgoing examination of the Holocaust and the "twelve-year empire." Living under Soviet tutelage in the east, the German Democratic Republic did none of these things. It chose instead to regard West Germany as the new home of all those fascists who had survived the Third Reich. The East, so its official statements and image insisted, was the successor to the only opposition wartime Germany had ever known: the Communist party. U-boat histories written in East Germany reflected this view.

Rolf Guddat's *Für jeden kommt der Tag* [Day Comes for Everyone, 1958] was such a book. Stamped as "Approved by the Ministry of Culture of the German Democratic Republic," it pronounced what would become a well-worn theme. In the words of the jacket blurb:

This novel deals with actual events of the fascist U-Boat Arm in the Second World War. In the centre of the action stands Kapitänleutnant Oeser who as the captain of U-213 is faced with difficult decisions. He believes he is a good German when he defends his Fatherland, when he causes enemy ships to be sunk. But then come doubts as to whether those whom he is destroying are really the enemies, and whether that for which he is staking his life is really the Fatherland.

Oeser is a fictional figure, and the real U-213 undertook none of the major missions described in the book. That, however, does not really matter, for the author's primary interest lies in unmasking the past: in laying bare the "criminal" orders that sent such boats to war; in pillorying Admiral Dönitz's "inhuman orders" not to pick up survivors from Allied ships; in undercutting wartime mythology. From the Eastern perspective, the U-boat is a "floating coffin"; each U-boat mission is a "suicide mission" (Himmelfahrtskommando); and the coveted Knights Cross is nothing but "a tin medal for the perfect murder." Two excerpts typify the author's tendentious approach to narration and his commitment to now outdated literary clichés. In one of them, his description of a successful "fascist" torpedo attack invests a piece of machinery with primeval instinct: "fired from invisible ambush the torpedoes had ripped open the hull with claws of death when the dying ship rolled onto its side like a goared beast."[21] In another, the U-boat captain is plagued with questions about the

ultimate purpose of undersea warfare. Typically, he manages to sup-
press his humanity and transform himself once more into the "Nazi"
skipper he has been trained to be: "Oeser's nerves were taut to the
point of tearing. It's all senseless what we're doing here, it flashed
through him. They should put an end to it, soon, soon … But then
he pulled himself together. Suddenly he was ice cold again. No more
anguishing thoughts, no pangs of conscience, no gnawing doubts. He
was once again the soberly calculating u-boat commandant on whom
the success or failure of the attack depended … It was up to him to
destroy."[22]

The plot of "Day Comes for Everyone" opens with the meeting of
two brothers at the beginning of the war. They recall their youth and
how their paths had diverged. One, Kapitänleutnant Robert Oeser,
had been beguiled by the Nazi party and had joined the navy; his older
brother, Karl, had espoused Christian and humanistic ethics and had
spent three years in concentration camp because of his views. The
u-boat captain tries to explain and justify his decision to defend the
Fatherland, while his ex-prisoner brother tries to make blinded eyes
see: "War for the Nazis is war for [the industrialist] Krupp … You have
been entrusted with a responsible military position, and will have to
make decisions for yourself." Ultimately, the book is about decision-
making. As a u-boat commander cast in a plot reminiscent of the
sinking of the British troop ship *Laconia* (called *Princess* in the novel)
by u-156 on 12 September 1942, Kapitänleutnant Oeser conceives of
a private plan. He intends to rescue the survivors of his attack by
putting them aboard a Portugese vessel and to scuttle his u-boat once
the good deed is done. This he does. As the waters close over the
sinking submarine "in the last light of evening [and as] gulls flew by
with a hoarse cry," the reader recalls the captain's words to his "Nazi"
first officer: "I am not a soul without a will; I am first and foremost a
human being."

The same year that Guddat's novel appeared in East Germany, a
different book appeared in the West: Wolfgang Frank's *Der Stier von
Scapa Flow: Leben und Taten des U-Boot-Kommandanten Günther Prien*
[Günther Prien, the Bull of Scapa Flow, 1958]. It was the very book
to bring "our unforgettable Prien" of Second World War fame back
before the readers' eyes. At least, that is how Admiral Dönitz's brief
introduction extolled it. One wonders just how many readers realized
that this was the very same preface that Dönitz had written for Frank's
first version of the book when it appeared in 1941, just after Prien's
death.[23] Now dressed up with a new title – and with no reference
whatever to this early version – the book resuscitated an old hero. In
fact, the author prefaced his text with the very same dedication as in

1941 – "to the Living as a model, to the following generation as solemn admonition, and in memory of Günther Prien and his men." And just as in the first version, he quoted lines made famous in Prien's own war book *Mein Weg nach Scapa Flow* (1940): "What is success? You can call it luck or grace. But the main thing for us men is just this: to have the heart of a fighter, and to be able to forget oneself for the sake of the cause one is serving." Here Frank has made no effort to place his book in the current of history that had been changing his country since 1945. The book was sheer nostalgia and gave no thought as to whether the cause that the submariners had served had really been worth the candle. The book was not the last of its type.

By contrast, Hans Herlin's *Verdammter Atlantik* [Damned Atlantic, 1959], as the subtitle claimed, was intended to provide "a factual report about the fates of German submariners." Using the lives of five famous u-boat skippers as paradigms, Herlin stressed the bitter fate-fulness that had drawn the German submariners' to their destruction. Like the suffering heroes of Greek tragedy – to whom Buchheim would refer in the 1980s – Herlin's men could not escape the avenging spirits, in this case the hounds of war. An anthology of novelettes, his book recounted lives sacrificed to battle: "the legendary" Günther Prien, the book's only representative of the "Happy Time" of u-boat supremacy; the desperate and despondent Peter Zech, commandant of u-505, who committed suicide because he could no longer find any Allied ships to attack; Werner Henke, skipper of u-515, who managed "to survive the war of nerves," only to be shot while attempting to escape an American prison camp; and Wolfgang Lüth, who survived the war as one of the most highly decorated aces, only to be accidently shot by his own guard on the grounds of the famous naval college at Mürwik when Germany was on the verge of capitulating. The last victim in the book was Heinz Eck, captain of u-852, who had been tried by a British court martial in Hamburg and shot for alleged war crimes. For Herlin, these men, "like the other 32,000 of the 39,000 submariners sent out to sea in 69 months of naval war," had all been victims. They had been sacrificed – but not for some political ideal or national dream; they had been the victims of the "damned Atlantic." The ocean thus emerged as the great enemy of sailors whose tragic flaw was single-minded devotion to duty and service.

Other narrators sought to clarify the ethical behaviour of Germany's submariners. For example, Jochen Brennecke's *Der Fall Laconia: Ein Hohes Lied der U-Boot-Waffe* [The Laconia Case: A Song of Songs of the U-Boat Arm, 1959] provided a freely narrated account of the famous Laconia affair. On 12 September 1942 Kapitänleutnant Hartenstein (u-156) had sunk the British vessel that had been transporting some

1800 Italian prisoners of war and a variety of passengers, including
women and children. Haste in effecting rescue was urgent. Unilaterally declaring the scene a neutral zone, Hartenstein had signalled in
the clear to both Axis and Allies alike; he remained on the surface
amidst the lifeboats and rafts and flew a jury-rigged Red Cross flag.
An American aircraft that had overflown the site before disappearing
over the horizon later returned to bomb the submarine. The lifeboats
scattered and U-156 submerged to escape. This now famous rescue
attempt led to Dönitz's famous "Triton Null" signal of 17 September
1942 forbidding U-boats to rescue survivors at sea. Former propaganda writer Brennecke was likely correct when he claimed to have
based his account on all data available at the time. He explained as
well that the International Military Tribunal at Nuremberg had used
the Triton Null signal in the war crimes trial as evidence against
Dönitz's inhumanity. Brennecke had two purposes in writing this book:
to portray "a convincing example of the U-Boat Arm's seamanlike
readiness to help" when humane action was called for, and to clear
the name of Dönitz.

The victorious Allied powers had reproached the German Grand Admiral with
having issued an order to kill ship-wrecked survivors; had reproached this
naval officer who on many occasions had had the courage to oppose his
Supreme Commander. This to an officer who in the Laconia case had even
disobeyed Hitler's instructions, and who, despite all the efforts of the prose-
cutors – together with the whole U-Boat Arm – finally had to be acquitted on
this main point ... Some people here and there in Germany may think
differently about Grand Admiral Dönitz whose greatest and final achievement
was to have saved two and a half million Germans from an uncertain fate in
the East; but in the end, of course, truth is victorious.

Ultimately, Brennecke's "Song of Songs" evoked what to his mind had
always been the grand tradition of selfless service. It was all the more
necessary to reiterate this theme now that Dönitz had been released
from prison.

This theme of undying service was repeated that same year in the
first comprehensive technical treatment of the German submarine to
appear after the war: Bodo Herzog's *Die deutschen Uboote 1906 bis 1945*
[German Submarines, 1906–45, 1959]. Its preface reminds us of the
author's intention: his book is to "mediate, awaken memories, admon-
ish, but also ... to reconcile, and encourage reflection." Aiming at a
general readership, the author doubtless hoped that his former opponents would learn much from his panorama as well. The book deals
with the development of various types of submarine and provides many

photos of men and equipment. It then summarizes "the most important submarine operations of the most successful year of the Second World War (1942)." Clearly a transitional work, it nonetheless draws upon the old iconography. Again, it is his preface that advertises his product best:

A small daring band of German seamen, a BAND OF BROTHERS, as Admiral Nelson once envisioned the [social] structure, waged submarine warfare on all the world's oceans.

Like mythical creatures of the primeval world they dashed through the seas, submerging as occasion arose into the glassy, silent depths – to deliver an attack – or else never to leave the bosom of the mighty ocean again.

The book's dedication – "To the U-boat crews of both World Wars, and their brave opponents in the Navies and Merchant Marines" – sheds further light on Herzog's intent, for it is followed by some revealing lines from German poet Hans Carossa: "Es gibt kein Ende / Nur glühendes Dienen / Zerfallend senden / Wir Strahlen aus."[24] "There is no end," the poet writes, "only glowing/ardent serving." These words, at once sentimental and specious, evoke the theme of a "higher service" that becomes an end in itself. By implication, this duty ends neither in victory nor in defeat, but continues to "irradiate" in the very process of "disintegrating." To the post-Hiroshima reader, Carossa's attempt at mysticism and metapolitics conjures up the vocabulary of all-transcendent atomic power.

Herzog includes former opponents in this paean to service and manages effectively to shield all sailors from ultimate moral questions. By claiming that those who serve do so at some "higher bidding," he begs the question as to precisely what or who was being served. Indeed, he suggests that the service of both Allies and Axis alike – no matter the regime or the circumstances – gives rise to the same "bursting and fading incandescence" of which, like the successive half-lives of a radioactive source, there is no end. This is perhaps stirring poetry indeed, but it is politically suspect. With his woolly minded emphasis on the "mysterious," and on "higher powers," the poet Carossa had been very popular during the Nazi period. In 1938 he had received the prestigious Frankfurt Goethe Prize, a prize traditionally offered to a person "whose creative work is worthy of the honour [of Germany's classical poet] Goethe."[25] Significantly, Carossa would not have won it if politics had not played a role. He had actually been the runner-up to Nobel Prize physicist Max Planck for the award; but propaganda minister Goebbels, abhorring the scientist's political views, swayed the committee into conferring the Goethe Prize on

Carossa instead.[26] Thus it was that a poetaster claimed the ten-thousand Reichsmark prize money – and of course the political cachet – that went with Goebbels's approval.

Carossa's evocative use of language was of course not an isolated case. Similar terminology had been in vogue for years and had found its expression at the highest political level. Thus Hitler too had spoken in the same vacuous, emotionally charged, and obscure terms, wielding them before mass rallies with demonic, persuasive effect. On a smaller scale, Air Marshal Göring also proved skilful at twisting language to met the ends of national policy. Just why U-boat author Herzog would want to endorse such poetry in 1959 remains unclear. Perhaps the lines from Carossa were little more than an unrationalized cultural artifact in his memory; perhaps an echo from a school lesson, taught by an enthusiastic teacher. Significantly, such influences have a life of their own in human memory and do not recognize the convenient divisions of "prewar" and "postwar" so frequent in pocket histories.

Traces of the period 1933–45 still clung to the Herzog work of 1959. The publisher's dustjacket pulled out all the stops in appealing to the ambient mythology of U-boats: "In the U-boat two typically male inclinations find their most consummate expression: the romanticism of seafaring and the adventure of modern technology. One may well regret that from this invention of the South German Wilhelm Bauer dangerous vessels of war, the grey wolves of the sea, had to emerge. But this treacherously secret submarine with its lethal style of attack was, by its nature, born to be a beast of prey."

The language is revealing. The ad writer sees a piece of technology as a living being ("beast of prey," "grey wolves") that fulfilled its supposedly innate characteristics and instincts by turning to war. This creature, now allegedly of sole German invention, appealed to "two typically male inclinations" – another word for instinct – which found "their most consummate expression in ... the romanticism and adventure" that the creature offered. The message seems clear: the creature of the deep had beguiled innocent men into a happy, macho servitude. The U-boat, the blurb tells us, is similar to the fighter plane, but with this important difference: "the U-boat required an especially high degree of 'blood brotherhood' achievement." The vocabulary is here critical. Conspiratorial cooperation – "verschworene Gemeinschaftsleistung" – was of the essence. For the ad-writer at least, this provocative term best characterized relationships not only among the crew members themselves, but between them and the beast they served.

Herzog published his next major U-boat work nine years later in 1968.[27] This time he wrote to celebrate the 60th anniversary of the commissioning of Germany's first operational submarine SMU-1 on 14 December 1906. Entitled *60 Jahre Deutsche Uboote 1906–1966* [Sixty Years of German Submarines, 1906–1966], the book offered a wealth of soberly related lore, together with some 118 U-boat technical drawings and 137 photos. Unlike Herzog's earlier work that claimed only Bauer as the father of the submarine, this edition drew on the more authoritative technical work of Gröner. It therefore conceded the international dimension of submarine experimentation and development – from van Drebel, Bushnell, and Fulton to the Germans' own Bauer. Despite the book's delayed appearance two years after the anniversary, Herzog hoped it would be "kindly received as an important complement to the history of technology, and encourage other writers to pursue further studies."[28] Although Herzog did not manage to inspire other works in this vein, the flow of memoirs by veterans continued. In these works of the 1960s, animal imagery of wolves and sharks prevailed as fitting symbols of stealth.

Marketed in like manner as the story of a "romantic and ghostly weapon" was Harald Busch's *Totentanz der Sieben Meere: Todbringende Gespensterjagd* [Death Dance of the Seven Seas: Death-Dealing Phantom Hunt, 1960]. Busch's attempt at describing the naval war of 1939–45 in four major "phases" employed many of the usual conventions of U-boat literature. Ad-writers needed little imagination in supporting his aims: the U-boat was a "milestone in human inventive genius"; the "merciless struggle for supremacy on the Seven Seas thrust friend and foe alike under the terrifying laws of the conflagration of the Second World War." Meanwhile, on the other side of the Berlin Wall, which had gone up on 13 August 1961 and had become the dreaded symbol of a divided Europe, East Germany's Military Press continued its tradition of anti-fascist historiography that year by publishing a work of fictionalized reminiscences. Ferdinand May's *Die Letzten von U-189* [The Survivors of U-189, 1961] claims to recapture the spirit of the 1952 reunion of those who had survived "the insane orders" of their commanding officer to attack a convoy with a damaged U-boat. The press announced the book as a "special edition for the home library." What in wartime literature would have been praised as heroism of the highest order is here condemned as a fascist crime.

That same year ex-propaganda writer Jochen Brennecke brought out his third postwar book: *Haie im Paradies: Der Deutsche U-Boot-Krieg in Asiens Gewässern 1943–45* [Sharks in Paradise: the German U-boat War in Asian Waters, 1961]. He described his purpose as "portraying in the form of a novel certain events and persons who have become history."[29] For the dust-jacket writer, this made the work "another genuine Brennecke ... a perfect synthesis of conscientious research and grippingly and dramatically portrayed reports of those who were there." As both journalist and popular apologist, he had a broad market in mind and gave his reasons for choosing historical fiction: "a wider circle of readers would not find the dry, documented results of research appealing." Indeed, the wider readership he envisaged "wants to experience what U-boat men experienced, to live through what it was and how it happened." Yet with an eye to the history-minded, he prefaced each chapter of his novel with a brief paragraph of "fact." Unfazed by overcharged prose and mixed metaphors, Brennecke tried to make history come alive. While historians would doubt his success, the ingenuous reader might have been drawn by such typical animations as "how steel sharks, those grey wolves of the German Commander-in-Chief, penetrated the waters of the tropical paradise of Asia." Such journalism had its appeal, for extracts from Brennecke's account appeared in serial form in the popular illustrated magazine *Quick*. Readers interested in less "literary" fare could reach for Jürgen Rohwer's picture-book. Its photos documented the feats of "grey wolves on a grey sea," while its captions, sometimes laced with sentimental lines like the popular song "reach me your hand, your little white hand" from the U-boat song "... denn wir fahren gegen Engeland," brought the "reality" of the war close to home.[30]

Karl Alman took a similar tack to Brennecke's "Sharks in Paradise" when writing his hackwork *Angriff, ran, versenken* [Attack, at 'em, sink, 1965]. It is worth noting that behind the transparent pseudonym Karl Alman ("Karl the German") was the prolific writer Franz Kurowski, who began publishing about this time. As he has since confided to a few veterans, he publishes his more serious work under his real name, Kurowski, reserving his nom de plume for his popularly written works of fiction. Alman's *Angriff* is the usual pulp-trade yarn, authenticated by a stock-in-trade preface by Grand Admiral Dönitz. Not unexpectedly, the army general who reviewed the book for the U-boat veterans' news magazine found it a grand "monument to the U-Boat Arm and its men."[31] The book had a ready market and was reprinted in 1975. Alman repeated the performance under the hackneyed title *Graue Wölfe in blauer See* [Grey Wolves in a Blue Sea, 1967]. With a curious twist of logic, a brief foreword by the former commander of the Mediterranean submarine squadron praised Alman's achievement as an important contribution to historical truth: "The book lays no claim to being a book of history that draws conclusions. [Its theme is] not what might have happened, but what actually happened. Here a monument is raised to the brave men who fought in the Mediterranean." In equating historiography with pure speculation, and novels with actual truth, the commander has reversed conventional concepts of the two disciplines. Nevertheless, the works of Brennecke and Alman highlight a consistent feature of U-boat literature: until the late 1960s the U-boat legacy and image had been delivered to the reading public largely through the medium of fiction, not through the professional discipline of history.[32] Unfortunately, some of the fiction amounted to willful distortion. Ex-submariner Werner's memoir is a case in point.

Herbert A. Werner's book *Die Eisernen Särge* [Iron Coffins, 1969] played a particularly important part in a literary phase of postwar Germany known as "coming to grips with the past" (Bewältigung der Vergangenheit). In literature, the phase marked the attempt to come to terms with the reality of the Nazi years by probing, questioning, and sometimes offering explanations. Published virtually simultaneously in both Germany and the United States, and a year later in Britain, Werner's narrative gave international currency to the term "iron coffins," which had been used before in East German historical novels. Werner, however, was not claiming to write fiction, but truth. In fact, he described the book as an attempt not only "to explain" what it was like to have been educated and trained for his military duties, but to show what it meant to have at first believed in his causes and to have gradually become disillusioned. His "factual report," as he dubs his memoir, runs the gamut from documentary to drama, from personal introspection to critical commentary. As the preface to his first German version explains:

This book, which reports my personal experiences in the U-Boat Arm in the Second World War, fulfils an old obligation. Since the end of that destructive war the role of the U-boat has been distorted and underestimated, particularly by writers of military histories on both German and Allied sides who claim to know the truth. As one of the few who survived the blood bath, I felt it my duty towards the fallen comrades to properly evaluate their desperate battle and to present the historical course of events from the standpoint of my own experiences.

In short, he had written to set the record straight. As one of the longest-serving submariners, he was in a good position to do so. He had served in submarines from the summer of 1941 until war's end in 1945, first while under training aboard U-557, then as officer-of-the-watch aboard U-230, and finally as commandant of both U-415 and U-953. In command he had undertaken ten missions for a total of 370 days at sea. It was a fine record. Shortly after the war he emigrated to Canada, and then to the United States where he established himself in business.

Werner gives the impression that the Nazi system had transformed thinking human beings into mindless automatons by extorting what Germans call "cadaver obedience." Bereft of free will, Germans merely followed without thinking. Earlier in his narrative he reveals an insidious type of seduction through the close identification of man and machine. This, we are to assume, was the peculiar fate of the U-boat men: "a new kind of feeling. I suddenly recognized how important this instrument of highest precision had become for me. I felt myself completely under the spell of the U-boat. Its power had become an important component of my life – if not of my very self."[33]

Like the key concepts of technical precision and obedience that crystallized around his reflections of war, so the terms duty and sacrifice underpinned the U-boat image. They suggested that the German submariner – and above all Werner himself – could not be tarnished with the Nazi brush. For he who "only" serves as a patriot cannot be guilty; he can at best be noble, at worst a victim:

Duty was the first and last word in the dictionary of submariners, and regardless of reports to the contrary we did our duty with a forthright courage unexcelled by any other branch. We were soldiers and patriots, nothing more. And in devotion to a lost cause our comrades died in horrendous numbers. The great tragedy of the U-Boat Arm was however not only that innumerable brave men faced a seaman's death, but that so many young men were sacrificed in inadequate U-boats and through the irresponsible measures of senior leadership.

Duty, devotion, sacrifice – and ultimate betrayal: the components of tragic action. Indeed, the word "tragedy" recurs throughout the book. His perspective on U-boats suggested a new identity for Germany's "wonder weapon": the machine was not merely one of many possible actors in the theater of war, but the very embodiment of war itself; the machine was an organic being, a protean element of tragic structure and action itself. The full scope of the "U-boat tragedy" emerges from the statistics of submarines and men sacrificed to the enemy; for Werner, they were pointlessly, uselessly lost. The war, he claimed, had clearly been lost from the very first day; Germany's "senior leadership" would have recognized the fact if they had faced up to the overwhelming industrial potential of the United States and the British Empire. Oblivious to the fact that Germany's ultimate defeat was a foregone conclusion, officialdom had preached heroism and valour in a just war that could be won. Having interpreted events in this manner, Werner explained what the loss of Prien and Kretschmer in 1941 had "really" meant; it was a "double tragedy that confused the German population" simply because they had now forfeited their "invincible heroes."[34] In portraying the matter in this way, Werner was attempting to debunk and demythologize the German submarine. Werner took the matter still further. Through brisk, if tendentious, narrative he made explicit what other writers had only implied: Germany's fortunes of war had paralleled the rise and fall of the U-Boat Arm. In thinking thus, Werner linked up with a number of other writers. The U-boat was the paramount German weapon and, as such, it was the primary measure and image of Germany's strength and weakness as a fighting nation.

Werner's "personal account of the German U-boat battles of World War II," as the subtitle of the American edition reads, is a lively and entertaining work. It serves up all the adventure and suspense one can find in the conventional pot-boiler. But he largely declines such wartime sobriquets about the U-boats as the stalking, hunting "grey wolves." He prefers instead the funereal "iron coffins" of his title. For him and for many other veterans, the days of heroic romanticism had long since past. Had the German leadership been honest, he points out, and had the submariners recognized in the so-called statistics of success the extraordinarily high mortality rate in the U-Boat Arm, then Germans from the earliest days of the war would have seen U-boats as the "iron coffins" they really were. Werner offers his views not as a wartime officer's gallows humour, but as a pragmatic judgment of history.

The title *Iron Coffins* derives in large part from one of the last scenes in the book. It is 1945, the last months of the war, and U-boat commander Werner has been summoned with others to meet Großadmiral Dönitz in Berlin. Werner claimed not to have seen Dönitz the "lion" since receiving the Knight's Cross from his hand in the autumn of 1941 at the French base of Lorient. Dönitz now looked different: "He had aged considerably. He had become leaner, more drawn and less dynamic."[35] Werner was by this time convinced of the utter futility of the war and of the suicidal nature of attempts at gaining the upper hand against overwhelming Allied forces. What struck him even more than the disturbing changes in Dönitz was the group of new commanding officers who had just completed their qualifying course. "I learned to my surprise that they were to command a new series of U-boat that was obsolete the day it was put into service ... Without any combat experience at the front, their U-boats were iron coffins. But it was not their fault. They were all young as I. We believed and obeyed; we had sworn obedience."[36] Such, at any rate, were Werner's views in 1969.

The dust-jacket of the German edition described "Iron Coffins" as a work "in which the events of the war are reflected unadulterated."

On closer examination, however, the book proved to be one of the worst distortions of the postwar period. It is, in fact, just as propagandistic in its own way as U-boat books that had appeared during the war. Jürgen Rohwer, Germany's premier naval historian, savaged the book in a scathing review. "If one wanted to underline the factual errors [in red], almost every page would be like a blood bath," he observed.[37] On the basis of documentary evidence – some of which consisted of reports submitted by Werner himself during his wartime service – Rohwer condemned the book as sheer hyprocisy. Werner had spliced other submariners' achievements onto his own record, had wildly exaggerated circumstances and events, did not have access to witnesses on whom he claimed to draw, invented orders that never existed, and distorted statistics and records – all to sustain his charge that the naval leadership had irresponsibly "fuelled up" submariners to undertake suicidal missions. Werner's book was motivated less by a sense of duty towards his fallen comrades than by cheap sensationalism in the attempt to make a literary hit. By this time, of course, Werner was already enjoying major sales on two continents.

Confiding to a former Crew-Kamerad in 1974, Werner commented on his book's continuing success. It had appeared in fourteen countries including Japan. It had given rise to tours across the United States for some 127 TV and radio interviews, and lectures at schools, universities, and naval bases. He had become, in effect, the paramount image-maker: "I was thus in the extraordinary position of informing our former opponents about the truth of our epic struggle. I know I have done more for the esteem of our U-Boat Arm and its men than all those little pen-pushers together."[38] Significantly, the Association of German Submariners had fully supported the findings of Jürgen Rohwer's debunking review; it had dissociated itself from any claims in the memoir and had rejected Werner's "hack-work as totally without foundation." Fortunately for Werner, however, his fame and his message outlived the review.

When Werner's book appeared in 1969, the German book market offered only two other main contenders for the position he claimed for himself. Paradoxically, the books had been written by Englishmen with no war experience whatever: Terence Robertson and Gwyn Griffin. Robertson's book had been on the market in English for almost fifteen years before the German edition appeared as *Der Wolf im Atlantik* [The Wolf in the Atlantic: War Experiences of Otto Kretschmer]. It strikes one as strange that the German subtitle had to remind the reader just who this famous protagonist was: "the most successful U-boat commander of the Second World War." First published in London in 1955 as *The Golden Horseshoe* – after the pictograph on the conning tower of Kretschmer's boat – the brisk account was a hero-maker. Its author had been motivated by admiration for a chivalrous warrior. After all, the German officer had been one of the grand three aces (Prien, Schepke, and Kretschmer) whose exploits had exhilarated Germany in the opening months of the war and whose submarine careers had come to an abrupt end in March 1941.

An American version of the book appeared as *Night Raiders of the Atlantic*, a title evoking the old mythologies that still had market value in the United States. Kretschmer himself had attended the launching of the original British edition in London, where he once again met the famous British "U-boat killer" Donald Macintyre who had sunk Kretschmer's U-boat in HMS *Walker*. Reconciliation was in the air in 1955. In a ceremonial gesture, Macintyre had returned the set of binoculars taken from his former enemy in 1941. A silver plate on the binoculars bore the inscription: "Returned to Otto Kretschmer – A Gallant Foe – Donald Macintyre, Captain, R.N., Oct. 24th 1955." Later, Macintyre had inscribed a gift copy of the book to Kretschmer as from "Your old foe and new friend." As Kretschmer recalled, Macintyre re-enacted the return of the binoculars during a live BBC-TV interview together, and the U-boat skipper took advantage of the opportunity "to stand up for Großadmiral Dönitz in public."[39] But as a German edition would not be available until 1969, none of this stage-craft would reach the German public in any significant degree. Thus Werner's iconoclastic "Iron Coffins" stood in sharp contrast to Robertson's "Wolf in the Atlantic" with its largely uncritical, though entertaining, tale of gallantry and derring-do. By this time, gallantry was a disputed virtue.

Gwyn Griffin's historical novel *Der letzt Zeuge* [literally, The Last Witness, 1969] had a different publication history. It was based on what was popularly regarded as the first war-crimes trial involving members of the German Kriegsmarine. Twenty-nine-year-old Kapitän-leutnant Heinz Eck, the commanding officer of U-852, faced a British court martial in Hamburg in October 1945, together with his medical officer, watch-officer, and two crewmen. Many regarded it as a show trial, an attempt by the British to gain evidence against Dönitz, who was then to face a military court in Nuremberg. In the event, Eck and his fellow officers were found guilty of having machine-gunned survivors of his torpedo attack on the Greek freighter *Peleus*. The Germans were executed by British firing-squad. No evidence was adduced that Dönitz had ever directly ordered that survivors of U-boat attacks be killed.

As early as 1951 a German illustrated magazine had recounted the events under the rubric "A dead man begs for justice."[40] The six-part series was a plea for an end to West Germany's "witch hunt" for war criminals. Just how much the Eck affair meant to veterans might be inferred from the first postwar gathering of the Association of German Submariners (Verband deutscher U-Boot-Fahrer). U-boat skipper Teddy Suhren had invited all former submariners to convene in Hamburg on 16–18 May 1954. Some 3000 attended. In a special ceremony marking the occasion, five hundred of them gathered at the grave of Heinz Eck and laid a wreath "to the fallen comrades." In this case, they recognized him as the victim of victor's justice. A British writer has confirmed the galling irony that well before trying Eck, British authorities had known of a similar war crime committed by one of their own submarine captains who had later been knighted and promoted to the rank of Vice Admiral. In July 1941 British submarine commander and Victoria Cross winner Anthony Miers of HMS/M *Torbay* had cold-bloodedly gunned down survivors of a ship he had sunk and later machine-gunned Germans found in an inflatable raft.[41] Despite the fact that Meirs's mission report had documented his breach of the Hague Convention, and that his report had been minuted by admiralty staff, it was withheld from Eck's defence. British authorities at the time deemed it more important to convict Eck, in the hope of gaining hard evidence against Dönitz, than to see that justice was served equitably on all sides. The "Eck case," as it is called, remains a bitter issue among U-boat veterans to this day.

Griffin's novel on the subject had first appeared in English as *An Operational Necessity* (1967). According to the subtitle of the German edition, this was "the shocking novel of German U-boats in the Second World War." Whereas the German version entitled *Der letzte Zeuge* [The Last Witness] highlighted the survivor whose testimony had launched the whole judicial process, the original English title was more accurate. For at issue was the behaviour of sailors when faced with decisions governed by an operational necessity: What were the limits of personal moral responsibility in the context of military operations? Is it morally defensible to be "merely a soldier doing one's duty" by obeying orders? Or might militarily legal commands sometimes be morally reprehensible and therefore worthy of rejection? Griffin's book is an especially fine achievement in the genre of U-boat literature. Well-crafted and insightful, it raises questions of exquisite ambiguity. Indeed, it invites critical examination of the traditional icon of the dutiful soldier who carries out his death-defying patrols as both patriot and hero. For Griffin, not even the winners of a war are heroes; all participants are victims.

Only in East Germany had the tone and thrust of U-boat books remained unchanged and unchallenged. Authors used axes instead of scalpels in order to lay bare the intricate problems of "coming to grips with the past." They exploited the past in order to accuse West Germany of the sins of its alleged fathers. Paul Herbert's *Der Tod auf allen Meeren* [Death on All Seas, 1970] is a case in point. It highlights celebrated and unusual cases of U-boat warfare in order to illustrate its narrow political aim. All U-boats are described as "fascist" U-boats; indeed, the adjectives "fascist" and "imperialist" are wielded with indiscriminate ease. The jacket blurb resorts to the same style and terminology as the text itself: "In depicting typical episodes from the U-boat war, the author of this factual report sheds light on the essential features of the conduct of war by fascist German imperialism ... He reveals the barbaric character and aspects of U-boat war that are contrary to international law, and shows the continuity between the fascist U-Boat Arm and the 'Kriegsmarine' [sic] of the Federal Republic of Germany."

Characteristically, the writer did not recount "typical episodes" as claimed; he chose instead important atypical ones fraught with complex moral and legal problems. His selective approach scarcely differed from writers in the West who chose to write about heroes. Significantly, however, the East German writer was content merely to denounce the German navy rather than to explore its past. For example, he highlighted U-30's sinking of the British liner *Athenia* on 3 September 1939; he emphasized U-852's machine-gunning survivors of the freighter *Peleus* on 13 March 1944, allegedly under orders from Admiral Dönitz (which was in fact not the case). Finally, by calling the navy of the Federal Republic of Germany the "*Kriegs*marine" instead of the technically correct "*Bundes*marine," he implied that West Germany's navy was in fact still the same old Nazi fleet. Not even when dealing with U-boats in the First World War could East Germans dispense with their politically obligatory whiplashes against the "fascist" and "imperialist" warmongers of the German navy.[42] Not until the Berlin Wall came down in 1991 did the general reader in East Germany have any other fare by which to judge political realities in both past and present. The book caused no ripples in the West until 1985, when a copy reached knowledgeable readers. As might be expected, the work was condemned; it was the subject of an address that year to the biennial conference of retired admirals convoked by the commander-in-chief of the Federal German Navy.[43]

Herbert's book "Death on All Seas" was, in fact, only one of many distortions published on both sides of the Berlin wall in 1970. To West German naval writer Bodo Herzog, a photo-documentary seemed the only way to counteract them. He dedicated his dual-language title *U-Boote im Einsatz: U-Boats in Action: Eine Bilddokumentation* (1970) to the victims of the atypical scenarios that the East German book had pilloried. His German-only preface outlines the curious fate of the U-boat image.

A strange mythology still lies over those boats and their crews who were often the cause for fanfares and special news bulletins during the Second World War. After the war the image of the U-Boat Arm was often enough distorted and misrepresented. If here [in West Germany] we sometimes have had a kind of successor to the old propagandizing literature, then the GDR [East Germany] has made little serious effort to document factually. Free from all emotion, only the photo documentary has special expressive capability.

His was the first of many photo collections which, like Mallmann-Showell's *Uboote Gegen England* [U-boats against England: Struggle and Demise of the German U-Boat Arm, 1939–1945], would provide virtually no text at all.

Yet the old War-Book style of narrative still found a market. The hackwriter Karl Alman remained interested in the great paladins of submarine warfare and saw to it that his brief accounts of their exploits lacked nothing of the pulp-novelist's flair. His *Ritter der Sieben Meere* [Knights of the Seven Seas – Knight's Cross Winners of the U-Boat Arm, 1975] characteristically avoided the burning moral issues surrounding submarines and politics; instead it restricted itself to wartime action as it "really" happened. Men of action, he would have us believe, had no time for effete reflection and must therefore be judged by their deeds. Subtitled a "Chronicle of a Sacrifice," his brief tales of the eighteen submarine commanders who had won the Knight's Cross drew heavily on already published material. Much of the data is correct: names, places, ships sunk, and medals won. But Alman is nothing if not eclectic; he is a journalistic quilt-maker who in this case provides a lean mix of fact and fancy, with photo-portraits of the major players. Not surprisingly, his dedication reveals a patchwork of allusions to already-marketed lore – "the 27,082 dead who bravely faced the opponent" – and splices selected elements that hearken back to recurring mythologies. Thus Alman dedicated his "book about the Knights of the Sea to the dead in honour, to the living as solemn admonition (Mahnung) and obligation." Connoisseurs of U-boat fare would have recognized that Alman had here borrowed sentiments and phrases from Frank's hagiographies of Günther Prien published in 1941 and 1958. In those years Frank had dedicated his texts not only "to the following generation as solemn admonition [Mahnung]," but "to the Living as a model." Times had now changed, and such models had fallen out of style.

Still, the old images of "Knights of the Deep" and "Grey Wolves" seem never to have lost their market appeal. Sometimes, however, they emerged with a different slant. A book by the photo-collector and former wartime press writer Bodo Herzog is a case in point. His co-authored work, published in 1976, included both of these epithets in its graphic title: "Knights of the Deep, Grey Wolves: The Most Successful Submarine Commanders in the World." Curiously enough, Herzog had lifted this first part of the title – "Knights of the Deep" – from the title of the German translation of Lowell Thomas's effulgent war book *Raiders of the Deep* that had appeared almost fifty years earlier, in 1928. Indeed, a fulsome quotation from Lowell Thomas – though without acknowledging the source – encapsulated Herzog's postwar view of submarine warfare: where the raiding exploits of Graf Luckner's high-seas sailing ship had once constituted a thrilling "romanticism" in the minds of an earlier generation, the new technology of submarine warfare projected a mesmerizing power that could determine the outcome of global war. Or in the words of the recycled passage from Thomas: "The U-boats held the world spellbound. One of the latest marvels of modern technology, striking a sweeping, fearful blow that threatened to decide the issue of the conflict of the nations – that surely was a thing to clutch the imagination with an iron grasp."

After a sketchy fifteen-page survey of the Battle of the Atlantic (1939–45), Herzog highlighted the exploits of the "ten most successful submarine captains in the world." Significantly, all of them were German, and not one of them was drawn from among any of the old Second World War heroes who might at the time have smacked of Nazism. Six of them had been captains in the Imperial Navy of the First World War (Arnauld de la Perière, Walter Forstmann, Max Valentiner, Otto Steinbrinck, Hans Rose, and Walther Schwieger), and four in the Kriegsmarine of Hitler Germany (Otto Kretschmer, Wolfgang Lüth, Victor Schütze, and Erich Topp). Topp would publish his own memoirs in 1991 long after his retirement as an admiral in the postwar German navy. In doing so, he would alienate many submarine veterans in postwar Germany by criticizing Dönitz's political opportunism; he would also question the ethical basis of wartime service in the U-Boat Arm.

Although Herzog's book is technically reliable for a non-specialist audience, it never addresses the political and moral issues that are beginning to be raised at this time. In 1976 Herzog was bent upon saving face. While extolling those mainstays of Germany's naval tradition who had fought gallantly in two wars, he was moved to console "the German seamen who had to deliver their Boats to the victors after the capitulation in May 1945, in often unworthy form under the black pirate flag." To this end Herzog cited words attributed to US General Douglas MacArthur in 1951: "German submariners were first class – there has never been a better submarine force than the German."

This was the first U-boat book to be dedicated to a shadowy group of officers who, in Herzog's phrase, had "safeguarded true naval tradition." Significantly, none of them was a member of the grand pantheon of German U-boat literature whose exploits had been told and retold, and who seemed to embody the essence of that "Band of Brothers" that had until now formed Germany's submarine tradition. Quite the contrary. All of them, in fact, had run against the grain during the war by participating in the German resistance movement, and four of them had actually been executed for their part in the failed assassination attempt against Hitler on 20 July 1944: Admiral Wilhelm Canaris, naval class of 1905; Korvettenkapitän Alfred Kranzfelder, class of 1927; Naval Judge-Advocate Dr Bertold Schenk; and General Graf von Stauffenberg, who had been a departmental chief in the operations division of the Naval War Office since 1939. Without committing himself to a reinterpretation of German U-boat history, Herzog had, in dedicating his book to the Resistance, taken a major step towards proclaiming an alternative tradition of naval service; he had tacitly swept away the tradition he had once evoked when quoting the poet Hans Carossa in his submarine book of 1959. Apparently rejecting Carossa's formulation of "higher service" which places sailors unthinkingly into the hands of a criminal regime, he had now recognized a valid sense of moral duty in a higher service to nationhood beyond political cabal. This moral duty, too, constituted an ancient tradition practised by the Brotherhood of the Sea. "Duty," in Nelson's oft-quoted words, "is the great business of a sea officer; all private considerations must give way to it however painful it may be." Just what that duty might be marked the next decade of U-boat debate.

5 Revising the Past: The Buchheim Wave, 1973–88

No book or film of the postwar era promoted the U-boat's image more successfully than Lothar-Günther Buchheim's literary memoir *Das Boot* (1973). In reaching the widest audience, his novel triggered often rancorous debate about just what that image was. It raised searching and often acrimonious discussion about the nature of the reality that the fiction portrayed. Veterans charged Buchheim with having distorted truth and having failed to communicate "the facts." Buchheim replied that his work was a product of the imagination; it was a novel, a historical novel. The positions of both Buchheim and the U-boat men became still more polarized once the film version appeared. Watching these debates in press and TV were younger generations of Germans who had not known the war. Of course, the book and the film projected different messages. So, too, did the subsequent three-part TV version.

Such was the temper of the 1970s and 1980s that war and the military were generally unpopular literary themes. This was so despite the strength of the now ebbing social process known as "coming to grips with the Nazi past" (Vergangenheitsbewältigung). The process, which had marked much political and literary discussion in the postwar years, tended to view supposedly historical accounts of war with some suspicion. With all the vigour of religious crusades, peace movements and green movements were now proclaiming an alternate reality. Of course, books and films that dealt with Germany's military past could still offer vicarious pleasure and "historical" insight. But apart from the Landser popular histories that continued to extol macho combat, the marketability of most books depended on the authors' having successfully linked storytelling with social criticism. This frequently meant rejecting the traditional ethos of soldiering as an absurdity of the past. It was Buchheim's achievement to have written a provocative and sophisticated novel that made "U-boat" once more a household word. His novel, followed by film, TV series, interviews, picture books, and public disputes, has kept the issue in the public mind up to the present day.

This wealth of material gathered its own momentum. The novel was Buchheim's personal and sometimes idiosyncratic view of life among the "grey wolves." The subsequent film reinterpreted Buchheim's novel. Produced and directed by Wolfgang Petersen with an eye to the American market, it concentrated on Hollywood-style action. The message of this carefully crafted film was both antiwar and anti-Buchheim. Bavaria Studios had turned the novel into what newspaper reviewers called an "underwater Western" and a "U-psycho-thriller." Petersen's lengthened TV version recast the material yet again, retarding the action as a means to approaching the numbingly dull reality of the U-boat war as it actually was. Submarine warfare, as Buchheim and many ancient warriors attest, was mostly a "Gammelfahrt": days and weeks of bone-wearying boredom and debilitating discomfort, broken only by shattered seconds of utter terror. With the appearance of the film, public and private castigations followed one another as veterans pilloried Buchheim and Buchheim taunted veterans. He then turned his ire against producers, who retorted by putting his own "unresolved past" on public display.

Buchheim, as we have seen, had begun his naval writing during the war years as a Propaganda-Kompanie man. As his articles attest, he had followed the party line with undisguised zeal. Even as late as 1990, U-boat veterans were quick to remind him and the general public of his National Socialist service. His wartime articles bore the marks of an experienced popular journalist; his reports were snappy, market-oriented, superficial, and hyped. He seemed at the time content to serve both a navy and a leadership that he would later make a profession of disparaging.

His major work of the war years, *Jäger im Weltmeer* [Ocean Hunters, 1943], is a case in point. Dedicated to "My U-boat Comrades," it bore a signed preface by Grand Admiral Dönitz, an honour not even accorded Prien's first edition about the attack on Scapa Flow in 1939. Yet over thirty years later, submarine veterans would evoke Buchheim's long-forgotten book as grounds for rejecting his self-righteous attacks against those who had served in the "Nazi" navy; his hands were clearly not as clean as he had at first claimed. Indeed, Buchheim's propaganda work provided the veterans further grounds for rejecting his qualifications as a writer on submarine matters: he had only been a PK-man promoting public relations in the service of the Nazi party, they taunted; he had experienced but a single patrol and had misused Dönitz's trust in him by inveigling a preface for his first book. For all these reasons, they pointed out, he did not measure up to the standards expected of a "U-boat comrade." But none of these arguments reveal anything about Buchheim as a creative writer. For him, the writing of *Das Boot* was a means of reassessing his wartime experience. For years after Germany's defeat, Buchheim has explained, his thousands of wartime photographs lay dormant. Gradually he re-examined them, until his own process of "coming to grips with the past" transformed images into an undisputed literary hit.

Das Boot (1973) is undeniably the finest piece of fiction in U-boat literature. Compelled to explore the human dimensions and depths of the U-boat experience, Buchheim had attempted to emulate the genre of the "non-fiction novel" in the manner of Truman Capote's *In Cold Blood.* With an eye to Herman Melville''s brooding epic *Moby Dick* and Norman Mailer's Pulitzer Prize winning war novel *The Naked and the Dead,* German critics have characterized Buchheim's achievement as evincing "Melville's obsession" and "Mailer's toughness." The national newspaper *Die Zeit* compared Buchheim's novel with Theodor Plievier's famous epic *Stalingrad* portraying the German army's campaign on the Eastern Front. Indeed, *Die Zeit* was careful to point out that our equating Buchheim's *Das Boot* with Plievier's documentary novel "must not obscure the judgment that Lothar-Günther Buchheim has written the best front novel of the Second World War, the first one that is valid; and objections that war, however you take it, is no longer a theme are swept from the writing table, and from the beer table too." Experienced observers have been equaly fulsome in their praise. Thus a wartime submariner who subsequently served as naval adviser to the Bavaria Studios' film production regarded the novel as "a superbly observed, powerfully expressed and realistic portrayal of a U-boat patrol in war."[1]

Buchheim projects a stark message: German submariners were not heroes, but victims. They were betrayed by their leader, Großadmiral Dönitz, who had driven them to their slaughter, and by the Nazi political system that had exploited their youth. The novel quickly sold more than two million copies worldwide in many languages. The first runs in Germany alone sold over a quarter-million copies. But in his relentless self-promotion, Buchheim was really no better than Werner in *Iron Coffins* (1969). The major difference between them, as an expert critic leads us to conclude, is that Werner had consciously lied from the outset when writing his supposedly factual account. Buch-heim, on the other hand, had written an honest novel in 1973, only to be later swept along by the emotional and commercial opportuni-ties created by the furore that both his best-selling novel and his subsequent U-boat films generated.

Responses to the novel in Germany were overwhelming. This at last was the U-boat as it really was, many thought. *Das Boot* was the war novel for our time; it was regarded as the successor to Erich Maria Remarque's classic war novel *Im Westen Nichts Neues* [All Quiet on the Western Front, 1929]. Of course, many veterans were not entirely convinced – just as an earlier generation of veterans had disdained Remarque. In defending themselves against Buchheim's portrayal and in rejecting his views, adherents of both naval tradition and the Grand Admiral have invoked everything in support of their cause from "com-mon decency" to Germany's constitution (Das Grundgesetz) and the Bible. Most ex-submariners who took issue with Buchheim did so because of his "distorted" representation of reality. Others largely supported Buchheim, while deploring the fact that artistic licence had led him to sensationalize the occasionally prurient interests of youthful German sailors in war. Many took specific exception to the drunken-ness, eroticism, and debauchery that the opening scene of both the novel and the film portrayed. This was certainly the position of Addi Schnee, then president of the Association of German Submariners, who otherwise praised Buchheim for his splendidly detailed portrayals of "submarine patrol with all its moods, excitements and dangers." Submariners had not been victims, the majority claimed; they had been loyal soldiers of the Fatherland who had simply been doing their duty. Like those of other nations, they had been – and still were – honour-able men. But veterans formed by no means a monolithic group. Thus when an article in the newsletter of the German Naval Officers' Asso-ciation deplored the novel as historically inaccurate and inveighed against its "disgusting smut," another veteran turned to the attack by arguing that the association had missed the whole point of Buchheim's novel. Echoing Alexander Mitscherlich's important and widely known book of Freudian psychoanalysis that in 1969 had dealt clinically with the problem of private and communal guilt for the Nazi era, he portrayed the anti-Buchheim stance as a psychological defence mech-anism.[2] Such a mechanism, Mitscherlich had argued, signalled the failure to have confronted German history realistically and frankly; it marked a failure to genuinely grieve and mourn. In the words of the pro-Buchheim veteran, those who supported the newsletter's rejection of the novel while endorsing its "Remembrance Day" commemoration of the Fallen showed little understanding of the war and of themselves.

These tributes and expressions of gratitude to the Fallen reveal at bottom only an "inability to grieve," to lament, to weep, an inability to come to grips with the horrors of the past just as they really were, through an honest process of grieving ... They signify trying to solve the problem by repression, by making the facts fit one's own scheme of things, by making legends. They are the vain attempt at making the terrible death of 30,000 young men less senseless and more bearable by promoting them to spotless heroes. As though anybody is helped by that.

Significantly, the letter was never published. In short, those who objected to the book tacitly decried the fact that Buchheim was demythologizing the past. That he should dare to do so was deemed an affront not only to the memory of the Fallen, but to the honour of those who had managed to survive. The passions unleashed by Buchheim's *Das Boot* intensified into what has become known as the Buchheim affair. The scope and intensity of these disputes about wartime reality hinted at deep-seated national problems that invited closer analysis. Intrigued by the phenomenon, German historian Michael Salewski teamed up with Buchheim to produce a hard-back volume of responses to *Das Boot*. It went into popular paperback publication the following year.

Salewski's *Von der Wirklichkeit des Krieges* [On the Reality of the War, 1975] was an important compendium and analysis of public opinion.[3] The nub of the Buchheim controversy, in Salewski's view, was that readers had come to the novel with different perceptions of historical reality than the one Buchheim had portrayed. Their reality had been a fusion of two sources: their own existential, and therefore subjective and isolated, experience of having gone to sea in U-boats; and the supportive cultural milieu of politics and propaganda that had gener-ated the politically appropriate fictions of what "really" was happening. Official stories throughout the war had exuded victory and heroism: "seagoing knights," "grey wolves," and "dedicated warriors" actually conquering their traditional enemy England with gallantry and bra-vado. Even death itself had been portrayed during the war years as an affirmation of glory. Whichever publication of the period one picks up – be it newspapers, reports, or journals such as *Das Reich, Signal, Angriff* – one finds the same thing. As Salewski put it: "the controlled press had filtered the war according to its own image, and this image was communicated to the populace with the tremendous resources of the media. Radio and film played their role." As we have seen in a previous chapter, novels and autobiographies also figured in what might be called the conspiracy of the book trade. Again, according to

Salewski, the wartime projection of reality was an "infamous mixture of truth and lie, propaganda and news."[4] Salewski's judgment is typical of his own and the younger generation. Born in 1938, he had not participated in the war, and thus enjoyed what Germans call "the Grace of late birth." Film director Wolfgang Petersen, who created the epoch-making film *Das Boot*, belonged to the same generation.

Buchheim next published a picture-book containing some of the excellent photographs on which his successful novel had in part been based. With a preface by Michael Salewski, Buchheim's *U-Boot-Krieg* [U-boat War, 1976] caused further stir. It was widely reviewed in the popular press. The illustrated magazine *Stern*, among others, discussed it at length. In step with the anti-U-boat fashion of the time, *Stern* called it "the story of the iron coffins" and described how "war reporter Buchheim had rescued his dramatic photos from the Gestapo thirty-five years ago." Of course, whether Buchheim had actually rescued them or simply purloined them can no longer be known. But his story of having snatched them from the Gestapo made good promotional fare and fit the mythology of the U-boat war which, we are to believe, was driven by evil Nazis. Buchheim's *U-Boot Krieg* is an example of history as advocacy, for he wanted to convert readers to his own viewpoint. Yet in drawing on a quotation from Henry Miller, he showed that he recognized the limits of his craft: "No one can write the absolute truth." Yet Buchheim nonetheless expressed his position clearly: Germany had wasted and exploited her youth, she had ruthlessly squandered what Dönitz had once called "Human material" (Menschenmaterial). Convinced that only eye-witness photographs could portray the reality of his claims, he selected superb pictures that spoke eloquently for themselves. A caption beneath a photograph of Admiral Dönitz brought the charge closer to home: "The training flotillas in the Baltic saw to reinforcements of 'Menschenmaterial' ... In the course of the war the U-Boat Arm bled itself out so quickly that crews became younger and younger." And, of course, the judgment is not inaccurate. Dönitz did indeed have to replenish the increasingly decimated manning pool with younger and less well-trained submariners. Transposed into Buchheim's context, however, Dönitz's terminology leads one to conclude that his conduct of the war was both wanton and base.

Indeed, Buchheim is deft at turning the spear by setting old words into new contexts. The result is acid social criticism. Wartime U-boat literature, for example, had extolled the vigour – and the youth – of the heroic submariners. Buchheim now shed a different light on it by taking Dönitz's statement of 8 October 1943 – a time when Dönitz must have known that he had irrevocably lost the Battle of the Atlantic – and republishing it in 1976. As Dönitz had said: "We will have to crew the majority of U-boats with many young people. There is nothing wrong with youth when splendid chaps are involved. But training must be all the more thorough, and its even more important that we get as much valuable human material as possible into the navy." Young people with "the right stuff" were just what he needed. As we have seen, wartime U-boat books directed at families and youth were not above trying to lure boys to sea. Such books proclaimed loftily that it was both honourable and sublime to sacrifice oneself for one's country. Death meant apotheosis, transfiguration, a transcendence of life. Those who had died young had fulfilled themselves; age would not weary them, nor the years condemn. But Buchheim saw death in a submarine differently, and in doing so cut against the grain of the navy's literary tradition.

Croaking in a U-boat is wretched and complicated. Nobody's shot to death, no sparks of life are simply snuffed out. The grim reaper likes his victims to squirm. A plunge into the depths takes its time. The water garotte chokes slowly. Pressure of the deep! At three thousand meters it reaches three hundred atmospheres.

Over the years, Buchheim would feel increasingly compelled, almost to the point of irrationality, to describe the horrors of U-boat war.

Prior to Buchheim's campaigning in the West, only East German U-boat novels had cast such harsh judgments. Typical of these was Gerhard Grümmer's lengthy *Irrfahrt: Ein Tatsachenroman* [Voyage Astray: A Documentary Novel, 1977]. It had told the story of three school chums drawn into the vortex of war to join the navy in 1941. The author explored the various influences that had led so many to watery graves: parents and friends, school, the idolatrous teaching of naval history, and ultimately the war itself with its opportunity to serve a grand tradition. Critical of the past from a narrow ideological point of view, Grümmer was as staunchly antifascist as the authors of all the other blandly mediocre war books coming out of East Germany. His primary purpose in writing was to uncover "the Nazi roots" of West Germany. Yet despite the invective of his programmatic approach, Grümmer was correct in assessing the atmosphere of the wartime literary tradition in the naval genre. "The ideals to which a German youth had to aspire distinguished themselves solely through combative spirit, courage, loyalty and a spirit of sacrifice."[5] As we have seen, these ideals were embodied in German heroes that both the propaganda service and the German Navy League had promoted: Horst Wessel,

Günther Prien, Joachim Schepke, and others. Young men were lured more to serve in the hope of emulating the deeds of the heroes than to fulfil the aims of the Nazi party. Yet as an ad on the jacket of Grümmer's *Irrfahrt* correctly put it: "Contrary to their notions of romanticism and great heroic deeds, they got caught in the merciless workings of the war machine."

Similarly mindful of the huge deceit that one generation perpetrated against another, Buchheim also added more derogatory terms to the "war machine" vocabulary of reconstructionist writers. For him, the u-boat was a "tube," a "crate under water," a "floating fighting machine," "a grey shark," "an insidious weapon," but above all else "an iron coffin."[6] The crews themselves were little better off than "the kaiser's coolies." Here he had picked up the title of Plievier's 1929 novel about the exploited German sailors of the First World War whose mistreatment had launched a revolution. Like the First World War, Buchheim argues, so the Second had also demonstrated "the senselessness of war."

By 1977, in response to Bavaria Studios' interest in his novel, Buchheim had begun working on a film adaptation.[7] While recognizing the story's potential for a feature film, Buchheim also knew that one could not dramatize an epic work without distorting its intent. The novel would have to be rewritten with the new medium in mind. Buchheim's successful public-relations tour of the United States in 1973, which had promoted the American version of the novel, had eventually aroused the interest of American movie producers. In the usual Hollywood way, American proposals had latched onto the easily marketable clichés about Nazis and action-packed skullduggery and adventure. Ultimately, Bavaria Studios rejected both the American script (because of its clichés) and Buchheim's (because of its inordinate length), and accepted instead that of Wolfgang Petersen.

Buchheim's script marks a critical stage in his writing. The script became what may be called the third part of his trilogy of u-boat trauma. As one critic rightly observed: "The novel was prose, reflection, fact, and memory; the picture-book brought documentary evidence and witnesses; the movie-script sketches the plan for the veritable reconstruction of the hell of war."[8] Buchheim's aggressive notes clarify the significance of the u-boat war for the lost generation that fought it. "We have been defamed [for having participated in the war], we have been attacked, many have been pilloried. This is a deceived, swindled generation that has been more viciously cheated than any other."

The world première of the film *Das Boot* took place on 18 September 1981 in Munich's Mathäser Palast cinema. It marked a watershed in the submarine's literary history. On the eve of the première, one newspaper typically promoted the event with a large-print article against a picture of a surfaced U-boat in a raging sea. It was meant to project a powerful image of the iron coffin, and of rugged men in a desperate situation. The thrust of the visual argument was unequivocal and clear: "Beneath them the depths of the ocean. Above them the destroyer's fire. In them, despair. For naval war knows no wounded." In U-boat warfare you either survive physically unscathed or you don't survive at all. And statistics long-since made public showed that most German submariners had perished.

A promotional campaign had prepared the movie market well. It had covered the shooting of the film in advance and had solicited feature coverage in the national magazine *Der Spiegel* in December 1980. A new U-boat image had emerged. In fact, the magazine's coloured cover-picture announcing "Das Boot – Germany's most expensive film" conjured up feelings of foreboding, mystery, and impending doom. One well-illustrated movie magazine promoted *Das Boot* with photographs, articles, and interviews with the actors. The film was about a "journey through the insanity of war" in which "enthusiastic young men go to sea in submarines only to experience fear and death."[9] It was "the story of young men – some still children, seduced by propaganda"; they had been enticed by war technology that offered "even a nobody the chance to become a member of an elite." In words attributed to lead actor Jürgen Prochnow, the story revealed "how dubious heroic figures and myths really are." According to a nineteen-year-old amateur actor who had joined the cast, "after this film no one can believe in heroic epics any more." The film depended on emotional impact, not rational argument. According to *Der Spiegel*, "the screams of fear, rage and pain had an authentic ring to them," while for Prochnow, the film laid bare a life that was "impressive insanity."[10]

Although Buchheim's work shaped much of the film, thirty-nine-year-old film director Petersen had his own message as well. In discussing the project with Buchheim, Petersen had explained what had attracted him to the novel. It had struck him as uniquely authentic: "For the very first time I had the feeling that a book was really saying what war was about; I had always been curious about it because I had never experienced war myself."[11] The whole point of the film was to convince the younger generation of the horror and futility of war. To that end, he followed his own lights: adding, deleting, inventing, and fantasizing in order to get remarkable effects. Bavaria Studios knew that the film audience of the day consisted chiefly of the seventeen to twenty-eight-year-olds who were "hot after action and destruction."

That is why Petersen insisted on fast-paced action, commotion, and exaggerated emotional expression as a means of communicating interior states. Bavaria Studios tried to reach the younger generation on both sides of the Atlantic Ocean by taking as its models such major box-office hits as *Star Wars, The Empire Strikes Back, Apocalypse Now,* and *Jaws.* These provided the standards for the high-tech glitz that the market seemed to demand.

By its own admission, Bavaria had no interest whatever in trying to attract "World War Two vets in their TV slippers." The naval adviser to Bavaria Studios, Hans-Joachim Krug, agreed that today's young audiences have different sensibilities to those of the 1930s and 1940s. Given Petersen's purpose, he pointed out, Petersen's often unhistorical approach made sense.

The generation [that experienced the Third Reich] was educated to rigour, commitment, self-control, and suppression of feelings – particularly that of fear. If we had had our actors behave according to the historical models which they were portraying, and had we dispensed with the overexaggerated reactions [shown in the movie], then the [young audience of today] would simply not have understood or even recognized the historically more genuine, stoic bearing up, nor the extent of strain, horror and dread they actually bore within themselves.[12]

The author of the *Spiegel* article on the filming of *Das Boot,* Wilhelm Bittorf, was himself a reconstructionist. Perhaps unwittingly so. At any rate, his survey of Germany's romance with the submarine was anything but congratulatory. Thus the "diving boats" of the First World War – beginning with Weddigen's "wonder weapon" U-9 that had sunk the three British cruisers – were no longer Germany's heroic stallions of the sea; they were "suicide weapons." They had not signalled Germany's ultimate victory, but had spelled her doom because the Germans had placed such implicit faith in them. Early U-boat successes, he insisted, had "strengthened the vain delusions of the German leaders" that they could actually take on Britain's stronger Royal Navy. In his litany of criticism against Germany's undersea war, Bittorf links the two wars. In the First World War Reichkanzler Bethmann Hollweg alone had raised his voice against the military, rejecting its adamant insistence on unrestricted submarine warfare which he correctly predicted would signal "Finis Germaniae" – the end of the German empire and nation. Nor had the lesson been learned in 1939–45, Bittorf urged: "In the U-boat was concentrated in its purest form the all-German feeblemindedness of the century: the stupidity, repeated by the Nazis but not invented by them, of leading a pointless and hopeless war of defiance against the states of Western civilization and against Anglo-American superiority."

For Bittorf, Buchheim's *Boot* is not about Nazism, but about a serious flaw in German character. "Buchheim's narrative deals ... with deep-rooted German-national stupidity and valour, with the blind logic of the Teutonic death-wish – perhaps that's why 'Das Boot' has become the paramount German novel about the Second World War." Later critics would speak of Buchheim's legacy as revealing the psychopathology of war.

The film had marketed a consistent and compelling image of the German submarine and its crew. In the words of one illustrated magazine: "As radiant heroes they set to sea, as old men marked by insanity they returned."[13] According to another observation, "never before have the sufferings and dying of German seamen been filmed [as in this film of] the grey sharks."[14] Jürgen Prochnow, himself a pacifist, observed of the lead character he plays: "I didn't regard the commanding officer as a hero, but as a man who is drawn into the war and who feels guilty because of helping to fight it." This poured salt in the wounds of those who had survived. For as one former submariner wrote, this sort of antiheroic posing had gotten it all wrong: "We were never how [Buchheim] has portrayed us in his bestselling novel, and more recently in his film – and we won't let ourselves be marketed in this way. We owe that to those of our comrades who fell between 1939–1945, and to those they left behind."[15] Criticism both for and against the film tended to divide along political lines. Those on the right decried the "base treatment" the film accorded Germany's u-boat veterans and their cause; those on the left tended to revise and reconstruct. As *The Times* of London reported of *Das Boot's* première, despite the ten-minute ovation at the end of the film, "the tin-can epic" continues to be attacked by 'the left' for lack of a clear anti-war stance."[16] It might have added that it was attacked from the "right" for failing to reveal the deep and abiding sense of honour, patriotism, and duty with which submariners had fought – and lost.

Media coverage of "The making of Das Boot" came into vogue. All quite rightly paid tribute to the meticulous attention to detail which attempted to recreate historical reality. Technology, models, special effects and trick photography, uniforms and location all called for a massive concentration of research, planning, ingenuity, and money. It was as though by reconstructing the submariners' external world one could actually recreate the internal and internalized worlds of the human psyche. Yet Buchheim's final judgment dissented; despite Petersen's approach – or perhaps because of it – "truth had remained submerged."[17] Nonetheless, all agreed on the film's message. The

U-boat, in short, was "a death trap for the crew," and the film was about demythologizing war.

Wilhelm Bittorf's TV-film *Die Feindfahrt von U-96* [The Patrol of U-96] about how the movie was made left no one in doubt about how to interpret the film.[18] Shot during the actual filming of the movie *Das Boot*, it revealed many fascinating aspects of rehearsals, trick shots, and special effects. It was sensitive to the irony of filming some scenes in the French port of La Rochelle, which had once served as a principal U-boat base in the Biscay. This film about the making of *Das Boot* was equally political, for, in the narrator's words, it was meant "to communicate the god-forsakeness of [U-boat] patrols." The narrator's editorializing decried submarine patrols as "suicidal undertakings, suicidal even for Germany itself"; they symbolized Germany's "obsessed yearnings for maritime supremacy." In the TV-script the letter *U* in the term *U-boat* took on a pejorative political meaning: the "wonder weapon" U-nderseaboat was now the U-ndoing of the whole German empire – "Das U-Boot war ein Untergangsboot für das ganze deutsche Reich." It was a machine Germany had mindlessly employed in order to assure its own self-destruction. The regime had "exploited and tortured" its youth by casting them into the arms of Moloch war; and "war turns everyone who takes part in it into murderers, even if against their will."

Few observers recognized that Buchheim's *Boot* had really been the work of Petersen. It is therefore Buchheim who continues to take the flak from its detractors, particularly when veterans – and only a very few of them are vocal – enter the lists in verbal combat. As Buchheim has commented:

My role is damnably difficult. Before the film came to be, everything was simpler. I had to put up with being dressed down by a few sclerotic old mental-midget navy vets for having fouled our own nest, and by ultra-left critics for singing heroic epics. Then came bundles of anonymous letters from old Nazis who didn't want to believe that the war years were not the best years for everybody, but a ghastly time of senseless suffering and of bending oneself to the fact of suffering; nor did they want to understand that this U-boat business was not as chivalrous as propaganda had stylized it; [U-boat warfare was] terrible.[19]

Buchheim took issue with the film in what became a best-selling large-format paperback, *Der Film, "Das Boot"* (1981). Here he focused on the power of images to communicate reality. He found he could authenticate "practically every page of his novel" with pictures he had gathered, most of which he had taken himself while in the Propaganda-

Kompanie. As we know, this had led to the photo documentary entitled *U-Boot-Krieg* (1976), "a report in pictures which had repeated the novel visually." By using Buchheim's photos, Bavaria Studios had initially dispensed with the usual story-boards. In fact, the story writers had simply cut up two copies of *U-Boot-Krieg* and tacked them to the studio wall. In all, some 5000 authentic photos would guide the filming. Bavaria had rejected Buchheim's film script because, in his words, "it was too complicated for an action film; it was also too long, good for a six-hour movie." (This would in fact become the TV version, filmed at the same time as the movie.) In short, Buchheim had wanted a "genuine portrayal" using, for example, black and white film (instead of the coloured film the marketplace demanded) and a much slower pace than the swift action sequences of the Hollywood style. He saw genuineness and authenticity as critical. For no matter how the film might ultimately turn out, he wrote, the general observer would always regard *Das Boot* as a historical document; relatively few would see it purely as entertainment. In fact, the audience's acceptance of the film's historicity became Buchheim's undoing. This was so because relatively few had had any personal experience of submarine warfare with which to compare it. For the non-historian, one's personal memory is the ultimate arbiter of the film's authenticity; similarly, memory had been the measure of the veracity of the original novel in 1973. In perhaps the most balanced judgment of the film, the astute naval adviser to Bavaria Studios called for caution. He knew that the detailed research into the Nazi period which had preceded the filming had also demonstrated the unreliability and doubtfulness of human memory – even that of Buchheim himself.[20]

Books on the subject of U-boats in the Second World War continued to appear on the market during the Buchheim wave. Thus Karl Alman's novel *U-Boot-Asse* [U-boat Aces, 1980] about the U-boat aces Prien, Schepke, Endraß, Topp, and Mohr was followed by his equally repetitive and run-of-the-mill *Günther Prien: Der 'Wolf' und sein Admiral* [Prien: the "Wolf" and His Admiral, 1981]. Alman had virtually stolen the title of the latter from Frank's book of 1953, with wholesale borrowings from Frank's *Prien greift an* [Prien Attacks Again, 1941]. In fact, the opportunistic Alman was publishing similar material under different titles in both Germany and Austria. All of them present the same heroics, for his heroes are little more than puppets with interchangeable heads. Hans Herlin's *Verdammter Atlantik* [Damned Atlantic, 1959] was reprinted in 1981, as it would be once again in 1988. But in reissuing the old tales about Prien, Zech, Henke, Lüth, and Eck, the publisher hinted that we might now interpret all these "U-boat fates" more along Buchheim's lines: "The book simply portrays human beings who wanted to live, but had to fight – or else go to pieces."[21] It is a measure of the popularity of the topic that U-boat books seemed to find a ready market whatever their hue. Thus in 1982 Heinz Straub's "adventurous life of Wilhelm Bauer" revived the memory of the German inventor of the submarine; it was a gentle and lightly entertaining read. Its distinctiveness lay in avoiding themes from the Second World War.

By this time, according to a reviewer, "there are piles of U-boat books about, and most of them are only worth scrap."[22] He deemed Günter Böddeker's *Die Boote im Netz* [Caught in the Net, 1981] strikingly different. Touted in advertisements as "perhaps the definitive representation of the triumph and tragedy of the German in the Second World War," it promised a story based on newly discovered secret documents. Indeed, despite the hype, the title "Caught in the Net" evoked an as yet unexplored entanglement and helped popularize a completely new aspect of the war. In drawing on a handful of recent scholarly books and articles on code-breaking, journalist Böddeker showed that from the earliest days of the war the German submarines had been facing hopeless odds. As scholars like Jürgen Rohwer and Patrick Beesly had now revealed, the British Code and Cipher School in Bletchley Park had repeatedly broken German codes. Despite often lengthy periods of blackout during which the Germans changed codes and code technology, the Allies had ultimately managed to divert their convoys with astonishing precision around the lurking wolf packs. Through such "Ultra" radio intelligence, as it was called, the Allies could also pin-point U-boat arrivals, departures, and the formation of packs, thus exposing them to attack. Repeatedly advised that the codes were unbreakable, Admiral Dönitz had suspected betrayal and sabotage instead, but doggedly persisted in sending his submariners to sea despite the heavy losses. As reviewed in a major German newspaper in 1982, Böddeker's submarine book had revealed that Germany's "grey wolves" had in fact always been the "sacrificed wolves" and that Germany's submarine warfare had been "unreservedly insane." He popularized a wealth of information in order to structure his narrative. Thus one chapter entitled "The Beginning of the End" reports the first decriptions of German codes and the capture of German cypher machines in 1941. This was followed by "Ultra Bears Fruit," in which the reader sees the Royal Navy's "Submarine Tracking Room on the Trail of Dönitz." Later chapters vividly entitled "Destruction from the Air," "Plunge into Defeat," and "The Last Hope" highlight the inexorability of the U-boat's swiftly approaching doom.

As the dust-jacket announces, Böddeker has delivered the "dramatic report about Karl Dönitz and the fate of the German U-Boat Arm."

This is trade parlance for "docu-drama" or "historical novel," for the author attempts to conjure up the immediacy of events by resorting to the conventional techniques of the popular novelist. While drawing largely on scholars for his information on Ultra, he resorts to well-known u-boat authors for texture, images, and colour: for example, Weddigen, "Our Naval Hero Weddigen" (1915), Lowell Thomas's "Knights of the Deep" (1937), Harald Busch's "The U-boat War: That's the Way It Was" (1952), Wolfgang Frank's "The Wolves and the Admiral" (1953), Hans Herlin's "Damned Atlantic" (1959), Jochen Brennecke's "Sharks in Paradise" (1961), Herbert A. Werner's "Iron Coffins" (1969), Karl Alman's "Grey Wolves in Blue Sea (1977), and of course Lothar-Günther Buchheim's "The Boat" (1973). These were deemed the books that allowed the reader to experience the truth, not merely to learn about it from a distance. Vicarious experience, and hence the genuine grasp of historical truth, is precisely the product that the popular u-boat novel was considered to deliver best. A reviewer of Böddeker's work put it this way: "Whoever wants to know how the u-boat war actually was, in those details in which truth dwells, still experiences it most precisely and most intensely in Lothar-Günther Buchheim's novel 'The Boat' (and not in the film of that name) ... And whoever wants to comprehend the u-boat war in its totality as the Germans conducted it and lost it [should read] this correct report." Böddeker had in fact succeeded in writing a lively tale of the sea, aimed at the broadest possible audience. But despite the new ground he had broken on the popular market, he could not escape the narrative tradition in which his theme was necessarily captive. Evidence suggests that he was assured of a market.

"Literature about the sea finds as much active interest as it always has, even in the interior of the country," wrote the *Berliner Morgenpost* when reviewing yet another u-boat memoir, Brustat-Naval's *Nasses Eichenlaub* (1983).[23] The "Soaked Oak Leaves" of the title was about the u-boat hero Teddy Suhren, one of the most decorated and rapidly promoted submarine commanders. Known in his day as a maverick, he was small, peppery, and vociferous. He seemed to be able to get away with every impertinence, and was, in a sense, a sort of anti-hero. The story is still told in veterans' circles of his return to Brest after a three-month patrol when, amidst the usual welcome of martial music, flowers, and salutes, he was heard to shout through his megaphone: "Are the Nazis still at the helm?" Dönitz cautioned him to weigh his words more carefully. He was later invited to Hitler's mountain hideaway in Obersalzburg to receive the sword to the Oak Leaf cluster. Here he was said to have danced with Hitler's mistress, Eva Braun – to the music of

American swing which official Nazi policy had banned. Such stories, of course, are retold in the book. "Here is a man who belonged to the elite of those days, who served as an example, and now gives account of what he thought, felt, and how he acted," the reviewer asserted. "Soaked Oak Leaves," he claimed, is therefore not "just one more U-boat book."

But unfortunately that is precisely what it is. Beginning in 1941 with a brief flashback to Suhren's youth, the narrative ends in 1946. It gives us nothing new and offers no hint of perspectives that might have arisen in the intervening years from 1946 to 1982. Indeed, its publication marks a lost opportunity to contribute meaningfully to the U-boat story. One must conclude that neither Suhren nor his author have any real insights into what his own life – or that of the U-Boat Arm – really meant. But in an attempt to round off Suhren's ideas in some sort of holistic and purposeful vision, the narrative ends with a gratuitous quotation from Goethe: "The Gods give all things, the Infinite Ones, / Everything to their Favourites / all joys, the Infinite, / All sorrows, the Infinite, all."[24] In short, Suhren had been the darling of the gods and had experienced his ups and downs. To the uninitiated, the closing verse is certainly very pretty, perhaps even moving. But it arises from a literary tradition that was embedded in eighteenth-century classical concepts of Fate which the twentieth century largely rejects. By appealing to Germany's classical tradition – without really understanding either the tradition or Goethe – the authors have side-stepped the crucial issues of responsibility. They have merely continued the iconography of the submariner as youthful knight-errant and have made no reference to events and issues after 1946. If an unreflected life is one not worth having lived, then Suhren may have revealed more about himself than he intended.

One of the most revealing, if not disturbing, events on the U-boat literary scene was the 1983 republication of Harald Busch's *So war der U-Boot Krieg* [That's the Way It Was: The U-boat War]. First published in 1952 and 1954 as a worthy piece of popular history, it now appeared in "an expanded and updated" edition, with a brief foreword by Teddy Suhren himself. It was a luxury edition with gold lettering on front and spine, and with some 120 photos and maps. Apart from some modest updating regarding the role of Allied radio intelligence in the defeat of the German submarine, only one major component is new: the attack against the Buchheim wave, and against modern Germany with its supposedly "aimless youth," its "softness" and "immorality." As both the publisher's launching-package and a review in a right-wing weekly make explicit, the current wave of "literary" distortions of German history had now made it mandatory to place truth before the reader. The jacket advertisements claim to lay bare the problem: wilful distortion of Germany's heroic naval past was rooted in those ideological positions throughout the country which "reject military virtues and [therefore market] a falsification of the German submariners' inner and outward bearing." A publisher's flyer announced that the book's "truth" has already sold well: "The standard work [by Busch] reached 420,000 copies in Germany, USA, England and France – and that says more than words!" Busch, we might recall, had published U-boat books in 1939 and 1942 while he was an officer in the Propaganda-Kompanie. Continuing his trade, he now used his well-known book of 1952 as a vehicle for reactionary polemics.

Typical of Busch's slanted view of history is his new chapter entitled "Seduced Youth?" It's a response to the Buchheim position that Germany of the 1930s and 1940s had deceived and cheated its young people – "seduced" is the media word – by steeping them in distorted views of national destiny and patriotic duty. Busch's revised version of 1983 vehemently rejected Buchheim's view, claiming that the young who had rallied to the flag in the 1930s and 1940s had quite properly recognized it as "their proud duty" to join "a band of brothers" in defence of "the more important life of their people."[25] This "more important life," by inference, was the grand abstraction "Deutschland" with all its mythopoeic baggage. Busch would not have recognized the fact that this kind of "Deutschland" was an essentially romantic construct. For him, a generation that had eagerly answered the call of duty in the Hitler era had not been responding to a mere political party, but to a higher calling in the service of a nationhood beyond politics. In this sense, then, fighting for Germany did not mean fighting for Nazism. The chapter continues with his social criticism and his interpretation of German history.

In strident, sweeping lines, Busch exhorts his readers to recognize the major fact of German existence: from the Stauffen kings of the Middle Ages, to the Thirty-Years' War (1618–48), to the revolution of 1848, to the Congress of Vienna (1815), to "the so-called Peace of Versailles" (1919) and beyond, Germany has been forced to suffer. She has been systematically "starved out, subjugated, carved up, and always kept down." What true citizen, his rhetorical question urges, would not have heeded her call for help? "The duly elected Führer" then began to rally the German people, until Germany once more faced "envious neighbours" bent on her destruction. Thus once again victimized, Germany had had to defend herself in a war that her neighbours had foisted upon her. Rallying to such a cause was "God's will, a natural law in which the individual defends its own kind." This, Busch would have us believe, was a noble instinct. Casting oneself into the breach for the Fatherland could only have been achieved by a generation "not yet divided in itself by intellect, that apple forbidden in paradise." According to such arguments so typical of the Nazi era, the "decisive" man of action is superior to the "effete" man of reflection. Anti-intellectualism – acting and not thinking – is in this light a virtue. Today's younger generation, by contrast, is simply not up to scratch. He sees young people today as the victims of "re-education" and revisionist views of German history; they have been "seduced by out-of-touch 'philosophers,' teachers, journalists and even pastors into believing that impudent, blasphemous slogan 'Life without Arms!'" They have been turned into "peaceniks and conscientious objectors." As might be expected, the reactionary weekly *Deutsche Wochen-Zeitung* acclaimed Busch's position enthusiastically.

But was that actually "the way it really was," as Busch's titles of 1952, 1954, and 1983 claim? Jochen Brennecke sought answers to this and other questions. His *Die Wende im U-Boot-Krieg* [Turning-Point, 1984] attempted an account of the causes and results of the critical opening phases of the Battle of the Atlantic leading up to what is now recognized as "the turning point" of his title in 1943. As a variety of studies had already shown, that year had marked the end of any real hope in a German victory. Rational analysis, Brennecke pointed out, should have shown the Germans that their faith in victory was sorely misplaced. For in their efforts to defeat the U-boat, the Allies had effected a massive convergence of the latest technologies. Yet, despite all evidence, leaders like Admiral Dönitz held firm in the faith of Germany's destiny and had urged the troops to fight on. For Brennecke, who had written his first U-boat book in 1943 as a member of the Propaganda-Kompanie, this amounted to a conflict between faith and reason. "The dictator Hitler," he argued, had "not managed to coalesce science, technology and the conduct of war." That was the achievement of "the democratic wartime prime minister Winston Churchill," and that was why Britain had ultimately won the war. As Brennecke concluded, "English Reason" had won where German faith had lost.[26] And the British had had time on their side. Seen in this light, Germany's submariners were indeed the deluded victims.

Alone among the "Knights of the Sea," only Peter "Ali" Cremer and Erich Topp would come to grips with the past in a major book. For both of them, times had changed and new historical perspectives had suggested different meanings to the great events in which they had participated. After taking us through gripping accounts of cool daring and desperate escapes, and after examining much of the historical record, Cremer's book *U-333* (1982) concludes with his release from prisoner-of-war camp. "I stood on the street a free man. Hamburg lay in ruins. All about me lay emptiness. Most of my comrades were no longer alive, the years of my youth were gone. Like so many others I too had given my best in a war which very few of us had wanted, and in which the faith and readiness for self-sacrifice of the German people, and the courage of their soldiers had been most horribly misused. Everything had been in vain."[27] Topp, as we will see later, was even more thoroughgoing. To many Germans who had fought in the submarine war, all this revision seemed a pernicious plot. The "Zeitgeist" – the "spirit of the age" – many said, was bent on undermining the eternal values of patriotism, loyalty, and ethics. The "Zeitgeist," if that indeed is what it was, would strike again.

Petersen's three-part, five-hour TV series *Das Boot* began on 24 February 1985.[28] Produced simultaneously with the feature movie, the TV-version was in fact the major epic from which the cinema version had been distilled. Advance notices prepared the audiences for yet another major "Kino-Hit" – a screen hit that would bring historical reality into the home. The TV magazine *Funk Uhr*, for example, published mini-interviews with six former submariners under the rubric "Every mission was a farewell from life."[29] Here were no steel-eyed heroes, but men coping silently with their fears and anxiety. In this case, according to *Die Zeit*, "viewers witnessed wrack and ruin in slow motion."[30]

The TV-host introduced the series by setting the tone for the audience's reflections: "For those of us of the older generation who took part in the war ourselves, this film means the confrontation with a past which we must neither transfigure nor repress. May it give the younger generation insight into an era, the burden of which all of us today have to bear." He explained that eight million British viewers had already seen the series during its BBC broadcast three months earlier. They had deluged the German television station with letters expressing a consensus: "This film reminds us that such a war must never take place again." As German reports would later explain, some twenty million German viewers had tuned in to Petersen's exposé in order to gain "an idea of what the inferno really looked like which historians and memoirists call the German U-boat War." Viewer ratings indicated that 23.9 million had watched the final episodes. According to *Der Spiegel*, the series had exposed the "mania of Germany's miracle weapon," the U-boat. The "media spectacle [had] shown that no weapon has so fascinated the Germans like the poor man's truncheon, the U-boat, had done."[31] Poignant dialogue and gnomic sayings delivered the new political message by punctuating the film's powerful images: the U-boat war was a grim "childrens' crusade" that sent the young and innocent to their preordained deaths; it was a cynical "experiment in probing the limits of our capacity to suffer."

Critical responses endorsed the TV version and found it even more forceful than Petersen's movie. The series was itself seen as a key event in the history of German warfare. With such stark and riveting realism, "the spell has been broken [and] an era of late-patriotic whitewashing has ended." Submarines had now been stripped of the veneer that wartime propaganda had given them. They had been liberated from the memories of nostalgic veterans. Now for the first time, it seemed, Germans could see U-boat warfare as it "really" had been: terrifying, numbing, senseless, and insane.

As it had done five years earlier in 1980, the mass-circulation magazine *Der Spiegel* once again surveyed Germany's U-boat history with a modern slant. It highlighted what it described as Germany's almost psychotic fascination with submarines. The sea and the German U-boat, it claimed, had done something that the army and the politicians could not do. Maritime forces had provided a stage far removed from occupied land masses, from battlefields and razzias, from troops carrying out "the final solution." The sea and submarining had thus provided scenarios for a "clean war." One could both narrate and enjoy U-boat yarns without having to account for concentration camps or the misery of the Nazi regime. But despite its "cleanliness," *Der Spiegel* argued, the U-boat war was a poor object for the nation's faith. "The German peoples' faith in their miracle weapon was macabre," especially so as they had hung their grandiloquent aspirations on it in two successive world wars. Indeed, "the miracle weapon U-boat had become an instrument of power-political harikari – that too a German phenomenon." The article in *Der Spiegel* delivered a scathing account of the navy's achievements. But the magazine correctly observed – though with undisguised dismay – that despite its aim of demythologizing U-boat warfare, the TV version had still managed to hold the viewers spellbound. "Even on this anti-war film there still clings something of that fascination which twice in one century lured the Germans and their leaders into the homicidal expanses of the oceans, bearing them on to a martial insanity-trip which perhaps can better be explained by psychiatrists than by military historians."[32]

An article in *Die Welt* suggested that the submarine appealed to subliminal depths of the German psyche. "Among weapons, the U-boat is closest to the mythical: a fish full of people, dangerously armed, and equipped with enormous power and a fine, wide-reaching sensory system."[33] Asked why so many women had wept when viewing the TV series, a woman psychologist replied: "Ships symbolize the uterus; and the sea is the amniotic fluid."[34] Only the submarine can dive into it and surface at will. Surrogate mothers were weeping for surrogate sons.

Buchheim was pleased with the TV version. In fact, he confessed that he was now "reconciled, for the TV version is better than the film."[35] A former U-boat skipper found the television version equally impressive; much more so, in fact, than the film. He had commanded U-711 at the age of twenty-six and had returned to the postwar Federal German Navy to rebuild the U-boat flotilla. He eventually became the Commander-in-Chief, Submarines. Now at the age of sixty-eight – younger than most of the vociferous anti-Buchheim veterans – he found himself in the limelight of discussions about the German past. To his mind, the three-part series had succeeded in revealing "the stress on board a U-boat, people living together in the tightest spaces." It showed that "of course the skipper knew fear as well; but he mustn't show it, he had to be credible and strengthen his men." It showed that "we too were suffering human beings [coping] with our task," similar to the opponents against whom the German navy fought.[36] Equally approving was Ali Cremer, former skipper of U-333 whose book of 1982 had just appeared in paperback. For him, the TV film had been realistic and had shown the war "the way it was." The television version's slower pace and downplaying of action had intensified the impression of grinding dread and sensory deprivation. Particularly "striking was the psychological portrayal of the atmosphere on board."[37]

Some veterans rejected the TV version outright – just as they had the film. They insisted that the TV series had tried to accomplish "something which the International Military Tribunal of Nuremberg did not do in 1946, namely condemn Großadmiral Dönitz and the U-Boat Arm for having conducted a criminal submarine war."[38] That, at any rate, was the assessment of Captain Kurt Baberg, one of the most outspoken former U-boat commanders in March 1985, the year the series first appeared. His widely published anti-Buchheim polemics and his unpublished letters fill two thick files in the U-Boat Archives in Cuxhaven. In time, he became a lone voice from which even the Association of German Submariners would distance itself. "Silence had proven itself in the past," the president of the association, Captain Kurt Diggins, would caution him, and silence now seemed the best strategy in the battle against Buchheim. Certainly, the president did not wish to associate either himself or the veterans with "the eternal has-beens," those ancient warriors who seemed never to have learned that times had changed. And in any event, he confided, it was better to lie low and let the controversy blow over. That was, after all, how many a U-boat had weathered a storm.

Buchheim produced his own TV film almost immediately after Petersen's successful prime-time show of February 1985. In a move that Buchheim regarded as overt criticism, German TV shifted his

U-boat film from prime time to the late show on 4 March 1985. His documentary's unusual title, *Zum Tode Gesiegt* [Victored to Death], with its echoes of "Sieg" and "Sieg Heil," is bitter irony, for it reveals that while German sailors had been touted at home as triumphant heroes, they were in fact being sent to a predictable and inglorious death sentence at sea. They had therefore been "triumphed to death"; they had been "victored" by their own misguided desire to vanquish the opponent. In the words of the show's host, the film is "a very personal, supplemental, and as [Buchheim] contends, a very necessary portrayal of the background and demise" of Germany's submarines.[39]

Buchheim's documentary film *Zum Tode Gesiegt* is a bitter, often vitriolic, frontal attack against the romanticism and idealism of U-boat warfare. By graphic and rhetorical means, the film continues a battle-line he had commenced with his perceptive novel *Das Boot* (1973). Familiar themes now find expression on the screen: the transformation of "highly praised technical wonder-weapons [into] iron coffins"; the beguiling influence of the First World War aces on a growing tradition of underwater seafaring; the exploitation of "U-boats with their mythology [as] propaganda-tools for persuading the German people" of their invincibility; the "propaganda mill's" distortions of reality which the populace accepted as truth. The great U-boat aces themselves had become deceived deceivers, beguiled in their own stead by the "party-whip" Dönitz and "the supreme battle-monger" Hitler. It was all part of the "infamous tactics of falsification and stultification" that prevailed "in the Nazi war." Buchheim debunks the concept of a hero's death, describing instead how water pressure slowly crushes a submarine like a compacting machine; his brutal honesty belies the euphemism "fallen for the Fatherland," exposing instead the reality of mangled men and machinery crushed beyond recognition on the ocean floor. Buchheim's film is a persuasive, if slanted, piece of journalistic craftsmanship. He engages his viewers with few historical or technical facts, opting instead to incite the emotions and to prompt reflection on a single idea: U-boats past and present are obscene.

A skilled and colourful debater, Buchheim confesses the sins his detractors accuse him of hiding. He, too, had once been taken in by the system in which he lived during the 1930s and 1940s. After much soul-searching and "coming to grips with the Nazi past" – an activity he claims the "mental-midget, sclerotic old farts" who assail him have never done – he recognized that he had been a participating victim of Nazism:

For me too this Dönitz was once the "grand Lion" ... until I finally saw behind it all that he was just an aged corporal with lots of gold on his arm, limited to a couple of idées fixes and infected with Nazi ideas. Until I finally saw behind it all that the U-boat war was not as glorious and clean as propaganda had hyped it up for us to be ... and that the U-boats were not such perfect constructions as they wanted to have us believe ... Until I finally saw behind it all that we were carting ourselves off to market for a lunatic [Hitler] whose most obsequious lackey was called Dönitz.

Buchheim admitted in the film that submarines had by this time become "an obsession" with him. This confession played into his opponents' hand and encouraged some veterans to publicize the view that he was clinically deranged. That sort of vilification reveals the depths to which the "debate" about the reality of the war has some-times sunk. In fact, Buchheim's preoccupation had been motivated as much by the mood of the mid-1980s as by the wartime past. It was triggered as well by an idiosyncratic view of naval warfare. As he pointed out, the very nature of the sea itself makes naval warfare the most horrible type of war imaginable; once the battle is done, the sea closes over the carnage and leaves no trace. Thus the sea creates the illusion of a "clean" war and provides warriors with aesthetic and poetic grounds for regarding battle at sea as somehow more moral than any other form of combat. Ultimately, the sea is the common enemy of all seafarers; where political leaders transform sailors into political opponents and then cast them as enemies into the vortex of combat, the sea binds enemies together in some remarkable way, despite the fact that they are bent on each other's destruction. (German submarine veterans still speak of their former opponents as "comrades of the other faculty.") For these reasons – no trace of battle and the comradeship between naval combatants – Buchheim regards naval war is especially perverted. Germany's U-boat history, Buchheim asserted in 1985, was the precursor to the major threat facing mankind today: superpower submarines. The nuclear-powered ballistic-missile equipped "grey monsters" that dominate the news are everywhere, from the Swedish archipelago to beneath the Arctic ice: "U-boats, U-boats, without end."

As with public response to Buchheim's other works, published opin-ions on his documentary were as polarized as might be expected. A lengthy illustrated article in the right-wing *Das Ostpreussenblatt* savaged Buchheim and his credibility as a witness, while defending Admiral Dönitz and the honour of former German submariners.[40] *Der Spiegel*, by contrast, accepted Buchheim's view of Germany's submarine war as a "lunatic odyssey"; it was a "war crime" even if not certifiable as such according to law.[41] By far the majority of published critiques shared the Buchheim view: thus Bonn's *Rundschau* provided photos and commentary with the message that "by the time the U-boat returns home from a lengthy mission, those spared a miserable 'hero's death' have become old men." War, in short, is hell, and Germany's youth had been wasted, cheated, and deceived. Meanwhile, inside the Association of German Submariners another kind of feud had long been brewing: whether to meet Buchheim's "distortions of history" head on with a well-organized campaign or simply to lie low. One ex-submariner suggested that the latter approach would at least have the advantage of letting the theme slip out of the public mind and thereby, perhaps, even of reducing Buchheim's income from royalties. The association president's reassuring suggestion that "nobody will be talking about Buchheim's documentation *Zum Tode Gesiegt* the day after tomorrow" proved wrong.[42]

Indeed, the U-boat image of the Buchheim wave was kept alive in a variety of newspapers and journals, and by repeat performances of the films and round-table debates. Both sides – for there really were only two – simply staked out their positions, without any hope of converting the other. Little is served in summarizing them here in greater detail. However, one curiosity in the wealth of published material does give us pause. The book, "We Submariners Say No! ... That's Not the Way It Was," is a vanity-press diatribe produced by two former "aces."[43] One of them, Karl-Friedrich Merten, excoriated the text of what he called Buchheim's "slanderous libel," *Die U-Boot-Fahrer* [The Submariners, 1985], while the other, Kurt Baberg, attacked the "dishonest" and "misleading" photos it contained. Arguing paragraph by paragraph and picture by picture against Buchheim's "falsification of history," they virtually defeated their purpose by obliging the interested reader to buy Buchheim's books in order to follow the argument. Particularly abrasive from the veterans' viewpoint were Buchheim's virulent attacks on Dönitz and on their concepts of patriotic duty and service discipline. One of the co-authors of the anti-Buchheim diatribe broke ranks with the Association of German Submariners in undertaking what amounted to a campaign to set the record straight. With circulars to the membership, and letters and telephone calls to both the press and to Buchheim, he even prepared himself for a class-action suit. The membership dubbed him an "Einzelfahrer"; that meant, in naval jargon, an "independently sailed vessel" that travelled without convoy or escort. Yet he managed to place lengthy articles in support of his cause in a number of right-wing publications: *National-Zeitung*, *Deutscher Anzeiger – Freiheitliche Wochenzeitung*, *Ostpreussenblatt*, and the *Deutsche Wochen-Zeitung*.

The reaction of the president of the Association of German Submariners to such broad and public campaigning against what he regarded as Buchheim's "falsifications of history" is symptomatic of the politically charged atmosphere in which discussions of German history still take place. The president explained to his "Einzelfahrer" that Bonn's Constitutional Court had declared two of the above newspapers to be "extreme right." In the best interests of the association, therefore, he himself had declined an invitation from the editor of the *Deutscher Anzeiger* to state his position on a number of "national" and personal issues. In summary, he declared himself "of the opinion, shared by a great many [in the association], that the above-mentioned newspapers are not the proper places to deal with the unqualified outpourings of a Buchheim." Indeed, he added, a critical related issue was at stake: "I have been endeavouring to bring submariners of the [postwar] Federal German Navy into the Association of German Submariners [vdU]. For many reasons, as you know, that is by no means easy. However, if the conduct of U-boat warfare and the role of Großadmiral Dönitz is handled in extreme-right publications, the third generation of submariners will be drawn into a situation of conflict which will bring about the very opposite of what we want."[44]

The association did not change its view even when a "radical right" editor explained the philology of the word "radical" (Latin: radix) as meaning "striking to the root of the matter." That meant, in the editor's argument, supporting both democracy and the national cause, NATO and collective security, and rejecting the concept of collective guilt.[45] The political problems to which the association president alluded, as we will see, would be addressed at the highest levels of the defence department when dealing with the question of military tradition. Discussions would lead to formulation of the so-called Tradition Protocol (*Traditions-Erlaß*) of 1992, which forbade any official link whatever with symbols, ideas, or conventions from the Nazi past.

Hard on the heels of Buchheim's documentary film followed his coffee-table picture-book *Die U-Boot-Fahrer* [The Submariners, 1985]. Advertised as a "photo epic in which the fate of Germany's U-boat men serves as a beacon against the insanity and inhumanity of every kind of warlike altercation," the handsome volume provided more photos and commentary in support of his claims. Evocative chapter headings signalled his interpretation of history: "Iron Coffins," "Entwined in Myth," "The Victims of Moloch," "The Schizoid War," "War as Propaganda," "Blind Faith," "Lost from the Very Beginning," and "Forgotten or Suppressed?" The publisher's launching-package touted the book as Buchheim's attempt to unmask "the Dönitz legend." The admiral had been "Hitler's obedient and pitiless party-whip who thrust his boys into the childrens' crusade at sea." This newest book was marketed as "an authentic contribution to the historiography of war" in which Buchheim "turns against the uncritical glorification of the U-boat war [perpetuated by] wreath-laying ceremonies and speechifiers on Remembrance Day." Significantly, *Die U-Boot-Fahrer* found its only balanced review in a naval magazine.[46] The reviewer found the photos in "the anti-war book impressive and shocking," but quite properly took exception to two issues. He objected in the first place to Buchheim's "attacks against the manner of honouring the war dead, especially the tablets at the U-boat Memorial in Kiel-Möltenort"; and he firmly rejected Buchheim's "comparison of the military leadership of the Federal German Armed Forces, which he sees as 'unscrupulous hell-drivers,' with the propagandists of the Nazi-era."

Buchheim's polemics show little subtlety of argumentation and little finesse in human psychology. He is a debunker pure and simple, and his graphic images sell well on a ready market. In fact, he remains what he always has been: a propagandist for whom effective propaganda depends upon communicating some elements of the truth. Again, it was the national magazine *Der Spiegel* that gave Buchheim's writings – and this newest book – broadest coverage. In the illustrated article "Drowned like Young Cats in a Sack," it surveyed Buchheim, the U-boat war, and what it called "the psychopathology of war."[47] This was a tall order, even for a major magazine article. Ultimately, however, the magazine offered its readers nothing new. Here again were the usual upbeat, easily digestible clichés and glib phrases that provided a "quick read" of complex issues. Dabbling in psychopathology, the reviewer promoted Buchheim's ruminations on military discipline and the German soul. Might there not be, the reviewer mused, some mysterious link between U-boat warfare and the cultic practices of ancient peoples in which the young were slaughtered to appease a god? Here he toyed with popular etymology, the German word for sacrifice (*Opfer*) being the same as the word for victim. Dönitz himself, as Buchheim correctly reminds us, had spoken of the final missions of his U-boats as an "Opfergang" (a sacrificial path, indeed a ritual procession). One thing seemed certain in Buchheim's reflections: the "victims" had to be made willing. Thus, scurrilous as it was, Dönitz had managed to prevent the very thing he apparently feared most: a repetition of the navy's revolution of 1918 when "the kaiser's coolies" had refused to offer themselves to the slaughter. As Buchheim expressed it: "These two warlords [Raeder and Dönitz] flogged the navy horribly for its disloyalty in that November [1918]. And the navy, completely uninvolved in the attempt on Hitler's life [on 20 July 1944], sailed off unresistingly and with incomprehensible stoicism into its destruction."

In his attacks against Admiral Dönitz, Buchheim repeatedly raised one of the toughest questions facing the military profession; it concerned the role and function of personal morality and ethics in the context of military duty. Can one shrug off personal responsibility for what transpired in the years 1939–45 by claiming one had been "merely a soldier"? Being a "Nur-Soldat," in Buchheim's expression, was surely unacceptable in the modern age. Those veterans who tried to refute this position, he claimed, were unredeemable has-beens caught in a time-warp from which they refuse to escape.

Books from such a time-warp continued to be published. Thus Martin Pfitzmann's *U-Boot Gruppe Eisbär* [U-boat Group Polar-Bear, 1986] served up material found elsewhere – errors and all – to "bear witness to the life of the U-boat crews and to the fascination with U-boating as such." It was a curious aim for the 1980s, but one directed to an undiscriminating public. That same year Heinz Schaeffer returned to the scene with a paperback rehash of his book *U-977*, which he had first published in 1950. His new title, "66 Days under Water: The Mystery-Enshrouded Long-range Mission to Argentina"(1986), espoused the time-worn technique of derring-do and high adventure. It repeated what for many ill-informed U-boat buffs was the intriguing suspicion that U-977 had actually transported Hitler and his untold treasures to Argentina. The tabloid *Bild-Zeitung* had marketed the story in 1983, and the theme would crop up intermittently throughout the next decade.[48] The image of the U-boat as an instrument of intrigues and subterfuge was common coin of the sub-literary realm. Against this lurid background, Hans Georg Hess's *Die Männer von U-995* [The Men of U-995, 1987] offered a collection of conversations with former crew members of the submarine now beached as a technical museum at Laboe near Kiel. Hess had been the second and last skipper of U-995. His compilation was "not a war book," he wrote, "but a mine of insights for leaders, psychologists and teachers, a book for tolerance and peaceful coexistence in every human community." A minor contribution to the literary canon, it aimed at revealing the essential humanity of those who had sailed on great waters in steel sharks. It was a book with neither bark nor bite. It would remain to photos and film to deliver the most lasting, if controversial, impressions.

On 22 April 1987 North German Radio broadcast a documentary film entitled ... *gegen Engeland*. As we have seen, the title "against England," derived from Hermann Löns's well-known battle song of 1914, although the TV magazine *Fernsehwoche* attributed it to "a combat-song from the period of the Third Reich." (Historicity was rarely an issue with writers of media program notes.) As the magazine erroneously reported, this film marked "the first attempt to examine and describe the Atlantic battle from both sides."[49] Ignorant of the wealth of academic and scientific studies that had long-since illuminated and analysed the Atlantic war, the TV journalist insisted on his own view. To his mind, the present state of our knowledge was grossly inadequate, for it consisted of little more than a collage of both German and Allied propaganda showing British iniquity on the one hand, and German skullduggery on the other. Now was the time for truth. But the magazine showed its bias: centre-page stood a reprint of a Canadian wartime poster showing a leering, monocled "Nazi" submarine captain. The caption "Danke Schön! THANKS for the Tip-off" warned the unwary about talking to strangers. It was one of many wartime posters admonishing Canadians that "Idle chatter sinks ships." North German Radio's own TV magazine increased the hype. Borrowing a fuller title from the rousing victory march "… wir fahren gegen Engeland" [we're sailing against England], it pictured anguished "survivors of a U-boat attack on a life-raft in mid-Atlantic"; it portrayed a powerfully armed U-boat surfacing in order to gun down an unarmed sailing vessel. The caption ran: "Unequal Opponents: U-boat vs a Cutter." "Scarcely a weapon in Germany of the First and Second World Wars had such a mystical ring to it as the U-boat," the article began, before launching itself into a thumbnail sketch of the German submarine.[50] Echoes from the Buchheim school of interpretation were unmistakable.

Despite such advertisements, the film documentary by Hans Brecht of North German Radio and Lothar Loewe of Radio Free Berlin provided an exceptionally balanced account of the Battle of the Atlantic (1939–45). In featuring the human experience of submarine warfare, it encapsulated the major outlines of strategy and highlighted the salient issues of tactics and technology. It drew upon such diverse visual sources as the Federal German Military Archives, the Imperial War Museum (London), the National Archives (Washington), and the National Film Board of Canada. Striving for vivid contrasts, the film team had interviewed veterans aboard the German U-boat museum U-995 at Kiel and aboard the Canadian museum ship, the corvette HMCS *Sackville* in Halifax. The film was a craftsmanlike blend of wartime newsreel clips and recent interviews with veterans of both sides. The interpretation, however, left no room for doubt that Germany had been in the wrong despite all the personal courage and tenacity. The opening scenes in the Stromness Museum (Orkneys) set the stage. As the camera panned across mementos from the scuttling of the German fleet in 1919, an uncompromising commentary introduced one of the film's major themes: "War again 20 years later. The chance for revenge had come." The film showed its bias in other ways too. For instance, the script soft-pedalled unpleasant Allied "incidents" – such as the American bombing of military and civilian survivors of the liner *Laconia*, and the Royal Air Force's strafing of dinghies bearing German survivors of U-852 – but came down hard on German "crimes." Thus Lemp (U-30) had sunk "the refugee ship *Athenia*" without warning; Heinz Eck (U-852) had been a war criminal who "spent the whole night machine-gunning survivors" of his successful torpedo attack on the freighter *Peleus*; and Admiral Dönitz had been "one of the Führer's most fanatic paladins." Interviewed in the film, Admiral Erich Topp himself bore witness to yet another abrasive fact: Dönitz had issued "suicide-commands" for a "kamikaze attack" against even the smallest Allied vessels during the Normandy landings. Of course, many of these representative incidents were complex affairs, open to wide-ranging interpretation. Yet despite its two-and-a-half-hour length, the film's broad sweep had little time for subtle analyses of complex matters. Effective communication in this medium depended on visual argument, and on visual impact alone. It was a successful piece of investigative journalism.

Articles and letters to editors of national and local newspapers leave no doubt that the film struck a chord in a broad spectrum of German society. "In pictures never seen before, [Brecht and Loewe] portray the suicide rides of the U-boat men in the Atlantic," wrote one typical commentator.[51] Some criticized the blithe manner in which U-boat veterans interviewed in the film had reduced the war to the statistics of tonnage sunk. Others were moved by the former submariner who at the age of twenty had lost his sight aboard his embattled U-boat and whose testimony concluded the film: "I must confess I was enthused [about the submarine war] at the time. But in retrospect it was utter insanity in 1944/45 to keep on thrusting our U-boats against the naked blade" of the Allied forces.[52] Another viewer found the film only partially successful, and that for reasons many others supported.

It seems as though the authors had fallen too much in love with the historical propaganda-material of the National Socialist newsreel productions. There were superfluous, irritating sequences: images of U-boat crews in action, burning and sinking ships, jubilant scenes of successful captains wreathed in high-sounding propaganda from the film archives – it's all much of a muchness, and awakens false heroic pathos, and is ultimately boring.[53]

This is indeed the film's major, if unavoidable, shortcoming, for the editors' recourse to propaganda film was all too readily misinterpreted. The president of Berlin's School of Art expressed his "outrage and shame" that this "repulsively dilettantish piece of hack-work" had marketed "Nazi newsreels which could arouse in the viewer nationalist feelings of the purest water."[54] His politically inspired and extreme remarks received broad national coverage. However, the majority of letter writers were positive. Having seen the première broadcast of Brecht's film – strategically programmed just before a replay of Buchheim's *Das Boot* – one typical writer expressed it as follows: Brecht's "'gegen Engeland' is an honest film well worth seeing; as an upbeat to the repeat performance of [Buchheim's] world-famous TV-film *Das Boot* he could scarcely have wished for a better one."[55] U-boats were still a prime-time event.

The vociferous few who felt themselves pilloried by the "tendentious" film ... *gegen Engeland* took the same stance they had taken with Buchheim. Thus a former "U-boat ace" criticized the "outpouring of material already seen and heard," and then attempted to set the record straight. The film, he insisted, had poured "poison and gall over an era and over [the U-boatmen] who had sacrificed themselves." "Like the soldiers of all nations, they had only done their duty."[56] Buchheim, too, joined the detractors of North German Radio's TV film, though for different reasons. As widely reported, he regarded the documentary as "a Nazi-spook." To his mind, the film ... *gegen Engeland* had allowed veterans the pernicious fantasy of thinking that it was still possible to have been "merely a soldier." Typical of the scenes that provoked his ire was the interview in the Lord Nelson Hotel in Halifax, Nova Scotia, in which survivors of U-boat attacks spoke casually and deferentially of their former opponents and the violence of the sea.

Buchheim and the "U-boat ace" Karl-Friedrich Merten then squared off at each other. The public squabble reduced itself to questions of image and to perceptions. Merten tossed out an old wartime photo of PK-man Buchheim lolling about on the bridge of a U-boat in a most unmilitary pose and had it published in newspapers. Such a man, he snorted, could not be a comrade who really understood the trade. Buchheim responded by publishing an official wartime portrait of the war-hero Merten with what Buchheim described as his steely eyed "rambo-zambo look." The lines seemed drawn between the "right" and the "left." Indeed, two books of this period by Alman and Buchheim reflect the stance.

In 1988 the prolific hack-writer Karl Alman published his hagiography *Wolfgang Lüth*. As the subtitle trumpets, Lüth had been "the most successful U-boat commandant of the Second World War." Such epithets come easily to writers like Alman, for his task has always been hero-making. Taking no issue with the vituperative criticism then current about German submariners and submarines, Alman dished up his usual yarns. Here he wished to commemorate "the meritorious soldier and human being Wolfgang Lüth [who is] forgotten neither by the old submariners, nor" – and this would have startled most observers of Germany today – "by the young submariners of the [present-day] Federal German Navy." In extolling the memory of the "30,000" who had given their lives, Alman endorsed the concept of the "Nur-Soldat." "Merely soldiers" doing their duty, they had been neither exploited nor victimized by their leaders, as a Buchheim would have it; they had been patriotic volunteers for sea service. Indeed, "they were members of that community – that [Nelsonic] band of brothers – into which their free decision had placed them, the former German U-Boat Arm." The book was precisely the kind of straw man Buchheim would have wished.

Buchheim's final book of u-boat pictures bore the same title as his documentary TV film, *Zu Tode Gesiegt.* Published in 1988, it offered more pictures (and some very familiar ones) in support of his antiwar campaign. As his preface explained, he had pondered giving it the title "Die verheizten U-boot-Fahrer" [The Hyped-Up Submariners], but found that too racy even for his own market. "Verheizen" means to "fire someone up"; in the army euphemism of the Great War it means to "send someone off to glory" in a suicidal dash. As always, Buchheim's intent was categorical. He had compiled yet another volume in order to prevent past horrors from being forgotten; he intended his book as a body blow against the "retrospective glorification of the u-boat war" in which he thought many veterans were still indulging. Indeed, he intended as well to confront "the unsuspecting younger generation" with the dangers militarism courts. Here, as elsewhere in Buchheim's work, the u-boat emerged as the paradigm of warfare at its most perverse.

The authentic wartime photographs are excellent. The inside cover photo projected the spirit of the book: U-353's captured survivors after a withering depth-charge attack and ramming in mid-Atlantic. Blindfolded and defeated, the young "Knights of the Deep" who had ridden Germany's "wonder weapon" had ironically been licked by one of the most ancient weapons in the naval arsenal: the ram. (They had been sunk by the British destroyer HMS *Fame* on 16 October 1942, just seven months after the u-boat had been commissioned.) Lack of vision and lack of technology had been Germany's Achilles' heel. And the photo seemed to show it. But Buchheim the artist injected a new emphasis into his collection of naval photographs: as though to sum up the series, he published a harrowing Allied photograph of the open mass graves of the death camp Bergen-Belsen. From Buchheim's perspective, we can no longer regard U-boat war as a "clean" war, nor even as a purely naval war. For him, the Nazi system was able to prevail only as long as the fronts held up; and the fronts could only hold as long as the U-boats dominated the seas. Thus by the late 1980s the U-boat had emerged as a holocaust machine. Meanwhile, in December 1986, Bavaria's Ministerpräsident Franz Joseph Strauss awarded Buchheim the Grand Cross of Merit (Großes Verdienstkreuz) for having "considerably strengthened, worldwide, the cultural esteem of the Federal Republic of Germany."[57] Though Buchheim had been specifically honoured as a benefactor of art, many observers suspected that the government was rewarding him as well for his strong anti-Nazi and antiwar stance.

6 Epilogue:
Legacies of History and Tradition

Among the relics of the U-Boat Archives in Cuxhaven hangs a poem of Second World War origin. Printed in the old German script and surmounted by an ink-drawing of a submarine crashing through daunting seas, the framed and glass-encased piece conjures up a storm-weathered, orphic tradition. The verses are as central to Germany's U-boat tradition as is John McCrae's "In Flander's Fields" to the Allies' Armistice Day. Though published anonymously and undated, its author was machinist's mate Fritz Thomas, who had been killed on 13 October 1939 in a naval action that none of his shipmates survived.[1] Behind his rhymed couplets and imitative harmonies, behind his alliteration and imagery, one discerns the authoritative hand of an insider who has lived through the scenarios he recounts. Only such writers, many veterans claim, can effectively inform the uninitiated about the cult of submarining. Each homiletic stanza of Thomas's poem evokes the "U-boat spirit" formed by shared experience. In dramatic sequence, the vivid verses evoke the stations of a young man's rite of passage: weeks on patrol where "a powerful spirit welded us together for life and death"; interminable days amidst the din of engines, with lungs and eyes scored by diesel fumes; a storm-tossed, churning hull in convulsive seas; then, the climax of it all, as his U-boat bursts through the cordon of enemy destroyers and cruisers, casting itself into the mêlée of torpedoes and depth-bombs while merchant ships explode overhead.

The visceral experience evoked by each successive stanza is followed by a rhetorical question: "Do you know what that means?" Obviously, we do not, for we surface sailors and shore-bound citizens to whom the poem is primarily addressed have never encountered submarine warfare. Nor can statistical facts give us such knowledge, the poet asserts, for even the wartime headlines that once had screamed "40,000 Tons Sunk" shed little light on that inner sanctum of private awareness where only submariners recognized what really lay behind it all: "we were just doing our duty; but you do not understand what that means, because you simply do not know." The cultic poem claims to hint at truths that the initiated alone can fathom, for the underwater band of brothers has been forged together by experiences branded in the bone. While historians, poets, novelists, and film-makers may perhaps come close in reconstructing and recreating what others have undergone, the poet implies that their portrayals will always fall short of what these German submariners have actually grasped as real. Thus the gap between insiders and outsiders remains unbridgeable. Of course, every human experience is unique, and therefore distinct and exclusive to the individual involved; submariners, however, plead the special uniqueness of what they themselves have undergone. Thus a mystique is created which sanctifies the belief that the submariners' duty and service were above reproach, whoever the master.

Devotion to duty often meant confronting the ultimate personal sacrifice: death for the Fatherland. This is a crucial theme in naval lore and has lent itself to expressions as diverse as myth and ritual, romance and defamation. Affirmed and endorsed in wartime naval literature, the theme encountered scorn and repudiation only in works published after 1945 when critics of Germany's past judged the wartime generation to have died in vain. But in their facile rejection of the concept, postwar critics have never really addressed the ethos of patriotism, nor what the term "Fatherland" might actually have meant. The protean character of patriotism in wartime Germany reveals itself in the varieties of human response to national emergency and duress: voluntarily rallying to the flag, inner emigration, actual emigration, and covert resistance to the government of the day. Among those who continued to live and work in Germany and its armed forces, the Resistance is a special case. Motivated in large measure by their love for a Germany that was being destroyed by the Third Reich, officers in the Resistance had plotted the assassination of their head of state, Adolf Hitler. Their failure on 20 July 1944 marked their martyrdom and became an important symbol for the postwar Federal Republic of Germany. When in 1993 the department of defence moved its headquarters from Bonn to the Bendler Block in Berlin, the military tradition of patriotism – even to the point of revolt against the government of the day – seemed confirmed. For it was in the Bendler Block that General von Stauffenberg had evolved the plot, and in its courtyard that he and others had been summarily executed.

Whether the sacrifice was noble or vain depended then as now upon perspective. Even in present-day Germany the actions of von Stauffenberg and his group still find detracters as well as supporters; reasoned arguments on both sides reveal complex subtleties in evaluating the conflicting priorities of tradition, honour, duty, and private morality. The frequent wartime evocation of the poem "Death for the Fatherland" which Friedrich Hölderlin had written in 1796, and which is cited at the beginning of this volume, stirred many emotions and responses: "Endure on high, o Fatherland, / Count not the dead! for Thee / Beloved! not *one* too many has fallen." Set against the statistics of submarine losses, it highlights much more than the tension between high-minded poetry and human sacrifice. It underscores the ambiguity in any commitment to the national political ideal. As recorded on a bronze plaque at the U-boat Memorial in Möltenort, 199 U-boats and 5249 sailors were lost in the First World War; 739 U-boats and 30,003 sailors in the Second.

Friedrich Hölderlin's fiercely idealistic romanticism of 1796 had portrayed Germany as a metaphysical reality without bounds or end; to die for such an ideal meant apotheosis. Living in the closing years of the Holy Roman Empire of the German Nation, Hölderlin had envisioned a rebirth of classical greatness, a dream culminating in his hymnic prophecy "Germania" (1801), which celebrated a new Germany as the reincarnation of Hellas. Many wartime orators accepted this expression of unconditional commitment to the nation. Yet they did so without considering the poem's original context or intent. Thus, almost 150 years later, on Memorial Day in 1940, the "Troubadour of the Hitler Youth," Hans Baumann, addressed a rally in Berlin's Schiller Theater on the theme of "the Solemn Promise of the Young."[2] Personal sacrifice called for the highest ideals he found expressed in Hölderlin's lines, which he proclaimed in full. Then in 1941 filmmaker Karl Ritter created a dramatic testament to the cult of youthful death by integrating Hölderlin's poem into his Luftwaffe film *Stukas*, which had extolled the exploits of the Stuka dive-bombing attacks in the battle against France in 1940.[3] Again, at Christmas 1942 when Germany's Third Empire, the Third Reich, was about to face the turning-point of the war, propaganda minister Joseph Goebbels exploited the lines in his radio address to the nation; at that strategic moment Goebbels quoted Hölderlin in order to sanctify the metapolitics of National Socialism's quasi-religious claims. And in April 1944 Admiral Rolf Johannesson had quoted precisely the same lines during a memorial service for the one hundred sailors killed during a British bombing attack against the battleship *Tirpitz*.[4] Baumann, Ritter, and Goebbels may well have shared a community of feeling and ideology despite their differences, but Johannesson did not share the same ideals despite his attraction to Hölderlin. Johannesson was a democrat whose cast of mind, as will be seen, enabled him to lead the postwar navy as its first Commander-in-Chief, Fleet. Just what this juxtaposition of Hölderlin's text with the statistics of battle losses means for us, today, readers will judge for themselves. That Hölderlin's lines are unattractively anachronistic, if not even repugnant, for contemporary German society will be clear to observers of the social scene. Yet in rejecting patriotism as a reasonable inspiration for military service, critics ignore the fact that soldiers without patriotism are mercenaries who can be bought for a price.

Military forces have traditionally been motivated by the challenge of serving the national ideal, and have couched their allegiance in elevated and uplifting terms that integrate the individual into a community bonded together by a common purpose and a common allegiance. The literary record of the German submarine provides ample evidence of this tradition. Naval literature during the First World War promoted the cult of the hero and projected images of chivalry, gallantry, and humanitarianism. It couched submarine exploits in the vocabulary of high-minded adventure and romance, and raised the Imperial Battle Flag (Reichskriegsflagge) as their symbol. U-boat ace Weddigen was typically the "Siegfried of the Depths," and his crew a "band of brothers." Authors of the period asserted that "U-boats have become the common property of all Germans," and that by 1917 the submarine had replaced the capital ship as Germany's major weapon. The U-boat itself emerged as a "miracle weapon," as "a hunter silently stalking his game" on missions of peace, and as Germany's sole defence against British hegemony and wile. British works, by contrast, claimed to see a darker side: the U-boat was an eerie weapon of primorial and illegal power, a "hideous monster of the under-sea," and its crews were deemed pirates and thugs.

For the next twenty years, from 1919 to 1939, German naval literature repudiated both British propaganda and the Treaty of Versailles. Popular literature endorsed the First World War view of submarining, rehearsed the old scenarios and images, and added entirely new themes: vengeance, retribution, and retrieval of lost honour. In narrating "heroic deeds," books of the interwar years promoted the concept of maritime prestige; they justified the past and affirmed the U-boat as "the only means of maritime warfare of decisive importance in the battle between Germany and England." Writers blamed Germany's defeat on inept political leadership and on the failure of senior leaders to have grasped the principles of naval warfare. Many voices had suggested that "continentalism" had caused the strategic downfall; the surface navy's arrogance and ineptitude had triggered the Sailors' Mutiny and revolution. Amidst a wave of self-justification and glorification of the past, submariners emerged in the pulps as the true patriots. They argued that the mutineers and slackers of the surface fleet had prevented any hope of peace with honour, while the U-boat men alone had kept the faith. In the effulgent words of propaganda writer and submarine veteran Fritz Otto Busch, the record showed "how dutifully, unflaggingly and radiant with hope our U-boat crews, the truest of the true, did their best to win the war for Germany." Small wonder, then, that writers of the period also regarded their naval history as a signpost to the nation's future, and in the 1930s actively promoted recruitment for the hoped-for U-Boat Arm. When the new submarine force actually began service in 1935, its inauguration marked for many both a confirmation of faith in Germany and a "redemption" from the burden of Versailles. Submariners, we are told, had always been driven by the Categorical Imperative to pursue the principle of maritime prestige, and "our young people, who are our hope in the Third Reich," must now take up the torch and carry on the great naval tradition.

Literature of the Second World War heightened the features that earlier cults of the hero had promoted. This was the era of the "grey wolves" and "steel sharks," when wolf packs, officially designated by such predatory names as "robber baron" (Raubgraf), "shredder" (Reisswolf), "incendiary" (Mordbrenner), and "bludgeon" (Schlagetod), attacked the Allies' transatlantic convoys. Widespread popularization of the U-boat aces, of their images and deeds propagated the cult of the personality which even today finds positive resonance in the popular market, especially in the United States where the entrepreneurial U-boat fan-club Sharkhunters continues to foster a sometimes lurid fascination in the cult. Literature of the war years 1939–45 marketed swashbuckling exploits and showed the submariner as the true believer both in Germany's invincibility and in the Führer's mission. Man and machine merged in the German submarine. Günther Prien had explained to his youthful readers in 1940 that, as U-boat skipper, "you are the brain of this steel beast ... one must think in iron and steel – or perish." Or again, the submarine is "a remarkable and miraculous synthesis of spirit and heartblood of comrades, of steel body and cable-nerves." In appealing for recruits, U-boat literature promised adventure and self-fulfilment in a unique brotherhood in which one could forget oneself in the great cause one served. Here, too, history and tradition were shown to endorse the highest ideals that had supposedly motivated Germans since the earliest days of their nordic "Viking exploits" on dangerous seas. In elevated tones and mannerisms, popular literary fare ultimately revealed the U-Boat Arm as the embodiment of Germany's national purpose. Despite its clichés and stereotypes, its narrative conventions and sometimes naive lore, popular narratives and lyrics had lionized the nation's submarine service in its righteous struggles against a "duplicitous" Britain.

The tone of U-boat literature shifted radically after Germany's defeat in 1945. This new phase marked the period of the "iron coffins" in which writers attempted to reconstruct the past by rescuing positive traditions from the rubble of Nazi Germany's defeat. The Allies' policies of denazification and re-education were "cleansing" the nation and repudiating all that the past seemed to have meant. Where some German writers still acknowledged "great and noble deeds" and aimed at communicating "authentic" experience untarnished by the political past, others evoked wartime heroism in a new atmosphere of reconciliation. Thus it was possible, in the words of popularizers like Busch and Frank, for U-boat history to emerge as both "triumph *and* tragedy." Believing in the imperatives of duty, service, and humanity, the argument ran, submariners had ultimately been betrayed; innocence had been their tragic flaw. In Germany at large, reassessment and exoneration were in the air. For some writers this meant defending submariners as simply having done their duty in the service of the highest national ideals. Others found the claim unsatisfactory. Submariners, they countered, may well have been a band of brothers whose submarines had fought "like mythical creatures of the primeval world"; but being "nur Soldat," a narrowly focused soldier content to leave moral and ethical questions to others, now struck observers as a barrier to moral living. This was the principal argument of the movie *U-47 – Günther Prien* (1958), the first popular work to introduce the theme of the 'Nur-Soldat' which would become a focal point for debate and official dictum in the 1980s. Yet war books based on the old model of "death and glory" continued to avoid issues of moral or political probity. Occasionally, however, new heroic ideals emerged from among the pulp-trade stereotypes, ones that were quite unexpectedly revealed as having fostered "genuine" naval tradition all along. The "true" role models were now shown to have been vested in two types of officer: those who had undertaken an "inner emigration," and those who had supported the Resistance. Both, of course, had outwardly supported the Nazis by serving in the navy. Yet where the former had emigrated inwardly to a world of private apolitical integrity, the latter had struggled to bring down Hitler's Reich.

The literary trend in naval war books reflected in striking degree a number of psychosocial concerns being investigated by the research team of Alexander and Margarete Mitscherlich. Drawing on clinical data then crystallizing from their psychoanalytical practice with patients suffering guilt-complexes and denial of the nation's Nazi past, their widely discussed book *Die Unfähigkeit zu trauern* [The Inability to Mourn: Bases of Collective Behaviour, 1967] popularized key concepts underpinning the Federal Republic of Germany's political life. In doing so, the book extrapolated from the evidence of case studies onto contemporary politics. Conscious of addressing taboos, the researchers' examination spanned antidemocratic attitudes prevalent in Germany since the Weimar Republic, the national penchant for authoritarianism, and the collective denial of the past. Denial was found to express itself in three critical historical phases beginning at war's end: first, by averting one's emotions from reality when facing overwhelming postwar evidence of the concentration camps and the defeat of the German army; second, by the nation's all-too-ready identification with the Allied victors and their cultural values; and third, by Germany's "manic attempt at making things as though they had never happened" by its zeal for reconstruction. Motivated by a desire to help Germany on the road to political health, the Mitscherlichs showed the nation how to come to terms with itself and its history. "The work of mourning," they explained, "is less concerned with restitution, than it is with accepting the definitive transformation of reality brought about by the loss of the beloved object."[5] Among the examples of the nation's inablity to undergo this process (hence the title of their book), they cited postwar Germany's higher esteem for winners of the Knight's Cross than for those (like future chancellor Willy Brandt) who had emigrated from Nazi Germany rather than become an instrument of its policies. Where the Knight's Cross winner was deemed even in postwar Germany to have served his country as a patriot, the emigrant or conscientious objector was frequently disdained for neglect of duty. The Mitscherlichs explained this in psychoanalytical terms as derealization (Entwirklichung), a defence mechanism involving a process of "unmaking" the present in order to hold on to a dream of the past. At the root of this inability to mourn lay both a faulty grasp of the past as it actually had been and continued self-indulgence in an illusion. When introducing the second edition of their book in 1977, the Mitscherlichs noted a shift in the national psychosis. The crucial issue now was less the question of guilt than the fact that distorted versions of German history were being passed on to the younger generation. Despite the evidence provided by scholarly and well-documented studies of the Nazi era, the older generation who had lived through it, and therefore deemed itself the best judge of what had "really" happened, was communicating self-delusions to its children. This "decline of well-founded historical understanding," the Mitscherlichs argued, was continued proof of Germany's inability to mourn.

Conflicting versions of what constituted historical truth emerged in the reconstruction period of naval narratives from 1973, the year in which Buchheim's historical novel *Das Boot* appeared. Bent on demythologizing the submarine, writers in both East and West Germany laid siege to the German navy's literary and cultural tradition. The war at sea had not been an honourable undertaking waged by chivalrous heroes, reconstructionists explain; it had been deceitfully planned by perverse politicians who had sent Germany's youth to needless and certain death in a "children's crusade." Submariners were now seen as having constituted a lost generation seduced as much by the Nazis as by popular "war books" that had lured them into the armed forces in hopes of emulating great deeds. In this light all military tradition became suspect, particularly the concept of the warrior as apolitical servant of the state. In their most virulent form, such facile arguments of the 1970s and 1980s denounced all military tradition, even that of home defence. They deemed honour and loyalty anachronistic, and heroism a pernicious lie. Struggling under the burden of German history, journalists and commentators supported the antiwar mood by labelling all war as insane, all heroism as sham, and devotion to duty as moral turpitude.

Significantly, however, popular critics of Germany's U-boat war debated not on the basis of hard evidence and analysis, but according to their position on the political spectrum. The right argued that soldiers could indeed fight honourably and decently, whatever the politics of the government in power; the U-boat was therefore but one weapon among many. The left rejected this as moral bankruptcy, as an anachronistic attempt by nostalgic old men to justify their past; the U-boat was therefore the most obscene weapon in the German arsenal. The left-of-centre media exploited the U-boat as a foil for encouraging national self-flagellation. One of the more strident voices encouraged the view that the U-boat was the end product of a dangerous flaw in national character, a "Teutonic death-wish." Whatever the perspective, each view betrayed an almost voyeuristic fascination with the theme of the submarine, a spell cast as much by beguilement as loathing.

Judging by its impact on the popular imagination, the U-boat, as an instrument radiating destructive power and stealth, is a modern example of the sublime: aesthetically enervating, morally ambiguous, spelling danger and pain.[6] For in its classical expression, the sublime is a mixed feeling of pleasure and pain, in which our instincts and desires are themselves in conflict; we are fascinated by dreadful objects and scenes because they trigger in us contrary emotions by making us want to involve ourselves in the very thing we find repugnant. The market success of novels and films on the U-boat even during the antiwar euphoria of the 1970s and 1980s offers some confirmation of the view. Their success suggests that the theme has appealed more because of the feelings it engenders than the ideas it promotes.

Yet questions about value and priorities have punctuated even this literary tradition, and occasional voices have questioned the navy's hierarchy of values. One thinks, for example, of such historical novels as Ott's *Haie und kleine Fische* (1956) and Buchheim's *Das Boot* (1973), as well as of numerous witnesses like Martin Niemöller and Erich Topp who had once fully embraced the wartime national ideals, only to reject them years later. Thus, when introducing the third British edition of Niemöller's autobiography, *From U-Boat to Concentration Camp*, in January 1939, the dean of Chichester Cathedral recalled a poignant banquet speech delivered during an ecumenical gathering in Berlin thirty years earlier, in June 1909. In raising the theme of patriotism that had inspired both British and German alike, the speaker had asked his mixed audience of church people whether even greater value systems might not exist. In ascending order he had listed three: the Christendom of Europe, the human race, and the Kingdom of God on Earth. "Patriotism is a noble ideal; let us not make of it an idol," he had said. Niemöller's postwar career had frequently reminded the dean of these words. Writing now thirty years later in 1939, on the eve of what was to become Part Two of the war to end all wars, the dean captured the nexus in which the priorities of conflicting loyalties are worked out.

[Niemöller] was – and is – an ardent patriot, who gave to his country all that he had to offer when the call came. The reader will feel as he reads his autobiography the exhilaration that comes from the forgetfulness of self in a common cause and that tang of the sea which gives a special gusto to the life of the sailor. But he will see also how by the inevitable march of events – or, in other words, by the hand of God – the sailor patriot found himself committed to the greater loyalties of religion, which to have disobeyed would have been to cut at the roots of his patriotism.[7]

As the dean expressed it, Niemöller's assent to the higher service of his religious beliefs had been nothing less than a stance that "refuses to disown the universal brotherhood of all the children of God." Admiral Erich Topp's sea-change fifty years later, on the other hand, had been caused by historical, not theological, reflection.

Topp had published his memoir, *Fackeln über dem Atlantik* [Flares over the Atlantic, 1990], after exemplary careers in two successive German navies: the wartime Kriegsmarine and the postwar Bundesmarine. Awarded the Knight's Cross with Oak Leaves and Swords, he had been credited during the war with sinking some thirty-nine ships in thirteen missions, for a total of 243,000 tons. He had also sunk the American destroyer USS *Reuben James* during the United States' period of belligerent neutrality and had survived a close-quarters gunnery attack from the Canadian corvette HMCS *Sackville.*[8] Famous as the skipper of the "Red Devil" U-boat, he had signed the 1946 protocol supporting Admiral Dönitz at Nürnberg and had figured in many literary and newsreel accounts of submarine exploits. He was, in short, a U-boat ace – doubtless reason enough to write a memoir just as other aces had done.

Indeed, the subtitle of his book, "a report about the life of a U-boat commander," hinted at yet another U-boat book attempting to recapture the old spirit of duty and high adventure. In his case, however, the meaning was actually quite different, despite the vivid title of the revised American edition that touted his story as an "odyssey."[9] Topp had in fact undertaken the far more difficult task of pondering the inner life that the U-boat experience had engendered: memories, moods, and pervasive ambiguities. Ultimately, he delivered a frank, if fragmented, historical evaluation of his generation's place in the flow of events. It was an attempt at exploring the ambivalence of human existence and at confronting the disturbing question of why his generation had "followed the siren tones of the totalitarian regime whose deeds lie upon us like a shadow." Such questions demanded honest answers, without concession to selective editing or wilful repression. As the opening words of his preface explained, he had "not written a book of memories in order to escape them." Nor did he accept the bland assertion of the U-boat ace who had recently swept all analysis aside by introducing his biography with the flourish: "we did our duty in war just as our opponent did."[10] Compiled from personal diaries, letters, and current reflections, Topp's autobiography is a meditation, not a salty yarn. He did not take the easy route.

Conversant with both the popular and professional traditions of the submarine service, the admiral took a view from the top. He drew not only on a wealth of personal experience, but also on a firm understanding of published research on the years he contemplated. He was not a nostalgic veteran. Indeed, he cut against the grain of much thinking by the "old guard" and sided – though without polemics – with those who were revaluating their wartime years in the light of the new knowledge postwar research and personal reflection afforded.

When writing to a veteran who had assailed his sea-change, Topp pointedly claimed "not to have been changed by the prevailing Zeitgeist" with its pressures to conform to a 1980s kind of political correctness; instead, he pointed out, "I am open-minded and critical, and am not afraid to change an opinion that is no longer tenable."[11] Once a strong adherent of Dönitz, he has over the years become an outspoken critic of the admiral and his policies. His concluding thoughts captured the essence of his philosophical and political intent.

I have recalled the fear and the courage, the mendacity and the truth ... My book does not dwell on the sting of all that I have missed experiencing [because of the war], nor upon the missed opportunities. Nor have I hesitated to call even myself into question again and again. I have reported on a period of our history which only my generation really knows, [and we know it] because we suffered through it – and helped shape it. It will continue to lie like a shadow upon us unto the end of our days. But it must not and shall not burden our children and grand-children.[12]

As we have seen, advocates of the U-Boat Arm had begun their memoirs and popular histories within five years of war's end, as soon as Allied rules on censorship and denazification had permitted. Topp himself had consulted on the very first of these, thereby helping to launch the popular surveys of that era.[13] He had begun by encouraging and advocating Harald Busch's account of the u-boat war, *So War der U-Boot-Krieg* [That's the Way It Was, 1952], which had for years remained a rallying point for veterans' memories. It had struck Topp at the time as a book whose vivid images and graphic narrative style had indeed told important features of the u-boat story "the way it was." (Topp was doubtless familiar with Busch's wartime picture-book, *U-Boot auf Feindfahrt*, 1942, which had extolled the "hunt in the Atlantic" against Allied shipping.) Not long thereafter he was attracted to Wolfgang Ott's *Haie und Kleine Fische* [Sharks and Little Fish, 1956]. Ott's historical novel was the first postwar u-boat book to evoke the perversion of Nazism and to promote the idea of submariners as a deceived and lost generation. Topp later described the novel as "a confessional book of our generation."[14] Convinced of the truth of its message, he had written a favourable review, and later served as technical adviser when the book was filmed in Hamburg in 1957.

Topp's involvement in fictional reconstructions of the u-boat experience reflected his concerns with the literary creative process. Having become an architect immediately after the war, he had pondered the impact of Nazi ideology on art and architecture. Both had been enslaved by an ideological system bent on eradicating individuality and authenticity. Topp grew convinced that only a politically unfettered art could evoke the genuine meaning of experience, and when looking at U-boat literature he found the first expressions of this freedom in the novels of Ott and Buchheim. As his autobiography reveals: "[Ott's] book was for many a provocation, but every provocation illuminates a complex situation in a striking way ... That I later took up the cause of Buchheim's novel *The Boat* was an [equally] personal concern. Here the reality of U-boat patrol – just as I had experienced it – was mastered in literature."[15]

Buchheim's detractors, as we have seen, had been attempting all along to debunk the novelist by claiming that he had been nothing but a propaganda writer during the war and was therefore not a "real" U-boat comrade. Offended that someone uninitiated into the cult would presume to criticize Großadmiral Dönitz, they resorted to sometimes hysterical ploys that revealed just how little they understood the nature of literature and its function in society. They wanted, in fact, a chronicle of deeds, not a history of social process, and were merciless whenever their sense of historicity was betrayed. By insisting that writers and film-makers tell the story as it was, they neatly managed to avoid the deeper question of responsibility. Unfortunately, their insistence on a reproduction of exactly what happened also marked a refusal to broach the question of what these wartime happenings might actually mean now. Yet Topp, reading for meaning behind the events, had rallied to Buchheim's defence in 1986 with an open letter to the German Naval Officers' Association.

I am of the opinion that Buchheim understands a great deal about submarines. Like the chief engineer of U-96 [aboard which Buchheim went to sea], I believe he describes technical procedures with astonishingly detailed knowledge, and I think that his books come closer to the psychological situations on board such as no other U-boat book among the many I have seen. [I am convinced] that he has reproduced the experience "Sea" so impressively in word and image in a manner unequalled in German literature.[16]

For Topp, the meaning projected by the novel *Das Boot* (1973) was unequivocal and just; it had been enhanced by Buchheim's trilogy *U-Boot-Krieg* (1976), *Die U-Boot-Fahrer* (1985), and *Zu Tode Gesiegt* (1988). As Topp concluded in his letter to the association: "This trilogy is the great epic of the struggle, suffering and demise of the German Submarine Arm of the Second World War. It has the inevitability and futility of a Greek tragedy." Six years later he would write in his autobiography that Buchheim's trilogy had graphically "brought the murderous battle and defeat of the U-boats and their crews into the consciousness of the German people." It had done so, Topp added, in a way that purely historical argument could not have done. Buchheim's books, particularly the novel and the film, had to his mind destroyed the ugly clichés and stereotypes coursing abroad about the u-boat sailor as "brutal ss man."[17]

Topp's advocacy of re-examining the past has brought him into conflict with some veterans who continue to regard him not only as turncoat, but as an officer who has "fouled his nest" and has had the temerity to challenge the revered status of Großadmiral Dönitz. In fact, however, Topp is not the loner his few vocal detractors – almost invariably diehard veterans – make him out to be. For his approach embodies reflections common to many senior leaders who had been invited to return to the postwar forces. What is at issue is not just the nature of historical truth, but of military tradition.

One of the major problems facing the new Federal Armed Forces in the postwar period had been the question of its links with the past. In attempting a new start, senior leaders pondered the meaning of military tradition and wondered whether such a thing as "patriotic continuity" was possible.[18] By 1965, when the forces were barely a decade old, the department of defence issued a Tradition Protocol (Traditionserlass) dealing with the topic. Entitled *Bundeswehr und Tradition*, the protocol investigated the extent to which the military virtues of the past, specifically those of the wartime Wehrmacht, were either applicable to, or even necessary for, the postwar Bundeswehr. It raised a number of sophistic questions, including that of moral responsibility: "The soldier who, in following a false tradition as an apolitical soldier, simply restricts himself solely to the military trade, neglects an essential part of the service duty which he confirmed by oath as a soldier in a democracy."[19] In other words, there was no room in the new armed forces for what was now regarded as the "Nur-Soldat" of the Nazi period; there was room neither for what the Germans call "Kadaver-Gehorsam" (zombie-like, mindless obedience), nor for the person who was content to be "only a soldier" without moral and democratic principles.

Many Second World War veterans saw this aspect of the protocol as a direct attack on their integrity and honour. They defended themselves against a wave of literature and film in the 1970s and 1980s in the only way they knew: by protesting that while they had indeed been "merely soldiers" doing their patriotic duty with honour and distinction, this was precisely the profound ethos (Soldatentum) on which the military of other great nations had also been based. That was doubtless true, and many an honest veteran has been unfairly pilloried in this process of redefinition. But historical perspectives had changed, and records had shown that time and again such a stance had served to cover up moral turpitude. In his plea for clemency, for example, the commandant of concentration camp Bergen-Belsen had insisted on just this excuse. He had been only a soldier ("Ich war nur Soldat"); he had merely followed the orders of his military superiors and had never killed anyone on his own initiative.[20] Although some 45,000 prisoners had died in his camp between 1943 and 1945, he refused to assume responsibility for their deaths. Doubtless to ensure that individual resonsibility could never again be so conveniently side-stepped, the formulators of the protocol *Bundeswehr und Tradition* (1965) felt obliged to make the new conditions abundantly clear. In the post–Second World War era, members of the armed forces were in all circumstances forbidden from relinquishing the responsibility for making ethical judgments. Only the "false traditions" of the past had fostered irresponsibility in such matters. False traditions, the protocol declared, were now to be understood as those that arose under dictatorships. This formulation had not only prepared the ground for rejecting the traditions of the Nazi regime, but it had laid the theoretical basis for rejecting those of the East German navy if ever the reunification of Germany should occur. (When in 1991 selected personnel of the East German Volksmarine were eventually taken over by the Bundesmarine, they were integrated only after a period of re-education.)

In 1983 yet another study, this time in the form of a volume of scholarly essays, examined the German navy's self-image and identity. It did so by comparing the four successive German navies, much as Vizeadmiral Friedrich Ruge, a wartime rear-admiral who became the first head of the Federal German Navy, had done in his autobiography of 1979.[21] Recognizing the importance of the sea for Germany's national well-being, the editor claimed to have found the key to the German navy's sometimes tarnished image: German naval prestige had in the past been erroneously predicated on overt competition against the major European navies, rather than on cooperation with them. He argued persuasively for the modern perspective. "For the first time in its history, the [German] navy no longer has an isolated national task. For the first time, after two lost world wars with all their devastating effects, something came about that neither the Imperial Navy nor the Kriegsmarine had been granted: alliance with the maritime powers of the west."

Yet despite the twenty chapters by as many authors, the scholarly anthology reveals one striking omission: the U-boat. Only one very lean chapter attempted to deal with the subject, and then it contributed little to the topic at hand.[22] In searching for Germany's naval identity, scholars had missed the crucial issue: the public image is not to be found in capital ships, but in the submarine. It is the U-boat, and not the big-ship blue-water navy, which lies at the heart of Germany's naval tradition. In striking contrast to then prevailing lore, Konteradmiral Rolf Johannesson seemed to confirm this view when writing in his autobiography of 1989 that "the tradition of the *Bundesmarine* should be based on the spirit of the men of the U-Boat Arm."[23] That was perceptive praise from an experienced seagoing officer who had never been a wartime submariner.

The West German policy study of the Federal German Armed Forces, *Tradition und Reform* (1985), illustrates the practical implications of the complex process in which the forces find themselves. As the conscious heirs of both a technological and a political past, the restructured postwar armed forces have had to divorce themselves from their historical stereotypes – in particular the Nazi image. At the same time, they have had to affirm those positive qualities of tradition – valour, humanity, duty, honour – which survived the tyranny. Not until 1970 had the question of the navy's self-image and identity been subjected to serious scientific scrutiny. Significantly, these studies found their key determining factors to lie in Germany's strategic policy and practice. Thus their conventional approach to naval history overlooked the primary role of the media in forming the navy's image.[24]

As late as 1991 Germany's department of defence was still attempting to set legal parameters to what "tradition" ought to mean by preparing drafts of a protocol that was ultimately never promulgated.[25] In doing so, it proposed a series of assumptions: "National Socialism has not only scorned traditions, but destroyed them"; therefore "the political leadership of the [Second World War] Wehrmacht and the conduct of Wehrmacht leadership ... do not admit of any link between the Wehrmacht and the [postwar] Bundeswehr as an institution." Consequently, the legacy of "National Socialist rule demands of soldiers of the Bundeswehr a high degree of sensitivity in the development of their understanding of tradition."[26] Ultimately, "the Bundeswehr fosters its own traditions." The very fact that such a Tradition Protocol was formulated at all continues to raise difficult questions about bureaucratic intrusions into the national consciousness. Indeed, officialdom's revaluation of the past involved a delicate balancing act, for it had to repudiate one aspect of its national past while affirming and building on a historically established military ethos commensurate with democratic principles.[27] "Duration in change," a principle once solely associated with themes in Germany's classical literature, was no less operative in naval history.

Unique among Germany's postwar armed services, the Federal German Navy (Bundesmarine) had begun its process of "coming to grips with the past" in 1960 almost as soon as the new navy was born. It had been firmly led in this enterprise by Rolf Johannesson, one of six of the 200 admirals of the former Kriegsmarine to be taken into the new Bundesmarine. He became the Federal German Navy's first Commander-in-Chief, Fleet. A strong leader with deep roots in the Confessing Church – the "resistance church" of the war years – Johannesson had worked under Pastor Niemöller in the immediate postwar years as bureau chief and financial adviser in the foreign office of the Evangelical Church. The link is important, for this was the same Niemöller whose autobiography *Vom U-Boot zur Kanzel* [From U-boat to Pulpit, 1935] had traced his path from submariner to pastor and whose opposition to Hitler had landed him in Sachsenhausen and Dachau concentration camps. Concerned that his officers learn from history, Johannesson had instituted the annual Fleet Historical-Tactical Conference. Here officers would tackle problems of German naval history, and were given academic freedom to address themselves to issues without regard to rank or station. Provided they exercised intellectual honesty, they could argue against past or present assumptions and against traditions and policies. The conference has become a firm tradition of the fleet, and the late "Johann Nelson," as the old admiral had been affectionately known since the early years of the war, is among the most revered admirals of the postwar era.

At a time when the navy's tradition was once again under public and official scrutiny, it was perhaps significant that the theme for the 1993 conference was "The Image of the German Navy in the Media, from the Turn of the Century to Today," and that for 1994, "Leadership and Trust: Influences on the German Navy's Combat Readiness." One of the specialized sessions in the 1994 conference enquired into the motivation of German crews during the First World War; it examined the roles of patriotism, comradeship, trust in the leadership, and pride in one's branch of the service. Another examined what motivated U-boat crews of the Second World War to continue taking up the battle after 1943 in the face of Allied superiority. Common elements were found to have linked the sailors of the two wars beyond the overarching conviction that they were fighting a just war: as patriots, submariners saw themselves as members of a historical community in the service of a super-political concept; as citizens, they were persuaded through faith in authority that the right men were in the right positions in the hierarchy; as military men, they felt bound to one another through an implicit, fraternal trust in each other's technical competence; as submariners they formed a tightly knit band of brothers destined to share a common, and possibly sudden, fate. Either the u-boat would survive, or it would not. There would be no half measures. Submariners of the Second World War still laboured under the shadow of the Sailors' Mutiny and the revolution of 1918; they knew that insurrection must never happen again, and that loyalty at all costs was of the essence. These elements have contributed to the navy's identity, to its myths of origin and self-definition. They constitute for many a trans-epochal commitment to duty and honour.

Yet whatever advances the navy makes in establishing an unsullied identity, it is always haunted by the past. For, as the senior admiral and chief of the defence staff explained in 1990, "German history is burdened in a way that makes it difficult for Germans to be patriots without Ifs and Buts."[28] Yet "if we take Germany as a whole in its history and cultural achievement, then Germans still have cause to be proud of their Fatherland despite the sombre periods." Certainly, the u-boat's literary tradition largely extols the submarine service for its chivalrous ethics and high-minded devotion to duty.

But the trend that the Buchheim wave established in the 1970s and 1980s has continued into the 1990s. Writers still find cause to attack Germany's military traditions by claiming to have found skeletons in the closet of the "sombre periods" of the country's past. Once exhumed, these skeletons are held up as alarming omens about military traditions. Reconstructionism is central to each case.

Thus in May 1990 a lead article in the international edition of *Die Zeit* reviled the sinking of the *Lusitania* as "a cold-blooded" act by one of Germany's self-styled "wonder weapons."[29] Surmounted by large graphics showing the stricken liner plunging into the depths, the story underscored the horror and criminal nature of Germany's undersea warfare. Such exposés were typical. Again, in December 1991, *Die Zeit* published u-boat author Bodo Herzog's abrasive account of the formerly top secret "Operation Ursula," a clandestine u-boat intrusion into Spain's internal politics in 1935. Allegedly constituting Germany's "first war crime," this "pirate" operation led to the sinking of Spanish submarine c-3 on 12 December 1935. For Herzog, the savagery of the torpedoing anticipated the "terror attack on Guernica" of 26 April 1936. Rejecting the received tradition about the apolitical and "clean" Submarine Service of the 1930s and 1940s, Herzog charged the German U-Boat Arm with having been thoroughly tainted by Nazi doctrine from its earliest days. U-boat operations in Spain seemed to him proof enough: "here we see all the dirty tricks of a navy thoroughly infected by National-Socialism." This was harsh criticism indeed. But Herzog took matters even further when attacking the "unconscionable" silence of the navy's prewar leaders. "Even Grand Admirals Raeder

and Dönitz, who had been convicted in Nuremberg as principal war
criminals, took their secret [about the Spanish campaign] with them
to the grave. As early as three years prior to the commencement of
the Second World War, they had already dropped all moral and ethical
reservations. They have no business in the honour role of the German
navy."[30]

As a member of the Association of German Submariners, Herzog
had thereby horrified many a veteran who felt he had broken ranks
in publishing this article. Both for this and for his support of Buchheim, some veterans proposed that Herzog's name be stricken from
the membership list. The motion failed for lack of support.

In subsequent stories, *Die Zeit* condemned Germany's unrestricted
submarine warfare of the First World War as "'Finis Germaniae!': the
stupidly audacious, fateful decision for ruthless U-boat war."[31] (In the
event, this perception was well founded, for the decision to pursue a
strategy of unrestricted submarine warfare had in fact spelled Germany's doom.) The article in *Die Zeit*, topped by a dramatic photograph of a surfaced U-boat crashing through heavy seas, explored how
"seventy-five years ago Germany provoked America's entry into the
war." The newspaper page conjured up all the visual tradition of
derring-do and bravado – and then undercut it all with a caustic
critique not only of Germany's admiralty but of the regime of the long-
revered Kaiser himself. The author pilloried an era of German politics
that had committed the cardinal error of regarding the U-boat as the
"miracle weapon"; he described the mobilization of public opinion in
support of U-boats, and the orchestrated public euphoria when their
repeated successes were announced. He claimed that Germany's promotional campaign about U-boats "was successful precisely because it
conformed to Germany's widespread expansionistic wishful-thinking."
As a result, yet another generation was deceived, for the promotional
campaign had drowned out any and all criticism of the U-boat war.
The U-boat reality that coursed through the public mind at the time
had been little more than a controlled fiction.

The problem of separating reality from fiction also arose in the case
of the problematic Martin Niemöller, whose journey from U-boat to
pulpit has left its traces in the submarine community. Marking on 14
January 1992 the 100th aniversary of his birth, *Die Zeit* published a
balanced article entitled "From Sea Devil to Angel of Peace" which
concisely explored his complex personality.[32] By 1981 the German
right-wing press had written Niemöller off as a "wooer of commies,"
and as "the idol of pacifists and capitulators."[33] It had later pilloried
Niemöller's "Jewish connection" when his name was honoured at New
York's Holocaust Center for his "courageous struggle against Hitler

and for human rights." As the old-line *National-Zeitung* pointed out when reminding its readers of the pastor's past, Niemöller had really been "one of us" all along: U-boat skipper and avowed nationalist.[34] Some things do not change, it implied, and loyalty was one of them. But matters were not quite so black and white for the article in *Die Zeit* of January 1992. Clearly comfortable with ambiguities, the writer raised a number of questions: Was this "fighter, U-boat skipper, Prussian and Protestant a saint, an old fire-eater, a prophet or a traitor?" He then surveyed the man's life in search of answers.

The writer in *Die Zeit* begged the question as to who this man really was. But he did decry the fact that "Germans do not like it when somebody changes his convictions and comes to a sounder understanding." (As we have seen, the right-wing press offers some evidence in support of this contention.) Yet those who do change provide a necessary provocation to a nation's often complacent assumptions. Indeed, in Niemöller's case, *Die Zeit* pointed out, "a church that can no longer produce and tolerate such characters would be narrower and poorer." The writer left little doubt that a nation without its dissenting characters would be equally poor. However, as far as the right-wing press was concerned, dissent was apostasy: for this reason it has attacked those submariners like Buchheim, Niemöller, and Topp who have changed their views about the U-Boat Arm. Such men are a source of provocation; both they and the issues they espouse are symptomatic of what another recent German writer called "the difficulties of dealing with tradition."[35]

The U-boat as a theme in literature and film continues to attract writers and audiences. Paradoxically, however, the submarines of the postwar Bundesmarine figure little, if at all. Unkind irony lies therein. The modern Federal German Navy has existed for almost forty years, longer than the Reichsmarine and the Kriegsmarine combined. Yet it remains overshadowed by a more intriguing past as the public remains fascinated by wartime exploits, U-boat aces, and all the old clichés fostered by popular literature and the press. Stories still appear about U-boats escaping to exotic South American ports at war's end carrying Hitler, his mistress Eva Braun, untold treasures, and a bevy of concentration-camp commandants and doctors. One is surprised at the apparent ability of such books as Norbert Lebert's kitchy novel *Eine Frau war an Bord* [A Woman Was on Board, 1968] and Karl Hans Koizar's, *U-91: Satan der Tiefe* [U-91: Satan of the Deep, 1979] to titillate the popular imagination. Indeed, the general fascination with U-boats also bubbled up with the recent discovery of what a diver had claimed in 1986 to be Hitler's real escape submarine. The tabloid *Bild-Zeitung* picked up news reports from Denmark and noised it abroad that there might be "Nazi treasure" in the wreck of U-534 lying on the bottom near the Danish island of Anholt; it suspected "gold, paintings and war documents" aboard. Even the more responsible *Frankfurter Zeitung* took up the tale, as did the *Kieler Nachrichten* in 1991, raising a question that haunted the popular U-boat scene for some considerable time: "Who was in U-boat 534?" Speculation was wildly imaginative: "those in the know suggest that, besides Nazi prominents like [the "Angel of Death"] Josef Mengele and Auschwitz-Kommandant Hoess and Hitler's mistress Eva Braun, there are treasures and explosive documents from Hitler's headquarters in Berlin."[36] (All that was found when the U-boat was actually raised in 1993 were cases of condoms and French wine.) Such unfounded stories and speculations do not disappear, for writers continue to recreate them for appreciative audiences.

Certainly, U-boat icons – especially those portraying the potentially scurrilous "Nazi" U-boats – are saleable items. Always eye-catching, they can either promote or criticize the past; they help market everything from T-shirts and shot-glasses to books. The image's effect depends not only on which feature one accentuates, but upon the context in which it appears. Thus even when discussing the economics of the German movie industry in 1992, the newspaper *Die Welt* caught the reader's eye by heading its account with a large sequence shot from Germany's biggest money-maker *Das Boot*. The photo portrayed neither a U-boat knifing its way through towering seas nor dashing young knights-errant at the onset of a mission. From among many possible icons, the editor chose the image of strident reconstructionism: a drunken U-boat captain being dragged by his comrades from the bistro's pissoir.[37]

Yet despite the tendency for the U-boat's past to be attacked in the media, "tradition presses" continue to keep heroism alive. Thus even in recent years the Landser series of military pulps has indulged in an exercise in hagiography by publishing some fifty pocket-histories and novelettes about Second World War U-boat aces; they glory in submarining as a naval skill devoid of any political or moral implications. Indeed, the right-wing documentary film *Die Grauen Wölfe* [The Grey Wolves, 1990] epitomized this stance. Compiled from wartime newsreels, it was a face-saving work whose purpose was "not only to recount the story of comradeship, self-sacrifice and many personal privations," but to honour the submariners' memory, "that we might never forget them."[38] It summarized the narrative with scenes shot at the submariners' shrine, the U-boat Memorial in Möltenort. Panning across the bronze tablets containing the names of the more than 30,000 fallen comrades, the camera paused on a panoramic view of the monument, while statistics recording the u-boats' successes scrolled by: 1170 u-boats in the Second World War had sunk 149 warships and 2882 merchant ships, for a total of 14,408,422 tons; 863 u-boats had been lost. The film ended with sentimental flair by overlaying the monument with a stylized portrait of Dönitz and bestowing upon a generation of heroic submariners the film's final accolade: "and all of them revered their C-in-C, Submarines, Grand Admiral Karl Dönitz." And for many, to borrow the assertive title from Harald Busch's famous *So war der U-Boot-Krieg* (1952), "that's the way it was."

Meanwhile, today, a variety of social and cultural artifacts continue to haunt the memory of old salts and to attract the attention of historians and curio-hunters. Such memorabilia include picture postcards and pop art from the earliest days of German seafaring, and music that once accompanied the "great" u-boat films and stirred the hearts of submariners.[39] Many postcards issued throughout the history of German submarining disseminated both stirring and sentimental verses about the "u-boat spirit": dash and daring, melancholy farewells and triumphant returns. Others proclaimed the words of songs easily sung in homes, messes, and taverns: "Lili Marleen," "… denn wir fahren gegen Engeland," and "Das deutsche U-Bootlied" [The German U-boat Song], to name but a few. Broadsheets with pictures and texts formed another component of the propaganda thrust. Thus the German Shipyards Deutsche Werft in Hamburg, a major builder of submarines, had issued a broadsheet with the words to its own "U-boat Song"; dedicated to "all the u-boats" it had built, it was meant to celebrate the "year of the great victories, 1941." In like manner a broadsheet with the words to Hermann Löns's old standby of 1914, "… denn wir fahren gegen Engeland!" was published and republished in the Second World War. Surmounted by a lone, outbound u-boat under the exaggerated air-cover of fifteen fighter-planes, the image exuded undaunted confidence in Germany's national security and destiny.

Cheap editions of piano scores provided yet another means of broadcasting submarine culture: "Das U-Boot-Lied" by the famous composer of the international wartime hit "Lili Marlene," and the rousing "Kretschmer-March" commemorating the deeds of the "Golden Horseshoe" skipper of u-99 spring to mind.[40] Musical hits from the u-boat movie *U-Boote Westwärts* [U-boats Westwards, 1941] were also marketed in piano scores. The film's signature tunes "Warte, mein Mädel, dort in der Heimat" [Wait Back Home, My Darling] and "Irgendwo, in weiter Ferne" [Somewhere, in a Far-off Place] would long hold nostalgic appeal.[41] These songs helped popularize the mythology of the Knights of the Deep who entered the lists to defend the Fatherland's honour.

Veterans hear these tunes and lyrics today with a wistful sense of irony. By contrast, the haunting electronic sounds of the theme from the movie *Das Boot* have a different effect. Written neither to be sung nor hummed, they are a symphonic threnody without words. The theme's melodic strains embody dark presentiments about a type of human experience that can only be grasped in the emotions. This is not the melody of nostalgic affirmation such as earlier films had used; it is the music of a muted "Götterdämmerung."

German history since the collapse of the Third Reich has been aptly described as a narrative in search of meaning.[42] U-boat literature, by contrast, evinces quite a different character: it is a narrative in search of an audience. U-boat narratives have promoted political goals, justified the past, sustained a seafaring tradition, and attempted to revise conventional wisdom. U-boat literature actually strives to deliver historical meaning to those who might support the cause. Even at their subliterary worst, u-boat books have conformed to the classical literary principle *Prodesse et Delectare*: entertainment as the sugar on the pill of instruction.

As we have seen, much u-boat literature concerns itself with perpetuating and communicating certain cultic values. It extols and elucidates deeds, characters, and events in order to preserve the traditions of the seagoing military professional. Thus the literary achievement sometimes goes beyond simply trying to narrate historical experience the way it "actually" was; literature of this type often indulges in the dangerous game of myth-making. Yet, ironically, one needs a mystique and a mythology if men are to commit themselves to dangerous missions. One needs clearly understood traditions as testimonial to the fact that one's ventures are rooted in acquired and tested wisdom. One needs the cult of duty, truth, and valour if one is to know how to act and who to be when the chips are down. But these inherited and inculcated certitudes can thrust individuals into a vicious quandary. Indeed, isolated cases in the u-boat's literary record remind us that reflective and enquiring minds will grasp the latent ambiguities of these fearful abstractions and confront the conflict between private morals and public ethos. What seems the appropriate choice of one historical moment does not necessarily command the allegiance or assent of another.

As to whether these u-boat books have any significance today, Admiral Topp suggests an answer: "For the participants of the war, the books have evoked memories of all the hells and horrors that war brings. But also the memory of people who despite the collapse and insanity of bloodshed fought on 'as the law required.' As a [retired] member of the Federal German Forces [Bundeswehr] I read from these books that the soldier is neither a caricature nor a potential murderer, but that he spans the whole scale of human and manly life with all its strengths, weaknesses and even its errors."[43]

Readers who have not themselves experienced "the hells and horrors" of which Topp spoke, but who have enhanced their vision of life through the vicarious experience U-boat literature and film provide, may well share his view. Indeed, impressions gathered by insiders and outsiders alike contribute to the cultural understanding of what the U-boat experience actually was. As was mooted at the beginning of this book, this experience finds expression in a wide variety of interpretations whose impact on one another both created and reflected new mind-sets – in themselves the stuff of new experience. U-boat literature is part of this complex weave. Like all historical experience, it too provides substance and perspectives for asking questions about the future.

Yet much of the U-boat's literary record gives evidence of inflexible lines of argument. Popular literature's sometimes one-dimensional presentation of heroism, patriotism, duty, and truth seems predestined to marshall the ranks of supporters and revilers along rigid lines: insiders and outsiders, the left and the right, ancient warriors and postwar civilians. The recent Buchheim wave amply documents this aspect of sectarian bias. Occasionally, however, voices have been raised in support of a broader perspective. Thus in his autobiography "Flares over the Atlantic" (1990), Erich Topp attempted to see the phenomenon of U-boat literature in the context of the history of ideas. As he pointed out, the books and reflections about U-boats and the war could only have been written – and indeed can now only be understood – in the context of one of the greatest intellectual shifts in Western history. How else does one account for what Nietzsche would have called the "transvaluation of all values" which, in the U-boat case, has meant the reassessment of traditions once held sacrosanct and absolute? Topp refers somewhat tentatively to such epoch-making ideas as Einstein's Theory of Relativity and Heisenberg's Uncertainty Principle, both of which helped to topple the hierarchical certainties on which the nineteenth century was based, and on which the twentieth century has so often acted. Such pivotal insights and creative directional thrusts have forced us to reconsider many of our presuppositions; they have obliged us to rethink our notions about time and space, and about causality and determinism. Ultimately, perhaps, meaning depends upon perspective; and ultimate meaning, if such there be, can never be objectively known. As Heisenberg has explained it: "What we observe is not nature itself, but nature exposed to our method of questioning."[44]

Writing in 1990 prior to the end of the Cold War, Admiral Topp spoke of our living in an apocalyptic age, an era of super-power confrontation and "star war" technology. In order to prevent catastrophe, he wrote, "we need responsible people who see the danger zones and mark them precisely, and who buoy the navigable channel which the ship of the future generation must travel."[45] This made it vital to understand the past in order to deal with what might lie ahead, and to scrutinize the beguiling influences of the machinery of war. Operational and technical histories of Germany's submarines have taken us a long way down the navigator's track of which Topp spoke, for their fully analysed war record serves as a benchmark for assessing the potential for underwater combat even today.[46] By shedding light on both the creation of culture and the manipulation of myth, the U-boat's literary history is of special significance, too.

Notes

A short-form citation is used most often in these notes. For the full citation, turn to the Bibliography.

PREFACE

1 Jonathan Raban, *The Oxford Book of the Sea* (Oxford and New York: Oxford University Press, 1992), 33.

INTRODUCTION

1 "U-Boot-Krieg: Wahn der Wunderwaffe," *Der Spiegel*, Nr 11/85 (11 März 1985), 114–17.
2 Claus Happel, "... wir fahren gegen Engeland," *NDR-Magazin*, Nr 4/87.
3 Alfred von Tirpitz, *Erinnerungen*, 22.
4 Hadley and Sarty, *Tin-Pots and Pirate Ships*, 30.
5 Barry M. Gough, "The Influence of History on Mahan," in Hattendorf, ed., *The Influence of History*, 7–23.
6 For a brief account, see Herwig, "The Influence of A.T. Mahan upon German Sea Power," in Hattendorf, ed., *The Influence of History*, 67–80.
7 For example, *Salzburger Chronik*, 30 March 1889, Jg. XXV, No. 73.
8 See, for example, Bundes- und Militärarchiv (BA-MA): Allerhöchste Kabinetts-Ordres, I Vierteljahr 1915, RM3/2703; RM3/2705, 45–6; A-K-O, II Vierteljahr 1915, RM3/2704, 4 Juni 1915, 64; A-K-O, III Vierteljahr 1915, RM3/2705; A-K-O, IV Vierteljahr 1915, RM3/2706, 8 Dez 1915, 63; A-K-O, IV Vierteljahr 1916, RM3/2710, 23 Nov 1916, 71.

9 See "Entsendung von Kriegsschiffen nach der Ost- und Westküste von Amerika," Bd I, Feb 1872–Juni 1880, BA-MA: RM1/2398; Bd II, Juli 1880–April 1888, BA-MA: RM1/2399. "Entsendung von Kriegsschiffen ... Streitfall mit Nikaragua 26 Sept 1877–16 Feb 1879," BA-MA: RM1/2890. Also "Krieg zwischen Peru, Bolivia und Chile," RM1/2891; RM3/11608, RM1/2401. Also Assmann, *Kämpfe*, and Messimer, "German Gunboats on the Yangtse."

10 Assmann, *Der Krieg*, 17.

11 Wislicenus, *Deutschlands Seemacht*, 1909.

12 For the following, see Militärgeschichtliches Forschungsamt, *Deutsche Militärgeschichte*, 5, Abschnitt VIII, 167.

13 Herwig and Trask, "Naval Operations Plans," 40: the Tirpitz "bandwagon provid[ed] a scaffold of cultural, economic political, military and vulgar Darwinistic timber for the new structure."

14 Meyer, "Propaganda," 26. Cited also in Herwig and Trask, "Naval Operations Plans," 64n13. See also "The Press, Pressure Groups and Public Opinion," in Kennedy, *Antagonism 1860–1914*, 87–102, and "Material für Zeitungen und Zeitschriften," 1900–14, BA-MA: RM3/9707–9709.

15 Militärgeschichtliches Forschungsamt, *Deutsche Militärgeschichte*, 6, Abschnitt VIII, 189–93.

16 BA-MA: RM3/10236, 179, contains the blurb of the special publication *Die Flotten-Manöver 1901* (Berlin: E.S. Mittler Verlag 1901): "Die Oeffentlichkeit immer mehr für die Einrichtungen und Bedürfnissen der Kriegsmarine zu interessieren und mit denselben vertraut zu machen."

17 "Abonnements auf Flotten-Manöverberichte," BA-MA: RM3/10236, 93.

18 Thus, for example, a personal letter of 22 July 1899 from state secretary for the navy, Admiral Wilhelm Büchsel, Persönliches an Chef der Herbstübungsflotte: "Seine Majestät haben zu befehlen geruht, daß auch in diesem Jahre die Tagespresse mit Berichten über die Tätigkeit der Herbstübungsflotte zu versehen ist." RM3/10236, "Herbstübungen der Manöverflotte August 1898 bis November 1902," 19. Page 35 of this file, entitled "Denkschrift zum Immediatvortrag, betreffend Berichterstattung für die Presse über die Herbstmanöver," notes this has been going on for the past two years.

19 As reported and commented on in *The Times* of London, 20 Nov. 1901, in BA-MA: RM3/9687, 115–16. See also RM3/9703, "Deutschfeindliche Presseäußerungen" (Bd I), Oct 1901–März 1909; (Bd II) April 1909–Juni 1915.

20 This sentence concludes the brochure [Anon.] *Presse-Stimmen der Flotten-Parade bei Kiel*, 1911. BA-MA: RM3/10237, "Herbstübungen der Manöverflotte, Dezember 1902 bis Juli 1912," 287.

21 *Die Post*, 30 June 12, and *Neue Preußische Kreuz-Zeitung*, 29 July 12, BA-MA: RM3/v. 9697.

22 BA-MA: RM3/v. 9697.

23 Hauff, *Die unterseeische Schiffahrt*, 1859.

24 Cited ibid., Vorwort.

25 Weir, *Kaiser's Navy*, 23.

26 Anon., "Die neuesten Unterseeboote," in *Stadt Gottes*, 1903.

27 *Die Flotte*, 8 Jg, Nr 2, Feb 1905, BA-MA: RM3/9708, "Material für Zeitungen und Zeitschriften," Bd 7, Jan 04–Feb 06," 23.

28 d'Équevilley, *Untersee- und Tauchboote*, 187.

29 Vorwort, *Nauticus: Jahrbuch für Deutschlands Seeinteressen*, Hrsgg. von Nauticus (Berlin 1908). For the article in question see Anon., "Der heutige Stand des Unterseebootwesens."

30 Herzog, *Die deutschen Uboote 1906 bis 1945*, 11n1.

31 Doyle, *Danger and Other Stories*, v.

32 According to Spindler, *Handelskrieg* (I, 157), Doyle's story had no impact in Germany at all. It appeared in German as *England in Gefahr*. See bibliography.

33 Doyle, *Danger*, 45.

CHAPTER 1: U-boats in the Imperial Navy

1 Otto, *Das Unterseeboot im Kampfe*, 111.

2 Von Forstner, *U-Boots-Kommandant*, 15.

3 Ibid., 221.

4 Clark, "Der Erste Weltkrieg: Die Operationen zu Beginn des Krieges," von K.J. Müller übersetzt und bearbeitet, in Potter et al., *Seemacht*, 350. It remains a disputed question whether this move made any substantial difference, for his staff was already beginning to consider changing concepts of naval warfare.

5 Spieß, *U-Boot-Abenteuer*, 25. The word *Waffe* means both weapon and arm. Thus U-waffe is the U-Boat Arm of the navy. An otherwise fine cultural history of these years gives a rather skewed account of the U-boat by describing its deployment not as a strategic necessity, but as an example of Germany's Darwinian zest for innovation and renewal. See Eksteins, *Rites of Spring*, 166–8.

6 Lassen, *Handels-Uboot 'Deutschland,'* Vorwort.

7 See Ferber, *Hundert Jahre Ullstein*; and *Berliner Illustrirte Zeitung*, 1982.

8 See, for example, Gottberg, *U-Bootstaten*, 9.

9 Records reveal two earlier cases, from which there were no survivors. British submarine HMS/M C24 torpedoed U-40 on 23 June 1915, and HMS/M C27 torpedoed and sank U-23 on 20 July 1915. A total of fifteen

u-boats were destroyed by British submarines, and one by the French
Circé. See Michelsen, *Der U-Bootskrieg.*

10 Spieß, *U-Boot-Fahrten,* 46.

11 Spieß, *U-Boot-Abenteuer,* 45.

12 Scheer, *Hochseeflotte,* 73.

13 Carr, *By Guess – and by God,* 90.

14 Spieß, *U-Boot-Abenteuer,* 57.

15 "Denkschrift einer Weiterentwicklung der Marine nach dem Krieg," and
"Erster Etat nach Friedenschluß," Nachlaß Admiral Hollweg, BA-MA:
RM3/11703, 8.

16 Nachlaß Vizeadmiral Hollweg (Hollweg Papers), BA-MA: RM3/11679.
The papers include a clipping from the *Hamburger Fremdenblatt* of 14
November 1926 in which the reporter, K.E. Wiegand, describes "Mein
U-Boot-Interview mit Tirpitz."

17 "N, Seiner Exzellenz dem Herrn Staatssekretär vorzulegen, gemäß tele-
phonischem Befehl," undated, in Tirpitz Nachlaß (Tirpitz Papers),
BA-MA: N253/99.

18 Bethmann Hollweg, *Betrachtungen,* II, 121.

19 Cited in Edmonds, *A Short History,* 145–6.

20 James W. Gerard, to His Excellency Mr von Jagow, imperial secretary of
state, Foreign Affairs, 15 May 1915, "Auswärtiges Amt: Schriftwechsel
mit der Regierung der Vereinigten Staaten," BA-MA: RM8/100.

21 See, for example, the twenty-eight notes exchanged between 4 February
1915 and 10 May 1916, in "Auswärtiges Amt: Schriftwechsel mit der
Regierung der Vereinigten Staaten von Amerika, betreffend den Unter-
seehandelskrieg," BA-MA: RM8/100. Also "Notenwechsel mit Amerika,
10 Juni 1915–3 April 1917," BA-MA: RM5/4044, and "U-Bootkrieg, Februar 1915–1916," BA-MA: RM5/921.

22 "Befehl," 7 Sept 1915, BA-MA: RM3/2705, Allerhöchste Kabinetts-
Ordres, III Vierteljahr 1915, 71–2.

23 Gottberg, *U-Bootstaten,* 9.

24 Ibid., 214–15.

25 Kirchhoff, *Otto Weddigen und seine Waffe.* Kirchoff had first published a
volume on 17th- and 18th-century Baltic history: *Seemacht in der Ostsee*
(Kiel 1907).

26 Descovich und Seeliger, *Das U-Boot.* Descovich held the rank of "Linien-
schiffsleutnant" in Austria's Royal and Imperial Navy, and Seeliger that
of "Hauptmann."

27 Bachmann, to kaiser, Berlin, 4 Sept 1915, BA-MA: RM5/4044. "... daß
unsere opfermutigen U-Bootsbesatzungen von Franctireurs zur See
zugrunde gehen."

28 von Papen, Kaiserlich Deutsche Botschaft, Militär-Attaché, New York, 28
Juli 1915, BA-MA: RM5/4044.

29 *Denver Times*, "Germany's Navy Ready to Thwart Blockades," 31 Jan. 1916. BA-MA: RM5/v 2861. Article by Carl W. Ackerman, UP staff correspondent, with photo of von Holtzendorff captioned "Admiral von Holtzendorff."

30 See Beesly, *Room 40*, 93–4.

31 Cf. Michelsen, *Der U-Bootskrieg*, 187–94.

32 von Holtzendorff, Chef des Admiralstabes der Marine, Grosses Hauptquartier, to Scheer, BA-MA: RM5/902, 159–61.

33 Immediatbericht, 4 Juli 1916, Scheer, "Chronologische Entwicklung des U-Bootkrieges 1916," Nachlaß Konteradmiral v. Levetzow, BA-MA: N239/15, 103.

34 See Spindler, *Der Handelskrieg mit U-Booten*, I, II.

35 For details of this venture see Hadley and Sarty, *Tin-Pots*, and Messimer, *The Merchant U-Boat*.

36 See, for example, König's descriptions of events in Rose, *Auftauchen! Kriegsfahrten von U-53*, 55–6.

37 König, *Die Fahrt der Deutschland*, 99. See also König's more sober, but substantially similar, official report, BA-MA: RM5/2267.

38 For example, Lohmann to Toussaint, Admiralstab der Marine, 28 Juni 1916; Lohmann to Vanselou, Admiralstab der Marine, 8 Juli 1916; Lohmann to Toussaint, 7 Juli 1916; BA-MA: RM5/2267.

39 "Amerikafahrt eines deutschen Handels-U-Bootes," *Berliner Tageblatt*, 1 Juli 1916, Jg 45, Nr 350, 1.

40 Ibid., 13 Juli 1916, Jg 45, Nr 354, 3. *The Times* of London correctly pointed out at the time that Canadian-built H-class submarines had actually made the first Atlantic crossings in 1915, a fact ignored by the German press. See G.N. Tucker, *The Naval Service of Canada* (Ottawa: King's Printer, 1952), I, 235.

41 For example, "Glückliche Heimkehr der U-'Deutschland,'" *Berliner Tageblatt*, 24 Aug 1916, Jg 45, Nr 432, 1; "Vor der Einfahrt der Deutschland," and "Die Ankunft der Deutschland in Bremen," 25 Aug 1916, Jg 45, Nr 435, 1; "Die Begrüßung der U-Deutschland in Bremen," 26 Aug 1916, Jg 45, Nr 436, 4. Also *Berliner Illustrierte Zeitung*, 3 Sept 1916, Jg 25, Nr 36, 526; 10 Sept 1916, Jg 25, Nr 37, 545–6.

42 *Die Flotte*, Monatsblatt des Deutschen Flotten-Vereins, Okt 1916, Jg 19, Nr 10, 168.

43 For example, "Die Zweite Fahrt der Deutschland," *Salzburger Volksblatt*, 12 Dez 1916, Jg 46, Nr 284, 2; *New York Times*, 1 Nov. 1916, 1, and succeeding issues of the newspaper throughout November 1916. See also the *New York Times*, 3 Nov. 1916, 16; also *Army and Navy Journal*, 4 Nov. 1916. The *Daily Mirror* ("No One Allowed to Go Near the U-Liner," 16 Nov. 1916) published a photograph of the "hidden" submarine behind her barricade in New York. BA-MA: RM5/2268.

44 BA-MA: RM5/6360 contains a significant number of clippings, press cables, and summary reports gathered by German authorities through attachés and clipping services.

45 *New York Times*, 9 Oct. 1916, 2.

46 Wilhelm II to Kapitänleutnant Rose, Kommandant Meines Unterseeboots U-53," 2 Nov 1916, BA-MA: RM5/6360.

47 For example, *Berliner Tageblatt*, 10 Okt 1916, Jg 45, Nr 519, 1. The morning and evening editions for the period 9–11 October are particularly detailed.

48 Stöwer, *Kaiser Wilhelm und die Marine.*

49 See, for example, cover advertising in Heino von Heimburg, *U-Boot gegen U-Boot.*

50 Ajax, *The German Pirate*, vi. Though published in 1917, the book dealt with none of the events off the American coast.

51 See BA-MA: RM5/922. Scheer forwarded a copy to the kaiser.

52 "Die allgemeine Kriegslage in ihrer jetzigen Entscheidungsphase," 30 April 1917, BA-MA: RM5/922. For Germany's reasons for regarding it as a criminal act, see Vincent, *Politics of Hunger.*

53 For example, "Der Staatssekretär des Innern über den U-Boot-Krieg," *Berliner Lokal-Anzeiger*, 29 April 1917, Nr 216, BA-MA: RM5/922.

54 Admiralsstab der Marine. *Die Wirkungen des U-Bootkrieges*, 25. Also, Küster, *Das U-Boot.*

55 Corbett, *Naval Operations*, V, 424; Great Britain, Air Ministry, Air Historical Branch, *The RAF in Maritime War*, vol. I: *The Atlantic and Home Waters, The Prelude, April 1918 to September 1939*, app. 1.

56 Hollweg, *Unser Recht auf den U-Bootskrieg*, 14.

57 Ibid., 235.

58 Schulze's *Die Schwarze Waffe* includes a pocket history of torpedoes and mines, torpedo-boats and submarines.

59 Admiralsstab der Marine, *Wirkungen des U-Bootkrieges in amtlicher Darstellung* (abgeschlossen im August 1917) (Berlin 1917), 24–5.

60 Schloß, "Die Bilanz des schärfsten Unterseebootkrieges nach fünf Monaten," *Die Flagge. Zeitschrift für Seewesen und Seeverkehr. Organ des Österreichischen Flottenvereins*, Aug 1917, Jg 12, Nr 8, 169–71. He had been following U-boat warfare from the beginning. He confirmed the forecast in "Die Bilanz von sechs Monaten schärfsten U-Bootkrieges," *Die Flagge*, Okt 1917, Nr 10, 230–2. This was confirmed once more in April 1918 by Emo Descovich, co-author of *Das U-Boot*, 1915: "Ein Jahr Unterseebootkrieg," *Die Flagge*, April 1918, Heft 4, Jg 13, 72–80.

61 von Holtzendorff to Auswärtiges Amt, 26 Jan 1918, "U.K.-Verband," BA-MA: RM5/3902, 144.

62 See "Anlage zum Kriegstagebuch SMU-Kreuzer U-155" in "Acta betreffend Technische Erfahrungen der U-Kreuzer, Mai 1918–Okt 1918," BA-MA: RM5/2163.

63 "Ärtzlicher Bericht zum KTB/U-156, v. 12.11.17–11.3.18," BA-MA: RM5/ 2163; also report of Dr Mennerich, Mar. Oberassistenzarzt und Schiff- sarzt, U-155, BA-MA: KTB/U-155.

64 Gilson, *Submarine U-93*, 136. Other quotations at 3, 15.

65 Ibid., 95, 138.

66 Ibid., 250.

67 Kapitän z. See Horn, "Gesichtspunkte für die bisherige U-Bootskrieg- führung," 6 Aug 1918, BA-MA: RM5/6440, 180–5.

68 "Unsere U-Boote vor Amerika tätig." *Berliner Lokal-Anzeiger*, 6 Juni 1918, No. 285, Jg 36, 1.

69 "U-Boats Off America," *New York Times*, BA-MA: RM5/6430.

70 Meeting with Reichskanzler, Sunday, 23 June 1918, 11 am, regarding the introduction of blockade zones off the United States. BA-MA: RM5/ 6440, 121, 125.

71 Horn, *German Naval Mutinies*, 183. Horn's study is definitive. See also his *War, Mutiny and Revolution in the German Navy.*

72 Horn, *German Naval Mutinies*, 235.

73 Plievier, *Des Kaisers Kulis.*

74 Weir, *Kaiser's Navy*, 186. Weir cites the official document: Ludendorff, General Headquarters, to RMA [Reichs-Marine-Amt] et al., Berlin, 10 Februar 1918, in BA-MA: RM3/11227.

75 "Denkschrift über Weiterentwicklung der Marine nach dem Krieg" und "Erster Etat nach dem Friedensschluß" (36-page document), Nachlass Vizeadmiral Hollweg, BA-MA: RM3/11703.

CHAPTER 2: The Legacy of Versailles, 1919–39

1 Bethmann Hollweg, *Betrachtungen*, I, Vorwort.

2 *Die Flagge*. Zeitschrift für Seewesen und Seeverkehr. Organ des Öster- reichischen Flottenvereins, "Das Ende unserer Kriegsflotte," Jan–Feb 1919, Heft 1/2, Jg 14, 1–3. In the same edition, "Das Ende der kaiser- lich deutschen Kriegflotte," 4–6; and the same title again, März–April 1919, Heft 3–4, Jg 14, 12–15.

3 For example, Dönitz, in Langsdorff, ed., *U-Boote am Feind*, 93.

4 Gayer, *Die deutschen U-Boote in ihrer Kriegführung 1914–18*, Bd 1.

5 Michelsen, *Der U-Bootskrieg 1914–1918*, vii.

6 Raeder, *Das Kreuzergeschwader.*

7 Spindler, *Handelskrieg.*

8 Kirchhoff, *Seekriegsgeschichte.*

9 For instance, Friedrich von Kühlwetter, *Skagerrak*; Sethe. *Die ausge- bliebene Seeschlacht*; Gebeschus, *Doggerbank*. These writers explicitly encouraged German youth to emulate the patriotism and courage of naval leaders.

10 "Der alten deutschen Flotte zum Gedächtnis," in Scheer, *Die deutsche Flotte in grosser Zeit*, 169–72.

11 Spieß, *U-Boot-Fahrten*, 25.

12 Ibid., 56.

13 Ibid., 169.

14 Lothar von Arnauld de la Perière, in Langsdorff, *U-Boote am Feind*, 77.

15 Scheer, *Deutschlands Flotte*, 368.

16 Ruf, in Langsdorff, *U-Boote am Feind*, 346.

17 In *Der Film*, Nr 24 (26 Juli 1926), 35.

18 See Saunders, "Politics, the Cinema, and Early Revisitations of War in Weimar Germany," and "Weimar, Hollywood and the Americanization of German Culture, 1917–1933."

19 In *Der Film*, Nr 25 (2 Aug 1926), 33. The movie *U-Boot in Gefahr* was discussed in *Der Film*, Nr 27 (16 Aug 1926), 12. The film *Unsere Emden* [Our Cruiser Emden] had already premiered in 1926.

20 Saunders, "Politics," 31.

21 *Illustrierter Film-Kurier*, Archiv der Stiftung Deutsche Kinemathek, Berlin. I am grateful to Professor Tom Saunders for bringing this material to my attention.

22 Saunders, "Politics," 38. His source is the Nazi party newspaper *Völkischer Beobachter*, 17 Sept 1927.

23 *Der Film*, Nr 9 (15 Mai 1927), 16–17.

24 Rose, "Die Kriegsfahrt des U-53 nach Amerika: Zur 10-jährigen Wiederkehr des Ausfahrttages." Scrapbook in Michael L. Hadley collection.

25 Wegener, *Die Seestrategie*, 28. He was in fact thinking of Flensburg, and not of the Möltenort memorial, which was dedicated on 30 May 1936 and reopened by Hitler in 1938.

26 This fatal lack of grasp of naval warfare would be picked up in 1976 when Mirow (*Der Seekrieg in Umrissen*, 155) addressed the question.

27 Wegener, *Die Seestrategie*, 38.

28 See, for example, Jackson, *Romance of the Submarine*, 244.

29 Ibid., 101, 210, 234.

30 Carr, *By Guess – and by God*, x.

31 Köppen, *Die Überwasserstreitkräfte und ihre Technik*.

32 Thomas, *Raiders of the Deep*, 4.

33 Thomas, *Ritter der Tiefe*, übers. von Spiegel, 44.

34 Thomas, *Raiders of the Deep*, 3–4.

35 Ibid., 243–4.

36 See, for example, Hashagen, *U-Boote Westwärts!* and Schultz, *Im U-Boot durch die Weltmeere*.

37 Lützeler, *Die Schriftsteller und Europa*. See especially in this regard the sections "Die Nachkriegsjahre (1919–1923)," "Vor und nach der Weltwirt-

schaftskrise (1924–1932)," and "Die Zeit der Hitler-Diktatur (1939–1945)," 272–401.

38 Eksteins, *Rites of Spring*, 275–7.

39 Valentiner, *Der Schrecken der Meere*, 328.

40 Bauer, *Das Unterseeboot.*

41 Hashagen, *U-Boote Westwärts!*

42 Ibid., 8.

43 Kapitän zur See, Dr. h.c. Groos, review republished in Bauer, *Das Unterseeboot*, jacket blurb.

44 Spiegel, *Vom Seekadetten zum U-Boot-Kommandanten.*

45 Busch, *U-Bootsfahrten*, Vorwort.

46 Busch, *U-Bootfahrten*, viii: "Wiking Du kühner, wo ist Dein Grab, / Wo sank Dein grüner Lorbeer hinab?"

47 Wiebicke, *Die Männer von U 96*, 5.

48 Busch, *U-Boots-Taten*, Vorwort.

49 Preface to the 1935 edition, translated by Commander D. Hastie Smith, reprinted in subsequent editions. Quoted in Niemöller, *From U-Boat to Concentration Camp* (1939).

50 For details see J.S. Conway, *The Nazi Persecution of the Churches, 1933–45* (London: Weidenfeld and Nicolson, 1968); Ernst Christian Helmreich, *The German Churches under Hitler* (Detroit: Wayne State University Press, 1979); and Peter Matheson, *The Third Reich and the Christian Churches* (Edinburgh: T. & T. Clark, 1981). For eye-witness coverage see William L. Shirer, *The Nightmare Years 1930–1940* (Boston and Toronto: Little, Brown, 1984), 149–57.

51 See, for example, Dietmar Schmidt, *Pastor Niemöller* (1959), trans. Lawrence Wilson (Garden City, NY: Doubleday, 1959); Jürgen Schmidt, *Martin Niemöller im Kirchenkampf* (Hamburg: Leibniz-Verlag, 1971); and James Bentley, *Martin Niemöller* (London: Oxford University Press, 1986).

52 Grosse, *Bedeutung des Unterseebotskrieges 1914/18.*

53 König, *Fahrten der U-Deutschland im Weltkrieg.*

54 Langsdorff, *U-Boote am Feind*, 40.

55 Ibid., 185.

56 Ibid., 96.

57 Ibid., 350.

58 Helmut Lorenz concludes the volume with "Der letzte Salut"; ibid., 355. He concedes that the front-line soldier ashore has also done his duty, but that in naval matters it is the submariner who has prevailed.

59 Cited in Arnold Fischdick, *U 90*, 11.

60 Dinklage, *U-Boot-Fahrer und Kamelsreiter.*

61 Spindler, *Der Handelskrieg mit Ubooten*, Bd 3, 350.

62 In this case, Eckart, *Marineblau und Khaki*; and Jung, *Die letzten Korsaren.*

63 Marschall, *Torpedo Achtung! Los!*

64 Jung, *Krieg unter Wasser*, 218.

65 Ibid., 215.

66 Ibid., 215–16.

67 Ibid., 218.

CHAPTER 3: Dönitz's Men

1 Busch, *U-Boote gegen England*, 16.

2 Ibid., 63.

3 Frank, *The Sea Wolves* [original *Die Wölfe und der Admiral*], 32.

4 Winston S. Churchill, *The Gathering Storm* (Toronto: Thomas Allen, 1948), 491.

5 Frank, *The Sea Wolves*, 37.

6 Amelung von Varendorff, quoted in Prien, *Mein Weg nach Scapa Flow*, 176. Endraß, who would become a famous ace, was also aboard.

7 Prien, *Mein Weg nach Scapa Flow*, 182–3. (My translation. Cf. translation by Comte de la Vatine, 191–2.)

8 Ibid., 188.

9 Prien, *I Sank the Royal Oak*. Count La Vatine, translator, 9.

10 Werner Knoth, "Das U-Boot Gesicht," in *Elegante Welt*, 1940 (sole data, copies in U-Boat Archives, Cuxhaven). The article contains slight description but many pen drawings of submariners of various ranks, some of them famous ones like Dönitz and Endraß.

11 Schröder, *"UX" stand im Mittelmeer*, 6.

12 Rose, *Auftauchen!* 305.

13 Salewski, *Von der Wirklichkeit des Krieges*, 168–9.

14 Schepke, *U-Bootfahrer von heute*, 22.

15 "Programm anläßlich des Besuches der erfolgreichsten U-Bootsmannschaft unter Führung von Kapitänleutnant Schepke in München Hauptstadt der Bewegung," 29–31 Jan 1941. Copy held in U-Boat-Archives, Cuxhaven.

16 Groos, *Was jeder vom Seekrieg wissen muß*.

17 Ibid., 5.

18 Reinhard, *Wir an den Maschinen*, 257.

19 Dönitz. *Die U-Bootswaffe*.

20 Ibid., 65.

21 See, for example, Ambrosius, *Die Schlacht im Atlantik*.

22 Prien's loss is the subject of frequent reinvestigation. Analysis on the basis of fresh evidence suggested as late as 1992 that HMS *Wolverine* had actually sunk a different U-boat, and that Prien had been destroyed by a maverick torpedo from another German submarine.

23 Werner, *Die Eisernen Särge*, 46.

24 Collection of the U-Boat Archives, Cuxhaven.

25 Frank, *Das Stier von Scapa Flow.*

26 Frank, *Prien greift an,* 260.

27 Copy of film in U-Boat Archives, Cuxhaven, and in Deutsches Filmmuseum, Frankfurt a. M.

28 Thies, *Der Eiserne Seehund.* See also Heinz Straub, *Der Eiserne Seehund.* Straub seems not to have known of Thies.

29 Kaden, *Auf Ubootjagd gegen England,* 13.

30 Herzog, "Admiral Hermann Bauer," *Deutsches Soldatenjahrbuch 1983* (München 1982), 11.

31 Busch, *U-Boot auf Feindfahrt,* 94.

32 Hartmann, *Feind im Fadenkreuz: U-Boot auf Jagd im Atlantik.*

33 Reich, *Dem Tommy entwischt: Der Geist unserer U-Boot-Waffe.*

34 Frank, *The Sea Wolves,* 148.

35 *Meldungen aus dem Reich* [Reichssicherheitsamt, Amt III, SD Hauptamt]. These publications are held in the Bundes- und Militärchiv, Freiburg, Germany.

36 *Meldungen aus dem Reich,* 26 Jan 1942, Nr 254, 1.

37 Ibid., 29 Jan 1942, Nr 255.

38 *Völkischer Beobachter: Kampfblatt der nationalsozialistischen Bewegung Großdeutschlands,* 4 Nov 1942, 1.

39 See, for example, the editions of 6, 10, and 18 Dez 1942.

40 Ibid., 28 Dez 1942, 3.

41 See, for example, the editions of 30 and 31 Dez 1942.

42 For the reception of Operation Drumbeat ("Paukenschlag"), see *Meldungen aus dem Reich,* Band 12, Nr 257, 6; Nr 258, 1; Nr 259, 2, BA-MA.

43 Kreimeier, *Die Ufa-Story,* 349.

44 Glodschey, *Stürme im Mittelmeer, Auf allen Ozeanen.*

45 *Stürme im Mittelmeer,* 177. For detailed accounts, see my *U-Boats against Canada.*

46 Cited in Brennecke, *Unser Boot und wir im Mittelmeer.*

47 Schröder, *"UX" stand im Mittelmeer,* 6.

48 Buchheim, *Jäger im Weltmeer,* 14, 19.

49 Buchheim file, U-Boat Archives, Cuxhaven.

50 Buchheim, "U-Boot im Sturm," *Völkischer Beobachter,* 9/10 April 1944, 1; through 14 April 1944, 3.

51 Kptlt Mannesmann, "Fliegerbomben trafen das U-Boot," *Völkischer Beobachter,* 14 April 1944, 2.

52 For example, *Völkischer Beobachter,* 3 Okt 1944, 1.

53 Ibid., 14 Okt 1944, 1.

54 Kriegstagebuch/Seekriegsleitung (KTB/Skl), Teil A, 220, 10 April 1944.

55 Günther Rühle, ed., *Bernhard Minetti: Erinnerungen eines Schauspielers* (Stuttgart: Deutsche Verlags-Anstalt 1985), 127–9.

56 See my *U-Boats against Canada,* 134–5.

57 "André Müller spricht mit dem Schauspieler Bernhard Minetti," *Die Zeit*, Nr 27, 9 Juli 1993, 13–14.

58 Werner, *Die Eisernen Särge*, 283.

59 13 Okt 1944, 3.

60 *Völkischer Beobachter*, 17 Okt 1944, 1. See also the editions of 1, 2, 15 Nov 1944.

61 Ibid., 15 Nov 1944, 1.

62 Ibid., 27 Dez 1944, 1.

63 For a popular account, see Frank, *The Sea Wolves*, 213–15.

64 For the official judgment, see International Military Tribunal, *Trial of the Major War Criminals* (Nuremberg 1947).

65 Frank, *The Sea Wolves*, 220.

CHAPTER 4: Redemption of a Myth, 1945–76

1 Padfield, *Dönitz: The Last Führer.*

2 Dönitz, *Zehn Jahre und Zwanzig Tage.*

3 Ibid., 10. I have translated this passage, since the published English translation differs in important points. See Doenitz, *Ten Years and Twenty Days*, translated by R.H. Stevens, London: Weidenfeld and Nicolson, 5.

4 Dönitz, *Ten Years and Twenty Days*, 478.

5 Dönitz, *Zehn Jahre und Zwangige Tage*, 470: "Niemand sollte das Soldatentum des letzten Krieges herabsetzen; man verletzt sonst die Ehrfurcht vor denjenigen, die in Erfüllung ihrer Pflicht gefallen sind."

6 *Marine Rundschau*, 50 Jg, Heft 2/53, 65.

7 For details, see my *U-Boats against Canada*, 175–84.

8 Busch, *So war der U-Boot-Krieg*, 20.

9 Busch, *U-Boats at War*, translated by L.P.R. Wilson, 132.

10 Prien, *I Sank the Royal Oak* [*Mein Weg nach Scapa Flow*], preface.

11 E.G., "Grosse [sic] Atlantik, von Nickolas [sic] Monsarrat (Hamburg: Claasen Verlag nd), reviewed in *Marine Rundschau* Jg 50, Jan 1953, 33.

12 Monsarrat, *The Cruel Sea*, 235.

13 Metzler, *Die lachende Kuh*, 214.

14 *Marine Rundschau*, Jg 50, Jan 1953, E.S. Mittler & Sohn, Darmstadt. The quoted statement opens this first edition designated "50. Jahrgang." The incomplete 49th had appeared in 1944.

15 K. Assmann, "Der deutsche U-Bootskrieg und die Nürnberger Rechtsprechung," ibid., Jg 50, Jan 1953, 2–8.

16 *Illustrierte Woche – Badische Illustrierte*, Nr 5, Jg 8, 31 Jan 1953.

17 Ott, *Haie und Kleine Fische*, 360.

18 Ibid., 394.

19 Copy of film in U-Boat Archives, Cuxhaven. See also the contemporary movie magazine *Illustrierte Film-Bühne*, Nr 4481 [1941], also held in the Cuxhaven Archives.

20 But as late as 1942 the liberal newspaper *Die Frankfurter Zeitung* ran a "resistance" story that grappled with questions of moral responsibility. See my "Resistance in Exile: Publication, Context and Reception of Stefan Andres' *Wir sind Utopia* (1942)," *Seminar: A Journal of Germanic Studies*, 19, 3 (1983): 157–76.

21 Guddat, *Für jeden kommt der Tag*, 120.

22 Ibid., 222.

23 Frank, *Prien greift an*, 1941.

24 For the full text, which Bodo Herzog must have known, see Hans Carossa, *Gesammelte Gedichte* (Wiesbaden: Insel Verlag, 1950).

25 *Klassiker in finsteren Zeiten*, Catalogue of the Schiller-Museum, Marbach, II, 142.

26 For Carossa's acceptance speech, see *Klassiker in finsteren Zeiten*, II, 150.

27 Herzog, *60 Jahre Deutsche Uboote 1906–1966*. See also his earlier *Kapitänleutnant Otto Steinbrinck*; and *U-35*.

28 Herzog, *60 Jahre*, 10. It was reprinted in 1990 without any changes, although his bibliography was badly in need of updating.

29 Brennecke, *Haie im Paradies*, 7.

30 Rohwer, *U-Boote: Eine Chronik in Bildern*.

31 *Schaltung Küste*, 1966 (Heft 21), 209.

32 The major exception is technical books. See, for example, Lawrenz, *Die Entstehungsgeschichte der U-Boote*.

33 Werner, *Die Eisernen Särge*, 101.

34 Ibid., 46.

35 Ibid., 338: "Er war beträchtlich gealtert ... Er war mager geworden, schmaler und weniger dynamisch."

36 Ibid., 338.

37 Rohwer, "Herbert A. Werner: 'Iron Coffins,'" *Schaltung Küste*, 1970 (Heft 38), 502–5.

38 Herbert A. Werner to Horst Selle, 8 Sept 1974, in U-Boat Archives, Cuxhaven. "Ich war somit in der aussergewöhnlichen Lage unseren Gegnern von damals die Wahrheit über unsern epischen Kampf und von unseren toten und lebenden Kameraden zu berichten. Ich weiss, daß ich mehr für das Ansehen unserer Waffe und ihrer Männer getan habe als all die anderen Schreiberlinge zusammen."

39 See the inscribed edition of Robertson's book in the U-Boat Archives, Cuxhaven.

40 Dieter Beko, "Ein Toter bittet um gerechtigkeit," *Illustrierte Woche – Badische Illustrierte*, 22 und 29 Dez 1951.

41 Popularly in Kennedy, "War Crimes," *Telegraph Magazine*, 1 June 1991.

42 For example, Baldur Kaulisch, *U-Boot-Krieg: 1914–1918*.

43 See, for example, draft of an address by Horst Bredow, director of the Stiftung Traditionsarchiv Unterseeboote, to retired admirals of the biennial meeting arranged by the senior admiral of the Federal German

Navy, 1985. Traditionsarchiv Unterseeboote, insert in Herbert's book, *Der Tod auf allen Meeren.*

CHAPTER 5: Revising the Past

1 Krug, "Der Film 'Das Boot,'" 17.
2 Mitscherlich, *Die Unfähigkeit zu trauern.* For veterans' reactions to Buchheim's person and work, see the collection (Buchheim-Ordner) in the U-Boat Archives, Cuxhaven.
3 Salewski, *Von der Wirklichkeit des Krieges.*
4 Ibid., 167.
5 Grümmer, *Irrfahrt: Ein Tatsachenroman,* 11–12.
6 Buchheim, *Der Film "Das Boot,"* 39, 69, 70, 157, 162, passim.
7 For the following, see Krapp's foreword to Buchheim, *U-96: Szenen aus dem Seekrieg. Ein Film.*
8 For this and the following quotation see Krapp, in Buchheim, *U 96,* 17.
9 *Cinema Programm – Special: Das Boot,* 3. Kino Verlag, Hamburg, nd.
10 Bittorf, "'Das Boot': Als Wahnsinn imponierend," *Der Spiegel,* Jg 34, Nr 53, 29 Dez 1980, 78–87.
11 Buchheim, "Die Wahrheit blieb auf Tauchstation," 137.
12 Krug, "Der Film 'Das Boot,'" 14.
13 *Cinema. Das Kinoprogramm Oktober 1981,* Nr 10, Okt 1981 (Heft 41), 10–14.
14 *Bravo,* 1981, 39. Photocopies in Ordner-Buchheim, U-Boat Archives, Cuxhaven.
15 For a collection of published and unpublished responses to the novel and film see Ordner-Buchheim, ibid.
16 Georg Perry, "The Tin-Can Epic," *The Times,* 14 Oct. 1981. For other responses, see Buchheim-Ordner, U-Boat Archives, Cuxhaven.
17 Buchheim, "Die Wahrheit blieb auf Tauchstation," 130–46.
18 *Die Feindfahrt von U 96: ein Bericht von Wilhelm Bittorf.* Kamera Franz Brandeis and Ernst Schmid; Ton Dieter Schulze and Horst-Peter Brandt. ARD Television.
19 Buchheim, *Der Film "Das Boot,"* 67.
20 Krug, "Der Film 'Das Boot,' 13, 17.
21 Herlin, *Verdammter Atlantik* (1988), jacket blurb.
22 "Geopferte Wölfe – Der uneingeschränkt irrsinnige U-Boot-Krieg," *Die Zeit,* Nr 9, 5 März 1982.
23 *Berliner Morgenpost,* 25 Nov 1983.
24 As the author expresses it: "von Goethe stammen die Verse: 'Alles geben die Götter, die unendlichen, / Ihren Lieblingen ganz, / Alle Freuden, die unendlichen, / Alle Schmerzen, die unendlichen, ganz. /'" He then adds his final comment, "that I can subscribe to": "Das darf ich unterschreiben" (171). Goethe to Gräfin Auguste zu Stolberg, 17 Juli 1777. *Hamburger Ausgube,* I, 142.

25 Busch, *So War der U-Boot-Krieg*, 416ff.

26 Brennecke, *Die Wende im U-Boot-Krieg*, quotes R. Güth, "Unveröffentlichtes Manuskript zum Thema Dönitz und der Opfergang der U-Boot-Waffe," dated Bad Pyrmont, 1982.

27 Brustat-Naval, F. *Ali Cremer: U 333*, 269–70.

28 *Das Boot: ein Fernsehfilm in 3 Teilen*, ARD television.

29 Karl-Walter Reinhardt, "'Das Boot': Jede Fahrt war ein Abschied vom Leben." *Funk Uhr – Das Fernsehmagazin*, März 1985, 20–2.

30 Fritz J. Raddatz, "Das Boot ist leer – Untergang in Zeitlupe: Plädoyer für ein realistisches Lehrstück," *Die Zeit*, 8 März 1985.

31 "U-Boot-Krieg: Wahn der Wunderwaffe," *Der Spiegel*, Nr 11/1985, 114–17.

32 Ibid., 114.

33 Herbert Kremp, "Das Boot," *Die Welt*, 2/3 März 1985.

34 "Das Meer ist das Fruchtwasser," *Der Spiegel*, Nr 11/1985, 115.

35 *Hör Zu*, Nr 8, 15 Feb 1985, 38–9.

36 "Ex-U-Boot-Kommandant: Fernsehfassung von 'Das Boot' besser als der Kinofilm," *Die Welt*, 1 März 1985.

37 "Für die Überlebenden ist 'Das Boot' mehr als ein Film," *Die Welt*, 1 März 1985.

38 Kurt Baberg, "U-Boat Kommandant 1941–1945," *Die Welt*, 11 März 1985.

39 *Zum Tode Gesiegt: Vom Untergang der U-Boote – Ein Film von Lothar-Günther Buchheim*. Copy with text in U-Boat Archives, Cuxhaven.

40 Kurt Baberg, "Wie es Wirklich War: Die Obsession des L.-G. Buchheim, oder sein gestörtes Verhältnis zur U-Boot-Waffe," *Das Ostpreussenblatt*, 16 März 1985, Folge 11, S. 24.

41 Bittorf, "Der lange Atem dieser Irrsinns-Odyssee," *Der Spiegel*, Nr 8/1985, 191–3.

42 Kurt Diggins, Präsident, Verein Deutscher U-Boot-Fahrer, An Die Vorsitzenden der U-Boot-Kameradschaften, 12 März 1985. Folio Buchheim, U-Boat Archives, Cuxhaven.

43 Merten und Baberg, *Wir U-Boot-Fahrer sagen: Nein!*

44 Kapitän z.S. Kurt Diggins to Kurt Baberg, 21 März 1985, in Baberg file, U-Boat Archives, Cuxhaven. See also the full Buchheim files for further correspondence on these issues.

45 Kapitän z.S. Kurt Baberg, a.D., to Kapitän z.S. Kurt Diggins, 31 März 1985, Baberg file.

46 G.S., "Die U-Boot-Fahrer," in *Marine Forum* 1/86, 40.

47 Bittorf, "Ersäuft wie junge Katzen im Sack," *Der Spiegel*, 47/1985, 246–63.

48 For example, "66 Tage unter Wasser – 'Ich floh im letzten deutschen U-Boot,'" *Bildzeitung*, 6 Mai 1983. Also "Taucher ertrinkt in Grundschleppnetz: Unfall an einem alten U-Boot," *Frankfurter Allgemeine Zeitung*, 22 Juni 1988; "Wer saß im U-Boot 534?" *Kieler Nachrichten*, 26 Juli 1991.

49 "... gegen Engeland." *ARD Magazin*, 2/87, 17 März 1987.

50 Claus Happel, "... wir fahren gegen Engeland." *NDR Magazin*, Nr 4/87.

51 "In nie gesehenen Bildern ... das Himmelfahrtskommando der U-Boot-fahrer im Atlantik," *Hören und Sehen*, 10 April 1987.

52 Wilfried Mommert, "'... denn wir fahren gegen Engeland,'" *Donau Kurier*, 16 April 1987.

53 Wolfgang Schneider, "Von Jägern und Gejagten," *Donau Kurier*, Ingolstadt, 24 April 1987.

54 "Hochschulpräsident: U-Boot-Film 'Gipfel der Menschenverachtung,'" *Ruhr-Nachrichten*, Nr 95, 24 April 1987. This story was repeated in a number of newspapers.

55 Herbert Schmitt, "'Es ist anzugreifen, auch wenn ...'" *Frankfurter Allgemeine Zeitung*, 24 April 1987.

56 Karl-F. Merten, "Gift und Galle über eine Zeit," *Die Welt*, Nr 95, 24 April 1987.

57 *Süddeutsche Zeitung*, München, 4 Dez 1986. For reactions, see Buchheim-Ordner, U-Boat Archives, Cuxhaven.

CHAPTER 6: Epilogue: Legacies of History and Tradition

1 Two U-boats were destroyed on 13 October 1939: U-40 (Kptlt. W. Barten), which struck a mine in the English Channel, and U-42 (KKpt. Rolf Dau), which was sunk in the North Atlantic west of Ireland by the British destroyers HMS *Imogen* and *Ilex*. It is uncertain which U-boat was Thomas's.

2 Baird, *To Die for Germany*, 165–6.

3 Ibid., 196–9.

4 Johannesson, *Offizier in kritischer Zeit*, 103.

5 Mitscherlich, *Die Unfähigkeit zu trauern*, 89.

6 Cf. Friedrich Schiller, "Über das Erhabene" (1801): "Wir werden begeistert von dem Furchtbaren, weil wir wollen können, was die Triebe verabscheuen, und verwerfen, was sie begehren."

7 Duncan-Jones, in Niemöller, *From U-Boat to Concentration Camp*, 9–10.

8 For this action, see my "HMCS Sackville and the Myth of U-26."

9 Topp, *The Odyssey of a U-Boat Commander*.

10 Hardegen, in Gannon, *Operation Paukenschlag*, 10: "Wir taten unsere Pflicht im Krieg genauso wie unser Gegner. Mögen unsere Enkel davor bewahrt bleiben."

11 Letter to Hermann Wien, 2 Jan. 1987, in the Buchheim collection, U-Boat Archives, Cuxhaven: "... mich hat der Zeitgeist nicht geändert. Aber ich bin aufgeschlossen und kritisch und scheue mich nicht, eine Meinung zu ändern, die sich nicht halten läßt."

12 Topp, *Fackeln*, 282.

13 Ibid., 168.
14 Ibid., 198.
15 Ibid., 198.
16 Erich Topp, "Gegen Glorifizierung wie Verdammung," *Marine Forum,* 11/ 1986, 399–400. Re the Baberg/Buchheim debate.
17 Topp, *Fackeln,* 199.
18 "Fragen an Dieter Wellershoff, Admiral and Generalinspekteur der Bundeswehr," *Information für die Truppe.* Hrsg. Bundesministerium der Verteidigung, Heft 6/90, 25–46.
19 Cited in *Fackel,* 266. See also Dieter Stockfisch, "Vom schwierigen Umgang mit der Tradition," *Marine Forum,* 4/1987, 120–22.
20 Plea for clemency from Josef Kramer to Field Marshal Montgomery, British Army of the Rhine, 27. XI. 1945, in Imperial War Museum, London, Bergen-Belsen display. In a hand-written note he explained his grounds: "Ich bin kein Kriegsverbrecher"; "Ich habe noch keinen Menschen aus eigener Initiative getötet"; "Ich war nur Soldat und habe als solcher die Befehle meiner militärischen Vorgesetzten ausgeführt." He was executed on 12 December 1945. About 60,000 were still in camp Bergen-Belsen when they were liberated by the British; about 45,000 deaths had occurred between 1943 and 1945.
21 Liebig, *Die Deutsche Marine,* Geleitwort. See also Ruge, *In Vier Marinen.*
22 Horten and Wilhelms, "Führung und Einsatz von U-Booten"; Horten was a naval captain, and Wilhelms a commander.
23 Johannesson, *Offizier in kritischer Zeit,* 91.
24 Salewski, "Selbstverständnis und historisches Bewußtsein," 65–122. Also Wegener, "Selbstverständnis und historisches Bewußtsein," 321–40.
25 "Richtlinien für die Traditionspflege bei Umgliederung in die Heeresstruktur 5," Bundesministerium der Verteidigung, Fü H 1 3 – Az 35-08-07, Bonn, 25 Juli 1991. [Draft of proposed Traditionserlaß, copy in U-Boat Archives, Cuxhaven].
26 See Kapitel 4, "Innere Führung und Tradition," Zdv 10/1, in "Richtlinien für die Traditionspflege," note 25 above.
27 Harder and Wiggershaus, *Tradition und Reform.*
28 "Fragen an Dieter Wellershoff, Admiral and Generalinspekteur der Bundeswehr," *Information für die Truppe.* Hrsgg. Bundesministerium der Verteidigung, Heft 6/90, 25–46.
29 "'Hier große Freude …' Der Kronprinz jubelte zu früh: Die Versenkung der 'Lusitania' …" *Die Zeit,* 18 Mai 1990, 10–11.
30 Herzog, "Piraten vor Malága." *Die Zeit,* Dez 1991, 17–18.
31 Zank, "Finis Germaniae!" *Die Zeit,* 6/7 Feb 1992, 17–18.
32 Gerlach, "Vom Seeteufel zum Friedensengel," *Die Zeit,* 17 Jan 1992, 12–13.
33 For example, *Deutscher Anzeiger,* 26 Juni 1981, 4.

34 *National-Zeitung – Deutscher Buchdienst*, München, Nr 49, 27 Nov 1987, 4.

35 Stockfisch, "Vom schwierigen Umgang mit der Tradition."

36 "Wer saß im U-boot 534?" *Kieler Nachrichten*, 26 Juli 1991, in the regular column "Ostsee-Report."

37 *Die Welt*, 27 Mai 1992, 21.

38 *Die Grauen Wölfe*, narrator's text. See bibliography under U-boat Feature Films.

39 For example, Kludas, *Die kaiserlichen Marine auf alten Postkarten.*

40 "Das U-Boot Lied: vom Kaleu bis zum letzten Mann," Gesang und Klavier, Worte Kurt E.Walter, Musik Norgert Schultze. Leipzig: Hans C. Sikorski. "Kretschmer-Marsch – Marsch der Deutschen U-Boot-Fahrer," von Hans Thissen, Aachen: Welt-Ton-Verlag. These pieces of music were also arranged for military band.

41 *U-Boote Westwärts!*, Inhalt: 1), "Warte, mein Mädel, dort in der Heimat," Marschlied, Text von Bruno Balz; 2), "Irgendwo in weiter Ferne," Lied, Text von R.A. Stemmle, Musik von Harald Böhmelt. Berlin: Ufaton Verlag, 1941.

42 Saunders, "Nazism and Social Revolution," in Gordon Martel, ed., *Modern Germany Reconsidered.*

43 Topp, *Fackeln*, 200.

44 Werner Heisenberg, *Physics and Philosophy* (New York: Harper and Row, 1958), 58. His concept had become familiar to a wide readership through popular philosophy, science, and literature.

45 Topp, *Fackeln*, 280.

46 Canadian and Australian submarine acquisition projects in the 1980s validated the role of submarines in part by reference to the German example. A British futurist saw global strategic significance in "The U-boat war in the Atlantic." See, for example, Andrew J. Withers, Introduction to Hessler, *The U-Boat War in the Atlantic 1939–1945*, iii.

Bibliography

A Primary Sources Published in German
B U-boat: German Feature Films and Documentaries
C Selected Secondary Sources

BIBLIOGRAPHICAL NOTE

Complete bibliographical data such as date of publication were frequently omitted in early editions of such ephemera as the Landser military paperback series (Rastatt/Baden: Erich Pabel Verlag). Wherever possible they are listed here by estimate.

The abbreviation BA-MA refers to the Bundes- und Militärarchiv in Freiburg, Germany's Federal and Military Archives.

A. PRIMARY SOURCES PUBLISHED IN GERMAN

Admiralsstab der Marine. *Die Wirkungen des U-Bootkrieges in amtlicher Darstellung* (abgeschlossen im August 1917). Berlin, 1917.
Alman, Karl (pseudonym). See also Kurowski, Franz.
Alman, Karl. *Angriff, ran, versenken: Die U-Boot-Schlacht im Atlantik.* [1965] Mit einem Vorwort von Großadmiral a.D. Karl Dönitz. 2. Aufl. Rastatt/Baden: Erich Pabel Verlag, 1975.
Alman, K. *Albrecht Brandi: Ein Brillantenträger der U-Boot-Waffe.* Landser [Military paperback series] No. 416. Rastatt/Baden: Erich Pabel Verlag, September 1976; Neuaufl., Landser No. 733, November 1988.

Alman, K. *Helmut Witte: Der Kommandant von U-159.* Landser [Military paper-back series] No. 438. 2. Aufl. Rastatt/Baden: Erich Pabel Verlag, Juli 1977.

Alman, Karl. *Heinrich Lehmann-Willenbrock. Der Kommandant von U-96.* Mit Magazin und dokumentarischer Bildbeilage. Landser-Grossband [Military 'big-book' series] No. 474. Rastatt/Baden: Erich Pabel Verlag, Dezember 1978.

Alman, Karl. *Graue Wölfe in blauer See: Der Einsatz der deutschen U-Boote im Mittelmeer.* Rastatt: Erich Pabel, 1967. München: Wilhelm Heyne Verlag, 1980.

Alman, K. *Kapitänleutnant Rolf Mützelburg: Kommandant von U-203.* Landser [Military paperback series] No. 1. Rastatt/Baden: Erich Pabel Verlag, 1971.

Alman, K. *Kapitänleutnant Werner Henke – U-515.* Landser [Military paperback series] No. 2. Rastatt/Baden: Erich Pabel Verlag, 1971.

Alman, K. *Korvettenkapitän Erich Topp: Kommandant der "Roten Teufel."* Landser [Military paperback series] No. 7. Rastatt/Baden: Erich Pabel Verlag, 1971.

Alman, K. *Hans-Günther Lange: Vor der Kola-Bucht bis zur Packeissgrenze – Schiffs-jagd im Eismeer.* Landser [Military paperback series] No. 18. Rastatt/Baden: Erich Pabel Verlag, Juli 1972.

Alman, K. *"Graue Wolfe" – Wilde See: Januar/Februar 1943.* Landser [Military paperback series] No. 326. Rastatt/Baden: Erich Pabel Verlag, April 1973.

Alman, K. *Die letzte Feindfahrt: Mai 1943 – Das U-Boot-Sterben im Atlantik.* Landser [Military paperback series] No. 331. Rastatt/Baden: Erich Pabel Verlag, Juni 1973.

Alman, K. *Johann Mohr: As der U-Boot-Waffe und Kommandant von U-124.* Landser [Military paperback series] No. 377. Rastatt/Baden: Erich Pabel Verlag, März 1975.

Alman, Karl. *Ritter der Sieben Meere: Ritterkreuzträger der U-Boot-Waffe. Chronik eines Opfergangs.* Mit 36 Bildtafeln. Rastatt: Pabel Verlag AG, 1975.

Alman, K. *"Kanonier" Lassen: Die Feindfahrten von U-160.* 2. Aufl. Landser [Military paperback series] No. 408. Rastatt/Baden: Erich Pabel Verlag, Mai 1976.

Alman, K. *Engelbert Endrass: Ein Eichenlaubträger der U-Boot-Waffe.* 2. Aufl. Land-ser [Military paperback series] No. 456. Rastatt/Baden: Erich Pabel Verlag, März 1978.

Alman, K. *Joachim Schepke: Der Kommandant von U-100.* 2. Aufl. Landser [Mili-tary paperback series] No. 510. Rastatt/Baden: Erich Pabel Verlag, April 1980.

Alman, Karl. *U-Boot-Asse: Roman.* Wien: Prisma Verlag, 1980.

Alman, Karl. *Günther Prien: Der "Wolf" und sein Admiral.* Druffel-Verlag, Leoni am Starnberger See, 1981.

Alman, K. *"Graue Wölfe": Januar/Februar 1943 – Der Einsatz deutscher U-Boote während der Winterschlacht im Atlantik.* Neuaufl. Landser [Military paperback series] No. 1193. Rastatt/Baden: Erich Pabel Verlag, Februar 1981.

Alman, K. *Günther Prien: Der legendäre Kommandant von U-47*. 2. Aufl. Landser [Military paperback series] No. 472. Rastatt/Baden: Erich Pabel Verlag, Dezember 1981. Neuaufl. Landser No. 784, Oktober 1990.

Alman, K. *Jagd auf "Graue Wölfe": 1943 – Das U-Boot-Sterben im Atlantik*. Landser [Military paperback series] No. 554. Neuaufl. Rastatt/Baden: Erich Pabel Verlag, Januar 1982.

Alman, K. *Georg Lassen: Der Kommandant des Unterseebootes U-160*. Neuaufl. Landser [Military paperback series] No. 566. Rastatt/Baden: Erich Pabel Verlag, Juni 1982.

Alman, K. *"Graue Wölfe" vor Marokko*. Landser [Military paperback series] No. 427. Neuaufl., No. 1438. Rastatt/Baden: Erich Pabel Verlag, Oktober 1985.

Alman, Karl. *U-Boot-Krieg: Graue Wölfe in blauer See*. Herrsching: Manfred Pawlak Verlagsgesellschaft, 1985.

Alman, Karl. *Wolfgang Lüth: Der erfolgreichste U-Boot-Kommandant des Zweiten Weltkrieges*. Friedberg: Podzun-Pallas-Verlag, 1988.

Ambrosius, Dr. H.H. Korvettenkapitän. *Die Schlacht im Atlantik*, Hamburg: Hanseatische Verlagsanstalt, 1941.

Anon. *Die Deutsche Flotte: Eine Mahnung an das deutsche Volk*, vom Verfasser der Gedichte eines Lebendigen. Zur sechsten Säcularfeier der Stiftung des Hansabundes. Zürich und Winterthur: np, 1841.

Anon. *Die Deutsche Flotte: Ein Traum Preussens und eine Forderung Deutschlands*. Vom Verfasser von "Was uns nicht retten kann." Leipzig, np, 1861.

Anon. "Die neuesten Unterseeboote," in *Stadt Gottes. Illustrirte Zeitschrift für das katholische Volk*. Missionsdruckerei in Steyl, 1903, Jg 26, Heft 1.

Anon. "Der heutige Stand des Unterseebootwesens," *Nauticus: Jahrbuch für Deutschlands Seeinteressen*, Hrsgg. von Nauticus. Berlin, 1908, 192–223.

Anon. *Presse-Stimmen der Flotten-Parade bei Kiel*. Berlin: Boll und Pickardt Verlagsbuchhandlung, 1911.

Anon. *Die Flotte: Monatsblatt des Deutschen Flotten-Vereins*, Jg 19, Nr 10, Oktober 1916.

Anon. *U-Boote im Eismeer*. Berlin: Verlag August Scherl, 1916.

Anon. *Die Flagge*. Zeitschrift für Seewesen und Seeverkehr. Organ des Österreichischen Flottenvereins, "Das Ende unserer Kriegsflotte," Jänner–Februar 1919, Heft 1/2, Jg 14, 1–3. In same edition, "Das Ende der kaiserlich deutschen Kriegflotte," 4–6; and same title again, März–April 1919, Heft 3–4, Jg 14, 12–15.

Anon. *Unter dem Kreuz des Südens: Unterseeboote U-68 und U-99*. Landser [Military paperback series] No. 73. Rastatt/Baden: Erich Pabel Verlag, nd.

Bartsch, Max Korvettenkapitän (Ing.). *Was jeder vom deutschen U-Boot wissen muß*. Berlin: Wilhelm Limpert Verlag, 1940.

Bauer, Admiral [Hermann]. *Das Unterseeboot. Seine Bedeutung als Teil einer Flotte; Seine Stellung im Völkerrecht; Seine Kriegsverwendung; Seine Zukunft*. Berlin: Verlag E.S. Mittler & Sohn, 1931.

Bauer, Hermann, Admiral z.V. *Als Führer der U-Boote im Weltkriege: Der Eintritt der U-Boot-Waffe in die Seekriegführung.* Leipzig: Koehler & Amelang [1942].

Bauer, Peter. *Gesunken im Atlantik 1940/41: Der Kampf deutscher Unterseeboote gegen westalliierte Geleitzüge.* Landser [Military paperback series] No. 1351. Rastatt/Baden: Erich Pabel Verlag, Februar 1984; Neuaufl., Landser No. 1696, nd.

Becker/Busch, [F.-O.] *Stählerne "Haie" 1940/1944: Die Feindfahrten von U-178 und U-57.* Landser [Military paperback series] No. 1085. Rastatt/Baden: Erich Pabel Verlag, Januar 1979.

Bernstorff, Graf von. *Ran an den Feind: vom Kampf und Tod auf See.* Leipzig: Amelangs Verlag [1914/15].

Bittorf, Wilhelm. "'Das Boot': Als Wahnsinn imponierend." *Der Spiegel,* 53/1980, 78–87.

Bittorf, Wilhelm. "'Der lange Atem dieser Irrsinns-Odyssee.'" *Der Spiegel,* 8/1985, 191–3.

Bittorf, Wilhelm. "Ersäuft wie junge Katzen im Sack." *Der Spiegel,* 47/1985, 246–63.

Block, Peter H. *Die Nacht der "Wölfe": Herbst 1940 – Deutsche U-Boote am Geleitzug SC-7.* Landser [Military paperback series] No. 804. Erich Pabel Verlag, July 1991.

Bock, Gerd, Hrsg. *Ubootsgeist: Abenteuer und Fahrten im Mittelmeer.* Nach Kriegstagebüchern von Maschinistenmaat Paul Ritter. Leipzig: Verlag von K.F. Koehler, 1935.

Brennecke, Jochen, Hrsg. [Artilleriemaat der Reserve]. *Unser Boot und wir im Mittelmeer: Die Feindfahrten eines deutschen Unterseebootes in Wort und Bild.* [Picture-book, limited edition of 1000 copies.] Berlin: Otto von Holten, 1943.

Brennecke. Jochen. *Jäger – Gejagte: Deutsche U-Boote 1939–1945.* Herford: Koehlers Verlagsgesellschaft, 1956.

Brennecke, Jochen. *Der Fall Laconia: Ein Hohes Lied der U-Boot-Waffe.* Biberach an der Riss: Koehlers Verlagsgellschaft, 1959.

Brennecke, Jochen. *Haie im Paradies: Der Deutsche U-Boot-Krieg in Asiens Gewässern 1943–45. Dramatische Originalberichte Überlebender und bisher unveröffentlichte Geheim-Dokumente.* Preetz/Holstein: Ernst Gerdes Verlag, 1961 [München: Wilhelm Heyne, 1976, Heyne Buch Nr 64].

Brennecke, Jochen. *Die Wende im U-Boot-Krieg: Ursachen und Folgen 1939–1943.* Herford: Koehlers Verlagsgesellschaft, 1984.

Brustat-Naval, F. *Ali Cremer: U-333.* Berlin, Frankfurt, Wien: Verlag Ullstein, 1982 [2. Aufl. Frankfurt a.M.: Ullstein Zeitgeschichte, 1986].

Brustat-Naval, F., and Teddy Suhren. *Nasses Eichenlaub: Als Kommandant und F.d.U. im U-Boot-Krieg.* Herford: Koehlers Verlagsgesellschaft, 1983.

Buchheim, Lothar-Günther. *Jäger im Weltmeer.* Berlin: Suhrkamp Verlag, 1943.

Buchheim. Lothar-Günther. "'U-Boot im Sturm' – vom Marinekriegsberichter Lothar-Günther Buchheim." *Völkischer Beobachter,* 9/10 April 1944, 1, through 14 April 1944, 3.

Buchheim, Lothar-Günther. *Das Boot.* München: Piper Verlag, 1973. [München: Deutscher Taschenbuchverlag, 1976].

Buchheim, Lothar-Günther. *U-Boot-Krieg.* Mit einem Vorwort von Michael Salewski. München: Piper Verlag, 1976.

Buchheim, Lothar-Günther. *U-96: Szenen aus dem Seekrieg. Ein Film.* [film script] Vorwort von Helmut Krapp. Hamburg: Albrecht Knaus Verlag, 1981.

Buchheim, Lothar-Günther. *Der Film "Das Boot": Ein Journal.* Hrsg. Dieter Struss. Mit über 250 Farb- und Schwarzweiß-Abbildungen. München: Goldmann Verlag, 1981.

Buchheim, Lothar-Günther. "Die Wahrheit blieb auf Tauchstation." *GEO-Magazin,* 10/1981, 130–46.

Buchheim, Lothar-Günther. *Die U-Boot-Fahrer: die Boote, die Besatzungen und ihr Admiral.* Stuttgart und München: C. Bertelsmann, 1985.

Buchheim, Lothar-Günther. *Zu Tode Gesiegt: Der Untergang der U-Boote.* Stuttgart und München: C. Bertelsmann Verlag, 1988.

Busch, Fritz Otto [Korvettenkapitän a.D]. *U-Boots-Taten.* Mit 16 Kupfertiefdruckbildern, 6 Gefechtsskizzen, 3 U-Boots-Schnittzeichnungen und 1 U-Boots-Tabelle. Berlin: Verlag Reimar Hobbing, 1934.

Busch, Fritz Otto [KKapt]. *U-Bootsfahrten.* Berlin und Leipzig: Franz Schneider Verlag, 1934, 2. Aufl. 1938.

Busch, Fritz Otto. Korvettenkapitän der Reserve. *U-Boote gegen England.* Berlin und Leipzig: Franz Schneider, 1939.

Busch, Fritz-Otto. *Großadmiral Karl Dönitz: Der große Stratege des U-Boot-Krieges.* Landser [Military paperback series] No. 105. Rastatt/Baden: Erich Pabel Verlag, nd.

Busch. Fritz-Otto. *... Torpedo ... LLLos! [sic] Die verwegenen Feindfahrten von U-110.* Landser Sonderband [Military paperback series, special volume] No. 181. Rastatt/Baden: Erich Pabel Verlag, nd.

Busch, F.-O. *Das Ende der "Ark Royal": Torpedos von U-81 versenkten den Flugzeugträger.* 2. Aufl. Landser [Military paperback series] No. 411. Rastatt/Baden: Erich Pabel Verlag, Juli 1976; Neuaufl., Landser No. 580, nd.

Busch, Fritz-Otto. *Jagd auf "Graue Wölfe": Deutsche U-Boote im Duell mit ihrem Todfeind Captain F.J. Walker, dem legendären englischen U-Boot-Jäger.* Landser [Military paperback series] No. 567; 2. Aufl. Landser No. 1031. Rastatt/Baden: Erich Pabel Verlag, Januar 1978.

Busch, F.-O. *Fritz Julius Lemp: Kommandant des U-Bootes U-110.* Landser [Military paperback series] No. 552. Neuaufl. Rastatt/Baden: Erich Pabel Verlag, Dezember 1981.

Busch, F.-O. *Duell im Atlantik: Jagd auf "Graue Wölfe."* Landser [Military paperback series] No. 1267. Neuaufl. Rastatt/Baden: Erich Pabel Verlag, Juli 1982.

Busch, F.-O. *Drama im Atlantik: Der Fall "Laconia."* Landser [Military paperback series] No. 482, März 1979; Neuaufl. Landser No. 612. Rastatt/Baden: Erich Pabel Verlag, März 1984.

Busch, F.-O. *Duell im Atlantik 1942/43: Wende im U-Boot-Krieg.* Landser [Military paperback series] No. 1520. Rastatt/Baden: Erich Pabel Verlag, Mai 1987.

Busch, F.-O. *Bomben auf Schiffbrüchige: Die Torpedierung des Ozeanriesen "Laconia" durch U-156.* Landser [Military paperback series] No. 772. Rastatt/Baden: Erich Pabel Verlag, Mai 1990.

Busch/Flachsenberg/Melke. *Gehetzte "Wölfe": Seekrieg im Atlantik.* Landser [Military paperback series] No. 1056. Rastatt/Baden: Erich Pabel Verlag, nd.

Busch, Harald. *U-Boot auf Feindfahrt: Bildberichte vom Einsatz im Atlantik.* Gütersloh: Verlag C. Bertelsmann, 1942.

Busch, Harald. *So War der U-Boot-Krieg,* Bielefield: Deutscher Heimat-Verlag, 1952. [*U-Boats at War,* trans. L.P.R Wilson, London: Putnam, 1955; American edition: *U-Boats at War,* trans. L.P.R. Wilson, New York: Ballantyne Books, 1955. *U-Boats at War,* (abridged version) London: Hamilton and Co., 1956]. Erweiterte Ausgabe mit Geleitwort von Teddy Suhren, Preussischer Oldendorf: Verlag K.W. Schütz KG, 1983.

Busch, Harald. *Totentanz der Sieben Meere: Todbringende Gespensterjagd für Freund und Feind. So war der U-Boot-Krieg.* Rastatt/Baden: Erich Pabel Verlag, 1960.

Busch, R., und H.J. Röll. *Die deutschen U-Boot-Kommandanten.* Landser Sonderausgabe [Military paperback series, special edition] No. 816. Rastatt/Baden: Erich Pabel Verlag, nd.

Crompton, [Iwan] Oberleutnant z. S. *Crompton "U-41" der zweite "Baralong"-Fall.* Selbsterzählt von Oberleutnant z.S. Crompton. [Preface signed in February 1917]. Berlin: Verlag August Scherl, 1917.

Crompton, Kapitänleutnant a.D. *Englands Verbrechen an U-41: Der zweite "Baralong"-Fall im Weltkrieg.* Herausgegeben von W. v. Langsdorff. Gütersloh: Verlag C. Bertelsmann, 1940.

d'Équevilley. *Untersee- und Tauchboote.* Übers. Oberleutnant zur See Weincke. Kiel: Robert Cordes Verlagsbuchhandlung, 1905.

Descovich, Emo, und Emil Seeliger. *Das U-Boot.* Wien: Verlag Österreichischer Flottenverein, 1915.

Dinklage, Ludwig. *U-Boot-Fahrer und Kamelsreiter: Kriegsfahrten eines deutschen Unterseebootes.* Stuttgart: Franckh'sche Verlagshandlung, 1939.

Dönitz, Karl, in Langsdorff, ed. *U-Boote am Feind: 45 U-Boot-Fahrer erzählen,* 1937.

Dönitz, Karl. *Die U-Bootswaffe.* von Vizeadmiral Karl Dönitz, Befehlshaber der U-Boote. 3. Aufl. Berlin: E.S. Mittler & Sohn, 1940.

Dönitz, Karl. *Zehn Jahre und Zwanzig Tage: Erinnerungen 1935–1945.* Mit einem Nachwort von Professor Dr. Jürgen Rohwer. 9. Aufl. München: Bernard & Graefe Verlag, 1985. [The first three printings, from 1958 to 1964, were with Athenäum Verlag. The next three, from 1967 to 1985, were with Bernard

& Graefe. The postscript containing Rohwer's insights into both Dönitz's autobiographical achievement and on the Battle of the Atlantic commenced with the seventh printing in 1980. British version, *Ten Years and Twenty Days*, translated by R.H. Stevens, London: Weidenfeld and Nicolson, 1959.

Enders, Gerd. *Auch kleine Igel haben Stacheln: Deutsche U-Boote im Schwarzen Meer.* Herford: Koehlers Verlagsgesellschaft, 1984.

Fechter, Hans, Marine-Oberingenieur. *In der Alarmkoje von U-35.* Berlin und Wien: Verlag Ullstein & Co., 1918.

Fischdick, Arnold. *U-90: Kameradschaft und Erlebnisse im Ubootkrieg.* Eigene Tagebuchaufzeichnungen mit ca. 75 Front-Aufnahmen, Vor- und Schluß-wort des Verfassers und einem Geleitwort des Kommandanten. Essen: Walter Bacmeisters Nationalverlag, 1937.

Fischer-Borken, Konrad. *Treibjagd im Atlantik: Deutsche U-Boote in den Weiten des Meeres.* Landser [Military paperback series] No. 374. Rastatt in Baden: Erich Pabel Verlag, nd.

Forstmann, Kapitänleutnant Walter. *U-39 auf Jagd im Mittelmeer.* Mit einem Vorwort von Kontreadmiral Hollweg. Berlin und Wien: Ullstein & Co., 1918.

Forstner, Günther Georg Freiherr v. *Als U-Boots-Kommandant gegen England.* Berlin und Wien: Verlag Ullstein & Co., 1916.

Forstner, Kapitänleutnant Georg Günther Freiherr v. *U-Boots-Leben.* Mit 15 Bildern des Marinemalers C. Bössenroth. Bielefeld und Leipzig: Velhagen & Klasings Volksbücher Nr 136 [1916?].

Forstner, Georg Günther Freiherr v. *U-Boot-ahoi! Deutsche U-Boote in Kriegs- und Friedenszeiten.* Berlin und Leipzig: Gustav Weise Verlag, 1937. 2. Aufl., 1938.

Forstner, Georg Günther Freiherr v. *Krieg in der Ostsee.* Berlin und Leipzig: Gustav Weise Verlag, 1938.

Frank, Wolfgang. *Prien greift an.* Nach Aufzeichnungen des Verfassers an Bord und der beim Befehlshaber der Unterseeboote vorliegenden dienstlichen Kriegstagebüchern des Korvettenkapitän Günther Prien. Hamburg: Deutsche Hausbücherei, 1941, 1942. Simultaneous paperback, Berlin: Zentralverlag der NSDAP, 1942.

Frank, Wolfgang, and Hans Meckel. *Was War Wirklich mit Prien?* Hamburg: Köhler Verlag, 1950.

Frank, Wolfgang. *Die Wölfe und der Admiral: Triumph und Tragik der U-Boote* [1953], Zweite erweiterte Aufl. Mit 54 Abbildungen auf Kunstdrucktafeln, einem U-Boot-Schnitt und der Karte einer Geleitzugschlacht. Oldenburg und Hamburg: G. Stalling Verlag, 1957. Reissued in paperback, same title, Bergisch Gladbach: Bastei-Lübbe-Taschenbuch [Band 65 025] 1. Aufl. 1980; 2. Aufl. 1981. [*The Sea Wolves*, translated by R.O.B. Long, London: Weidenfeld and Nicolson, 1955, and London: World Distributors, 1957 [in the series Viking War Giant]; later Maidstone: George Mann, 1973. Edition used, *The Sea Wolves*, New York: Ballantyne Books, 1955.

Frank, Wolfgang. *Der Stier von Scapa Flow: Leben und Taten des U-Boot-Kommandanten Günther Prien.* Nach Aufzeichnungen des Verfassers an Bord U-47 und den seinerzeit beim Befehlshaber der Unterseeboote vorliegenden dienstlichen Kriegstagebüchern des Korvettenkapitäns Günther Prien, sowie deutschen und englischen Dokumenten der Kriegs- und Nachkriegszeit. Oldenburg und Hamburg: G. Stalling, 1958.

Freiwald, Ludwig. *U-Boots-Maschinist Fritz Kasten: ein Frontbuch der Deutschen Marine.* München: J.F. Lehmanns Verlag, 1933.

Führen, Franz, Hrsg. *Kapitänleutnant Schepke erzählt.* Mit einem Geleitwort von Großadmiral Dönitz. Minden (Westf.): Wilhelm Köhler Verlag, 1943.

Fürbringer, Werner. Kptlt. a.D. *Alarm! Tauchen!: U-Boot in Kampf und Sturm.* Berlin: Im Deutschen Verlag [Ullstein], 1933.

Gayer, A[lbert]. *Die deutschen U-Boote in ihrer Kriegführung 1914–18.* Heft 1: *Von Kriegsanfang bis Februar 1915* [Berlin: Mittler & Sohn, 1920; 2. Aufl., Berlin 1930]; Heft 2: *Die U-Bootsblockade Februar bis Oktober 1915* [2. Aufl., Berlin: Mittler & Sohn, 1930]; Heft 3: *Der Winter 1915/16 und die Zeit bis zur Anordnung des reinen Kreuzerkrieges Oktober 1915 bis Ende April 1916* [2. Aufl., Berlin: E.S. Mittler & Sohn, 1930]; Heft 4, *Die Zeit des U-kreuzerkriegs und die Periode der Verwendung der Nordsee-U-Boote gegen feindliche Kriegsschiffe Mai 1916 bis Februar 1917* [2. Aufl., Berlin: E.S. Mittler & Sohn, 1930].

Gerlach, Wolfgang. "Vom Seeteufel zum Friedensengel," *Die Zeit,* Nr 3, 17 Januar 1992, 12–13.

Glodschey, Erich. *Stürme im Mittelmeer.* Berlin: Verlag "Die Wehrmacht," 1940.

Glodschey, Erich. *U-Boote: Deutschlands Scharfe Waffe.* Stuttgart: Union Deutsche Verlagsgesellschaft, 1943.

Gottberg, Otto von. *Kreuzerfahrten und U-Bootstaten.* Berlin und Wien: Verlag Ullstein & Co., 1915.

Griffin, Gwyn. *Der letzte Zeuge: Der erschütternde Roman der deutschen U-Boote im Zweiten Weltkrieg.* [Orig. *An Operational Necessity.* New York: C.P. Putnam's, 1967]. Trans. Hans E. Hausner. Wien, München, Zürich: Verlag Fritz Molden, 1969. MTV-Band, 29 Dezember 1976.

Grosse, Karl Friedrich. *Politische und Militärische Bedeutung des Unterseebootskrieges 1914/18.* Rosenheim: Rosenheimer Anzeiger, 1937.

Grümmer, Gerhard. *Irrfahrt: Ein Tatsachenroman.* Berlin: Verlag der Nation, 1977.

Guddat, Rolf. *Für jeden kommt der Tag.* Berlin: Verlag Sport und Technik, 1958; 4. Aufl. 1960.

Günther, Hanns [W. De Haas]. *Die Eroberung der Tiefe.* Stuttgart: Kosmos, Gesellschaft der Naturfreunde, Geschäftsstelle Franckh'sche Verlagsbuchhandlung, 1928.

Hardegen, Reinhard, Kapitänleutnant. *"Auf Gefechtsstationen!" U-Boote im Einsatz gegen England und Amerika.* Mit einem Geleitwort von Großadmiral Dönitz. Leipzig: Boreas-Verlag, 1943.

Hartmann, Werner. *Feind im Fadenkreuz: U-Boot auf Jagd im Atlantik.* Nacherzählt von Gerhart Weise. Mit einem Vorwort vom Befehlshaber der U-Boote Vizeadmiral Karl Dönitz. Berlin: Verlag die Heimbücherei, 1942.

Hashagen, Ernst. *U-Boote Westwärts! Meine Fahrten um England 1914–1918.* 2. Aufl. Berlin: E.S. Mittler & Sohn, [1931?].

Hauff, Ludwig. *Die unterseeische Schiffahrt[:] erfunden und ausgeführt von Wilhelm Bauer.* Bamberg: Verlag der Buchner'schen Buchhandlung, 1859. Auch Bamberg: C.C. Buchners Verlag, 1915. [Original im Deutschen Museum, München Signatur 1929 A 1937.] Photomech. Nachdruck, Weinheim: Physik-Verlag, 1982.

Heimburg, Heino von, Oblt. zur See. *U-Boot gegen U-Boot.* Berlin: Verlag August Scherl, 1917.

Herbert, Paul. *Der Tod auf allen Meeren. Ein Tatsachenbericht zur Geschichte des faschistischen U-Boot-Krieges.* [1970] Berlin: Militärverlag der Deutschen Demokratischen Republik, 1984.

Herlin, Hans. *Verdammter Atlantik. Schicksale deutscher U-Boot-Fahrer. Tatsachenbericht.* [1959] Düsseldorf und Wien: Econ Verlag, 1981; 12. Aufl. München: Wilhelm Heyne Verlag, 1980; Hersching: Manfred Pawlak, 1988.

Hersing, Korvettenkapitän Otto. *U-21 rettet die Dardanellen.* 2. Aufl. Leipzig: v. Hase & Koehler Verlag, 1932.

Herzog, Bodo. *Die deutschen Uboote 1906 bis 1945.* München: J.F. Lehmanns Verlag, 1959.

Herzog, Bodo. *Kapitänleutnant Otto Steinbrinck: Die Geschichte des erfolgreichsten U-Boot-Kommandanten in den Gewässern um England.* Krefeld: Hermann Rühl Verlag, 1963.

Herzog, Bodo. *U-35: Das erfolgreichste Unterseeboot der Welt! Kapitänleutnant Arnauld de la Perière, der erfolgreichste U-Boot-Kommandant der Welt.* Krefeld: Hermann Rühl Verlag, 1964.

Herzog, Bodo. *60 Jahre Deutsche Uboote 1906–1966.* München: J.F. Lehmanns Verlag, 1968. [Reprinted Herrsching: Manfred Pawlak, 1990].

Herzog, Bodo. *U-Boote im Einsatz: U-Boats in Action: Eine Bilddokumentation.* Dorheim: Polzun-Verlag, 1970.

Herzog, Bodo, und Günter Schomaekers. *Ritter der Tiefe, Graue Wölfe: Die erfolgreichsten U-Boot-Kommandanten der Welt.* 2. Aufl. München und Wels: Verlag Welsermühl, 1976.

Herzog, Bodo. "Piraten vor Málaga." *Die Zeit,* Nr 49 (6 Dezember 1991), 17–18.

Hess, Hans Georg. *Die Männer von U-995: Gespräche mit ehemaligen Besatzungsangehörigen des Bootes von Laboe.* Olden, München, Hamburg: Stalling Verlag, 1979.

Hildebrandt, Hans H. *Die Deutschen Kriegsschiffe.* 7 Bde, 2. überarbeitete Aufl. Herford: Koehlers Verlagsgesellschaft [1979] 1983.

Hirschfeld, Wolfgang. [Funkermaat] *Feindfahrten: Das Logbuch eines U-Boot-funkers.* Wien: Paul Neff Verlag, 1982.

Hirschfeld, Wolfgang. *Das letzte Boot: Atlantik Farewell.* München: Universitas Verlag, 1989.

Hollweg, Kontreadmiral Carl. *Unser Recht auf den U-Bootskrieg.* Berlin: Verlag Ullstein & Co., 1917.

Janssen, Jens. *Zwischen Sieg und Tod: die Feindfahrten von U-123 unter Kapitän-leutnant Hardegen.* Landser [Military paperback series] No. 855. Rastatt/Baden: Erich Pabel Verlag, August 1974.

Jonsen, Fred. *U-Boot 861: Feindfahrt um die halbe Welt.* Landser [Military paperback series] No. 57. Rastatt/Baden: Erich Pabel Verlag, nd.

Jonsen, Fred. *Das Duell im Atlantik: "U-Glasewald" im Kampf gegen feindliche Übermacht.* Landser [Military paperback series] No. 131. Rastatt/Baden: Erich Pabel Verlag, nd.

Jung, Hermann A.K. [Kptlt. a.D.]. *Krieg unter Wasser: Der Opfertod der Fünf-tausend.* Oldenburg i.O./Berlin: Gerhard Stalling Verlagsbuchhandlung, 1939.

Just, Paul. *Vom Seeflieger zum Uboot-Fahrer: Feindflüge und Feindfahrten 1939–1945.* Stuttgart: Motorbuch Verlag, 1979.

Kaden, Kapitänleutnant [Wolfgang]. *Auf Ubootjagd gegen England.* 2. Aufl. Leipzig: Verlag v. Hase und Koehler, 1942.

Kaulisch, Baldur. *U-Boot-Krieg: 1914–1918.* Reihe: "Illustrierte historische Hefte," Zentralinstitut für Geschichte der Akademie der Wissenschaften der DDR. Berlin: VEB Deutscher Verlag der Wissenschaften, 1974.

Kirchhoff, Hermann Vize-Admiral a.D. *Otto Weddigen und seine Waffe: Aus seinen Tagebüchern und nachgelassenen Papieren.* Mit einem Titelbild und 63 Abbild-ungen. [Band 11 der Reihe "Unsere Seehelden"]. Berlin: Marinedank-Verlag, 1915.

Kirchner, Johann. [Leitender Ingenieur]. *Das U-Boot bei der Arbeit: Seine Technik und Wirkungsweise in Wort und Bild.* Mit zahlreichen Abbildungen. Berlin: Ernst Siegfried Mittler und Sohn, [1917] [7. Aufl. 1917] 9. Aufl. 1918.

Köhler, Wilhelm, Hrsg. *Deutsches Heldentum zur See: Nach den von Mitkämpfern zur Verfügung gestellten Seekriegserlebnissen.* Minden: Wilhelm Köhler, Vaterlän-dische Verlagsanstalt, [1917?].

König, Paul. *Die Fahrt der Deutschland.* Berlin: Verlag Ullstein & Co., 1917.

König, Paul. *Fahrten der U-Deutschland im Weltkrieg.* Von Paul König, Kapitän des Untersee-Frachtschiffes "Deutschland." Berlin: Im Ullstein Verlag, 1937.

Koizar, Karl Hans. *U-91: Satan der Tiefe.* Wien: Omnibus Verlag, 1979.

Korten, Hans-Joachim. *Atlantik in Flammen: Mit Korvettenkapitän Lüth auf Feind-fahrt.* Landser [Military paperback series] No. 38. Rastatt/Baden: Erich Pabel Verlag, nd.

Korten, Hans-Joachim. *U-Boot-Kampf in heissen Zonen: Boote, Bärte und Pötte im Indischen Ozean.* Landser [Military paperback series] No. 93. Rastatt/Baden: Erich Pabel Verlag, nd.

Kramsta, E., geb. von Prittwitz. *Aus dem Logbuch des I. Wachoffiziers U-66: Auszüge aus Briefen und Tagebuchblättern.* Hannover: Verlag Industrie und Handelsdienst, nd. [1930s?].

Küster, Jul., Hrsg. *Das U-Boot: Motor-Tauch-Schiff.* Berlin: Verlag Klasing & Co., 1916.

Küster, Jul. *Das U-Boot als Kriegs- und Handels-Schiff: Technische Entwicklung, Motoren, Bewaffnung und Abwehr von Tauchbooten.* Berlin: Verlag Klasing & Co., 1917.

Küster, Julius, Hrsg. *Das U-Boot als Kriegs- und Handelsschiff: die technische Entwicklung und Anwendung der Tauchboote, deren Motoren, Bewaffnug und Abwehr,* 3. vermehrte Ausg. Berlin: Verlag Klasing, 1917.

Kurowski, Franz, see also Alman, Karl.

Kurowski, Franz. *Krieg unter Wasser: U-Boote auf den sieben Meeren 1939–1945.* Düsseldorf und Wien: Econ Verlag, 1979.

Laar, Clemens. *Das Geister-U-Boot.* In der Reihe "Kleine Wehrmacht-Bücherei," Bd 16 [paperback]. Berlin: Verlag "Die Wehrmacht," 1937.

Lakowski, Richard. *Deutsche U-Boote Geheim 1935–1945.* [Foto-Buch] Berlin: Brandenburgisches Verlagshaus, 1991.

Langsdorff, Werner von, Hrsg. *U-Boote am Feind: 45 U-Boot-Fahrer erzählen.* Gütersloh: Verlag C. Bertelsmann, 1937.

Langsdorff, W. von, [Hrsg.]. *Englands Verbrechen an U-41,* von Kapitänleutnant a D. [Iwan] Crompton. Gütersloh: Verlag C. Bertelsmann, 1940.

Lassen, Ernst. *Handels-Uboot "Deutschland": Fahrt nach Amerika.* Siegen und Leipzig: Hermann Montanus Verlagsbuchhandlung, 1916.

Lawrenz, Hans-Joachim. *Die Entstehungsgeschichte der U-Boote.* München: J.F. Lehmanns Verlag, 1968.

Lebert, Norbert. *Eine Frau war an Bord.* [Orig. title *Bordarzt Steffens II,* 1968]. Bergisch Gladbach: Bastei Verlag, 1975.

Lehnhoff, Joachim. *Die Heimfahrt: Roman.* München: Kindler Verlag, 1956. [The novel first appeared in the illustrated magazine *Revue.*] Also: *Die Heimatfahrt der U-720: Roman nach Tatsachen.* 8. Aufl. München: Wilhelm Heyne [Heyne Bücher Nr 905], 1977.

Lehnhoff, Joachim. *Quicksilber: ein dramatischer Roman um ein U-Boot.* Bergisch Gladbach: Gustav Lübbe Verlag, 1982. Also Stuttgart und München: Deutscher Bücherbund, 1982.

Lochner, Herbert. *U-425: Das Schicksal eines Eismeer-Unterseebootes.* Landser [Military paperback series] No. 806. Rastatt/Baden: Erich Pabel Verlag, August 1991.

Lüderes, Willi. *Tatsachenbericht eines U-Bootfahrers 1943–1945.* Rossdorf: Helen M. Brinkhaus Verlag, 1982.

Lüth, Wolfgang, und Claus Korth. *Boot greift wieder an! Ritterkreuzträger erzählen.* Von den Unterseebootkommandanten Korvettenkapitän Wolfgang Lüth,

Träger des Eichenlaubes mit Schwertern und Brillanten, und Kapitänleutnant Claus Korth. Berlin: Verlag Erich Klinghammer, 1944.

Lützow, Korvettenkapitän Friedrich. *Unterseebootskrieg und Hungerblockade.* Berlin-Dahlem: Verlag für volkstümliche Literatur und Kunst, 1921.

Lützow, Konteradmiral z.V., Friedrich. *Die Heutige Seekriegsführung: Mit U-Boot und Minen gegen englische Hunger-Blockade.* Berlin: Verlag "Die Wehrmacht," 1940.

Mannesmann, Kptlt. "Fliegerbomben trafen das U-Boot," *Völkischer Beobachter,* 14 April 1944, 2.

Marschall, Wilhelm, Konteradmiral. *Torpedo Achtung! Los!: Erlebnisse im U-Bootkrieg 1917–18.* [Preface dated Kiel, 12 April 1919]. Berlin: Im Deutschen Verlag, 1938.

May, Ferdinand. *Die Letzten von U-189.* Sonderausgabe für die kleine Hausbibliothek. Berlin: Deutscher Militärverlag, 1961.

Merten, Karl-Friedrich, und Kurt Baberg. *Wir U-Boot-Fahrer sagen: "Nein! … So war das nicht!" Eine Anti-Buchheim Schrift.* U-Boot-Fahrer nehmen kritisch Stellung zur Schmähschrift des Lothar-Günther Buchheim *Die U-Boot-Fahrer* [C. Bertelsmann 1985]. Neustadt b. Coburg: J. Reiss Verlag, 1986.

Metzler, Jost. *Sehrohr Südwärts.* Ritterkreuzträger Kapitänleutnant Jost Metzler erzählt; Niedergeschreiben von Otto Mielke. Berlin: Wilhelm Limpert-Verlag, 1943.

Metzler, Jost. *Die Lachende Kuh. Die einem spannenden Abenteuer gleichenden Erlebnisberichte der Besatzung von U-69 während des Zweiten Weltkrieges.* Unter Mitarbeit von Paul Heinsius. Ravensburg: Veitsburg-Verlag, 1954.

Michelsen, Andreas, Vizeadmiral a.D. *Der U-Bootskrieg 1914–1918,* 3. Aufl. Leipzig: Verlag von Hase & Koehler, 1925.

Mielke, Otto. *Unterseeboot U-977: Wir schnorcheln uns durch.* Landser [Military paperback series] No. 136. Rastatt/Baden: Erich Pabel Verlag, 1958.

Mielke, O. *Vor Afrikas Küste: Einsätze deutscher U-Boote in Südlichen Breiten.* Landser [Military paperback series] No. 1069. Rastatt/Baden: Erich Pabel Verlag, September 1978.

Mielke, O. *Vor Afrikas Küste: Deutsche U-Boote in südlichen Gewässern – Einsätze von U-69 unter Kapitänleutnant Jost Metzler und U-159 und Kapitänleutnant Helmut Witte.* Neuaufl. Landser [Military paperback series] No. 1306. Rastatt/Baden: Erich Pabel Verlag, April 1983.

Mielke, O., und Janssen. *"Rauchsäule Voraus!" 1942–44: U-Boot-Krieg im Atlantik und im Mittelmeer.* Landser [Military paperback series] No. 1345. Rastatt/Baden: Erich Pabel Verlag, Januar 1984.

Morath, Robert. *Die Versenkung des Danton: Meine U-Bootserlebnisse von der Ostsee bis zum Mittelmeer.* von Kapitänleutnant Robert Morath. Mit Illustrationen und während der Fahrt gemachten photographischen Aufnahmen. Berlin: Hutten-Verlag, 1917.

Moraht, Robert [KKpt a.D., Ritter des Ordens Pour le Mérite]. *Werwolf der Meere. "U-64" Jagt den Feind.* [1. Aufl. 1933] 13. Aufl. Berlin: Vorhut-Verlag Otto Schlegel GmBH, 1938.

Neureuther, Karl. *Wir Leben Noch! Deutsche Seehelden im U-Bootkampf: 26 Erlebnisse von Angehörigen der U-Bootskameradschaft München.* Gesammelt und hrsgg. von Korvettenkapitän a D. Karl Neureuther, Vorsitzender der U-Bootskamerad-schaft München, und Marinemaler Clauss Bergen. Stuttgart, Berlin, Leipzig: Union Deutsche Verlagsgesellschaft, 1930.

Niemöller, Martin. *Vom U-Boot zur Kanzel.* Berlin: Martin Warneck Verlag, 1935. [Translated by Commander D. Hastie Smith, *From U-Boat to Pulpit,* London: William Hodge, November 1936; Second "Cheap Edition," September 1937. Expanded and revised as *From U-Boat to Concentration Camp: The Autobiography of Martin Niemöller, Vicar of Berlin-Dahlem. With His Further Story by [A.S. Duncan-Jones] The Dean of Chichester,* London, William Hodge, January 1939.]

Nowarra, Heinz. *U-VII: Graue Wölfe auf allen Meeren.* Mit Poster. Reihe "Das Waffen-Arsenal: Bewaffnung, Ausrüstung und Einsatz der Streitkräfte im Zweiten Weltkrieg." Friedburg (Dorheim): Podzun-Pallas Verlag, 1977.

Ott, Wolfgang. *Haie und Kleine Fische.* München: Albert Langen–Georg Müller Verlag, 1956. [Sonderausgabe, Wien: Eduard Kaiser Verlag, 1956].

Otto, Friedrich. *Das Unterseeboot im Kampfe.* Leipzig: C.F. Amelangs Verlag, 1915.

Paus, P. *Die Jagd der "Grauen Wölfe."* Landser [Military paperback series] No. 751. Rastatt/Baden: Erich Pabel Verlag, August 1972.

Paus, P. *Die letzte Atlantik-Schlacht: Frühjahr 1943 – Die große Wende im U-Boot-Krieg gegen die alliierten Geleitzüge.* Landser [Military paperback series] No. 760. Rastatt/Baden: Erich Pabel Verlag, Oktober 1972; Neuaufl. No. 778.

Paus, P. *"Graue Wölfe" im Schwarzen Meer.* Landser [Military paperback series] No. 976. Rastatt/Baden: Erich Pabel Verlag, Dezember 1976; Neuaufl. Landser No. 1790, Juli 1992.

Paus, P. *Die "Nacht der langen Messer": Kriegsjahr 1940 – Die ersten großen Rudelschlachten deutscher U-Boote.* Landser [Military paperback series] No. 1003. Rastatt/Baden: Erich Pabel Verlag, Juni 1977.

Paus, P. *Die Schlacht im Atlantik 1939/41: Beginn des U-Boot-Krieges gegen Gross-britannien.* Landser [Military paperback series] No. 632. Rastatt/Baden: Erich Pabel Verlag, Dezember 1984; Neuaufl., *Die Schlacht im Atlantik 1939/41: Die erste Phase des U-Boot-Krieges.* Landser No. 778, Juli 1990.

Paus, P. *Die Schlacht im Atlantik, Kriegsjahr 1942: Großangriff der "Grauen Wölfe."* Landser [Military paperback series] No. 1061. Rastatt/Baden: Erich Pabel Verlag, August 1978.

Paus, P. *Unternehmen "Paukenschlag" 1941/42: Die ersten Einsätze deutscher Unter-seeboote vor der nordamerikanischen Küste.* Landser [Military paperback series] No. 1019. Rastatt/Baden: Erich Pabel Verlag, Oktober 1977; Neuaufl. Land-ser No. 1661, Januar 1990.

Paus, P. *Die erste Feindfahrt 1939/40: Der Beginn des U-Boot-Krieges.* Landser [Military paperback series] No. 1109. Rastatt/Baden: Erich Pabel Verlag, Juli 1979; Neuaufl. Landser No. 1718, März 1991.

Paus, P. *Duell mit dem Tod – Sommer 1944: Der opferreiche Kampf deutscher U-Boote gegen die Invasionsflotte.* Neuaufl. Landser [Military paperback series] No. 1226. Rastatt/Baden: Erich Pabel Verlag, September 1981.

Paus, P. *Feindfahrt im indischen Ozean 1943–1945: Die Einsätze deutscher "Monsun-U-Boote."* Landser [Military paperback series] No. 1650. Neuaufl. No. 1294. Rastatt/Baden: Erich Pabel Verlag, Januar 1983.

Paus, P. *Unternehmen "Paukenschlag." Der erste Einsatz deutscher U-Boote vor der amerikanischen Küste.* Landser [Military paperback series] No. 1334. Neuaufl. Rastatt/Baden: Erich Pabel Verlag, Oktober 1983.

Paus, P. *Durch alle Höllen: 1939–1941. Die dramatischen Feindfahrten von U-48.* Landser [Military paperback series] No. 1425. Rastatt/Baden: Erich Pabel Verlag, Juli 1985; Neuaufl. Landser No. 1748, Oktober 1991.

Pfitzmann, Martin. *U-Boot Gruppe Eisbär: Einsatz vor Kapstadt.* Raststadt: Arthur Moewig Verlag Taschenbuch, 1986.

Plottke, Herbert. *Ein U-Boot-Drama: die letzten Feindfahrten von U-172.* Landser [Military paperback series] No. 704. Rastatt/Baden: Erich Pabel Verlag, September 1987.

Prien, Günther. *Mein Weg nach Scapa Flow.* Berlin: Deutscher Verlag, 1940. [*I Sank the Royal Oak*, translated by Comte de la Vatine, London: Grays Inn Press, 1954].

Rehder, Jacob, Fregattenkapitän. *U-Bootsfallen.* München: J.F. Lehmanns Verlag, 1935.

Reich, Kurt. [U-Boot-Maat]. *Dem Tommy entwischt: Der Geist unserer U-Boot-Waffe.* Berlin: Im Deutschen Verlag, 1942.

Reinhard, Wilhelm [Korvettenkapitän des Marineingenieurwesens]. *Wir an den Maschinen.* Leipzig: v. Hase & Koehler Verlag, 1940.

Reinhardt, Karl-Walter. "'Das Boot': Jede Fahrt war ein Abschied vom Leben." *Funk Uhr. Das Fernsehmagazin.* Programm vom 23. Februar bis 1. März 8, 1985, 20–2.

Richter, Heinrich. *Otto Weddigen: Ein Lebensbild.* Bielefeld und Leipzig: Verlag von Velhagen und Klasing, 1916.

Rohwer, Jürgen, *U-Boote: Eine Chronik in Bildern.* Oldenburg und Hamburg: Stalling Verlag, 1962.

Rose, Hans. *Auftauchen! Kriegsfahrten von U-53* [1931]. 2. Aufl. Essen: Essener Verlagsanstalt, 1939; 3. Aufl. Essen: Essener Verlagsanstalt, 1940.

Sanders-Bremen, Friedrich. *Der Heldenkampf unserer U-Boote.* Berlin: Askanischef Verlag [1917].

Sauer, Herbert. [Kapitän]. *Die Höllenmaschine im U-Boot.* Vorwort von Admiral Scheer. Berlin: August Scherl, 1928.

Schaeffer, Heinz. *U-977: 66 Tage unter Wasser.* "SOS Sonderband" Series "Schicksale deutscher Schiffe," Moewe No. 23. München: Moewe-Verlag, 1959.

Schaeffer, Heinz. *66 Tage unter Wasser: die legendäre Feindfahrt von U-977 nach Argentinien.* Landser [Military paperback series] No. 900. Rastatt/Baden: Erich Pabel Verlag, Juli 1975.

Schaeffer, Heinz. *U-977: Geheimfahrt nach Südamerika.* Wiesbaden: Limes Verlag, 1974. [Original: *U-Boat 977*, W.W. Norton & Company, 1952; Bantam Books, 1981].

Schaeffer, Heinz. *66 Tage unter Wasser: Die geheimnisumwobene U-Boot-Fernfahrt nach Argentinien.* Rastatt: Erich Pabel Verlag, 1986.

Schepke, Joachim. *U-Bootfahrer von heute. Erzählt und gezeichnet von einem U-Boot-Kommandanten.* Berlin: Im Deutschen Verlag, 1940.

Schloß, Max. "Die Bilanz des schärfsten Unterseebootkrieges nach fünf Monaten," *Die Flagge.* Zeitschrift für Seewesen und Seeverkehr. Organ des Österreichischen Flottenvereins. August 1917, Jg 12, Nr 8, 169–71.

Schloß, Max. "Die Bilanz von sechs Monaten schärfsten U-Bootkrieges," *Die Flagge*, Oktober 1917, Nr 10, 230–2.

Schröder, Edgar. *"UX" stand im Mittelmeer: Mit einem deutschen U-Boot auf Feindfahrt.* Von Kriegsberichter Edgar Schröder. Mit 48 Aufnahmen des Verfassers und von Bildberichtern einer Marine-Kriegsberichter-Kompanie. Berlin: Steiniger-Verlage, 1943.

Schultz, Paul. *Im U-Boot durch die Weltmeere.* Bielefeld und Leipzig: Velhagen & Klasing, 1931.

Schulz, Johann. *Das Boot der "Roten Teufel": Die Feindfahrten von U-552 in den Weiten des Atlantik.* Landser [Military paperback series] No. 458. Rastatt/Baden: Erich Pabel Verlag, nd.

Schulz, Johann. *Fahrt ins Verderben 1943/1944: Deutsche Ein-Mann-Torpedos im Kampf gegen die alliierte Landungsflotte.* Landser [Military paperback series] No. 1093. Rastatt/Baden: Erich Pabel Verlag, nd.

Schulz, Joh. *U-861 auf grosser Fahrt: Vom Einsatz der "Grauen Wölfe" auf allen Meeren.* Moewe No. 14. "SOS Sonderband" Series "Schicksale deutscher Schiffe." München: Moewe Verlag, 1959.

Schulz, Joh. *Torpedo – los! Mit U-123 vor Amerikas Küsten.* Moewe No. 21. "SOS Sonderband" Series "Schicksale deutscher Schiffe." München: Moewe Verlag, 1959.

Schulz, Joh. *Zwischen Rio und Freetown: U-201 auf groer Fahrt.* Moewe No. 27. "SOS Sonderband" Series "Schicksale deutscher Schiffe." München: Moewe Verlag, 1960.

Schulze, Franz. *Unsere U-Boote: Geschichtliche Entwicklung und Wirkung dieser modernsten Waffe.* von Prof. Dr. Franz Schulze, Direktor der Navigationsschule in Lübeck. Kassel: Verlag von Max Brunnemann, 1915.

Schulze, Franz. *Unterseebootsbilder.* [Many photos from 1914, 1915]. Hat dem Nachrichtenbüro des Reichs-Marine-Amts zur Zensur vorgelegen. Kassel: Verlag von Max Brunnemann, 1915.

Schulze, Franz. *Erich Sarnekow der U-Bootsheld: eine Erzählung aus dem Weltkrieg.* Mit Genehmigung des Reichs-Marine-Amts. Stuttgart: Loewes Verlag Ferdinand Carl, [1917].

Schulze, Franz, Professor Dr. *Die Schwarze Waffe,* Bd 1 der Reihe "Die U-Boot-Bücher." Berlin-Friedenau: Verlag für U-Boot-Literatur, 1917.

Schütte, Otto F. *Deutschlands U-Boote – Der Schrecken Englands: Ein Bildwerk von der deutschen U-Boot-Waffe.* Minden (Westf.): Wilhelm Köhler Verlag, nd [1939], 2. Aufl. 1940.

Schütze, H.G. *Operation unter Wasser.* Herford: Koehlers Verlagsgesellschaft, 1985.

Schultze-Bahlke. *U-Boote.* Reihe: Motorschiff-Bibliothek, Bd. 3. Berlin: Richard Carl Schmidt & Co., 1918.

Spiegel, [Edgar] Freiherr von. *Kriegstagebuch U-202.* Berlin: Verlag August Scherl, 1916.

Spiegel, [Edgar] Freiherr von. *U-Boot im Fegefeuer.* Berlin: Verlag August Scherl, 1930.

Spiegel, E[dgar] Freiherr von. *Meere – Inseln – Menschen: Vom Seekadetten zum U-Boot-Kommandanten.* Mit 45 Abbildungen. Berlin: August Scherl, 1934.

Spiegel, Edgar, Freiherr von. *45 000 Tonnen versenkt.* Gütersloh, Verlag von C. Bertelsmann [nd].

Spieß, Johannes [Kptlt a.D.]. *Sechs Jahre U-Boot-Fahrten.* Berlin: Verlag von Reimar Hobbing, 1925.

Spieß, Johannes [Kptlt a.D.]. *U-Boot-Abenteuer. Sechs Jahre U-Boot-Fahrten.* Berlin: Verlag Tradition Wilhelm Kolk, 1932.

Spieß, Johannes [Kptlt a.D.]. *Wir jagten Panzerkreuzer: Kriegsabenteuer eines U-Boot-Offiziers.* Mit 16 Bildern. [Revised edition of his *U-Boot-Abenteuer,* 1932.] Berlin: Verlag Ernst Steiniger, 1938.

Spieß, Johannes. *U-9 auf Kriegsfahrt.* Gütersloh: C. Bertelsmann Verlag [nd].

Spindler, Arno. *Der Handelskrieg mit U-Booten.* Bde 1–5, Berlin: E.S. Mittler & Sohn, 1932–41.

Steen, Hans. *U-Bootfallen im Kampf: Zur Erinnerung an den heldenmütigen Kampf und Tode des Oberleutnants zur See Reinhold Salzwedel.* Stuttgart: Union Deutsche Verlagsgesellschaft, 1941.

Stöwer, Willy. Professor. *Deutsche U-Boot-Taten in Bild und Wort.* Hrsgg. von der Reichsmarine zu Gunsten ihrer Friedenswohlfahrtszwecke. [10 plates with one-page commentary]. Berlin: I. Buch. Jahrgang 1916.

Stöwer, Willy, Hrsg. und Illust. *Kaiser Wilhelm und die Marine,* mit Text von Admiralitätsrat G. Wislicenus. [np, nd].

Straub, Heinz. *Der Eiserne Seehund: Das abenteuerliche Leben des kgl. bayerischen U-Boot-Erfinders Wilhelm Bauer.* München: Süddeutscher Verlag, 1982.

Thies, Hans Arthur. *Der Eiserne Seehund: Wilhelm Bauer, der Erfinder des U-Boots, Tat, Schicksal und Abenteuer.* Berlin: Deutsche Kulturbuchreihe, 1941. Also, München: Verlag Knorr & Hirth, 1942.

Thies, Hans Arthur. *U-1: Ein Erfinderschicksal.* München and Ulm: Knorr & Hirth Buchverlag, 1952.

Thomas, Lowell. *Ritter der Tiefe.* Uebersetzt und bearbeitet von E. Freiherr von Spiegel, Kapitänleutnant a.D. Berlin: Deutsche Verlagsgesellschaft, 1930; 2. Aufl. 1931. [Also, Gütersloh: C. Bertelsmann, 1930; also Volksverband der Bücherfreunde, Berlin: Wegweiser Verlag, 1931. [Originally published as *Raiders of the Deep*, New York: Garden City Publishing Company, 1928].

Topp, Erich. *Fackeln über dem Atlantik: Lebensbericht eines U-Boot-Kommandanten.* Herford und Bonn: E.S. Mittler & Sohn, 1990. [*The Odyssey of a U-boat Commander: Recollections of Erich Topp.* Westport, Connecticut: Praeger, 1992].

Trapp, Korvettenkapitän Georg von. *Bis zum letzten Flaggenschuß: Erinnerungen eines österreichischen U-Bootkommandanten.* Salzburg, Leipzig: Verlag Anton Pustet, 1935.

Valentiner, Max. *300,000 Tonnen Versenkt! Meine Boots-Fahrten.* Berlin und Wien: Verlag Ullstein & Co., 1917.

Valentiner, Max, Korvettenkapitän. *Der Schrecken der Meere: Meine U-Boot-Abenteuer.* [Mit 25 Abbildingen]. Zürich-Leipzig-Wien: [1930], 2. Aufl. 1931.

Valentiner, Max, Korvettenkapitän, Ritter des Pour le Mérite. *Der Schrecken der Meere: Meine U-Boot-Abenteuer als "Kaiserlich-deutscher Pirat."* [16 Bilder] Zürich, Leipzig, Wien: Amalthea-Verlag, 1932.

Valentiner, Max, Kapitän zur See. *U-38: Vikingerfahrten eines deutschen U-Bootes.* Berlin: Im Deutschen Verlag, 1934.

Weddigen, Otto. *Unser Seeheld Weddigen: Sein Leben und seine Taten dem deutschen Volke erzählt,* von Dr. Otto [sic] Weddigen. Mit mehreren Bildnissen. Berlin: Verlag August Scherl, 1915.

Werner, Herbert A. *Die Eisernen Särge.* [Hamburg: Hoffmann & Campe Verlag, 1969, 1970]. München: Wilhelm Heyne, 1980. [Heyne-Buch Nr 5177.] [American version, *Iron Coffins*, New York: Holt, Rinehart and Winston, 1969; English version, *Iron Coffins: A Personal Account of the German U-boat Battles of World War II*, London: Barker, 1970; London: Pan Books, 1972].

Wetzel, Eckard. *U-995: Die Feindfahrten des U-Bootes unter Kapitänleutnant Köhntopp.* Landser [Military paperback series] No. 720. Rastatt/Baden: Erich Pabel Verlag, nd.

Wetzel, Eckard. *Feindfahrt im Eismeer: Der Nordmeereinsatz von U-995 unter Oberleutnant z. S. Hess.* Landser [Military paperback series] No. 722. Rastatt/Baden: Erich Pabel Verlag, Juni 1988.

Wiebicke, Karl. *Die Männer von U-96: Erinnerungen an Fahrten unseres U-Bootes.* Mit 33 Bildern und 3 Kartenskizzen. 2. Aufl. Leipzig: Verlag von K.F. Koehler, 1934.

Wiedemayer, Gerhard. *Waffe unter Wasser: Die Erfindung des U-bootes und seine Geschichte.* Berlin: Kyffhäuser Verlag, 1940.

Wolfslast, Wilhelm. *U-Bootsdämmerung: Der große Erlebnis-Roman über das Schicksal eines deutschen U-Bootes und seiner tapferen Besatzung.* Moewe No. 1. "SOS Sonderband" Series "Schicksale deutscher Schiffe," München: Moewe Verlag, 1957.

Wolfslast, Wilhelm. *Nacht der Vernichtung: der groe Tasachenroman einer Geleitzugschlacht.* Moewe No. 7. "SOS Sonderband" Series "Schicksale deutscher Schiffe." München: Moewe Verlag, 1958.

Wolfslast, Wilhelm. *Trotz Tod und Teufel: Der U-Boots-Krieg von der freien Jagd bis zur Radarhölle.* Moewe No. 18. "SOS Sonderband" Series "Schicksale deutscher Schiffe." München: Moewe Verlag, 1959.

Zank, Wolfgang. "'Finis Germaniae!'" *Die Zeit,* 6/7 Februar 1992, s. 17–18.

B. U-BOAT FEATURE FILMS AND DOCUMENTARIES
(copies of films held in U-Boat Archives, Cuxhaven)

1926: *U9: Weddigen. ein Heldenschicksal.* (69 min.) Deutsche Volksfilm G.m.b.H., Berlin. Premiere, April 1927. Directed by Heinz Paul, script by Willy Rath, photography by Hermann Grund and Willi Goldberger, naval adviser Kapitänleutnant a.D. Hermann Rohne, and starring Carl de Vogt, Mathilde Sussin, Fritz Alberti, Fritz Solm, and Gerd Briese.

1932: *Morgenrot.* (69 min.) Ufa-Tonfilm, Berlin. Directed by Gustav von Ucicky, produced by Günther Stapenhorst, script by Gerhard Menzel, photography by Carl Hoffmann, and starring Rudolf Forster, Hans Lelbelt, Adele Sandrock, and Fritz Genschow.

1941: *U-Boote Westwärts.* (96 min.) Ufa Berlin, with the support of the Oberkommando der Kriegsmarine, and with the cooperation of the Commander-in-Chief Submarines [Dönitz] and the officers and men of the U-Boat Arm. Premiere May 1941. Directed by Günther Rittau, concept and script by Georg Zoch, music by Harald Böhmelt, and starring Ilse Werner, Herbert Wilk, Heinz Engelmann, and Jochen Brennecke.

1942: *Geheimakte WB1: Das Leben und Schicksal des Artillerie-Unteroffiziers Wilhelm Bauer aus München.* (69 min.) Bavaria Film-Kunst, München. Based on the novel *Der Eiserne Seehund* by Hans Arthur Thies. Script by Curt I. Braun, directed by Herbert Selpin, and starring Alexander Golling, Eva Immermann, and Günther Lüders.

1957: *Haie und Kleine Fische.* (117 min.) Willy Zeyn-Film GmbH, München. Script by Wolfgang Ott, based on his novel of that name. Naval and technical adviser Fregattenkapitän a.D. Erich Topp. Directed by Frank Wisbar, and starring Horst Felmy, Sabine Bethmann, Wolfgang Preiss, and Heinz Engelmann.

1958: *U-47 – Kapitänleutnant Prien.* (86 min.) Arca-Filmgesellschaft GmbH., Berlin. Script by J. Joachim Bartsch, based on material by Udo Wolter.

Directed by Harald Reinl, photography by Ernst Kalinke, music composed by Norbert Schultze, and starring Dieter Eppleff, Sabine Susselmann, and Dieter Barsche.

1981: *Das Boot.* (118 min.) Bavaria Atelier GmbH, München. Based on the novel by Lothar-Günther Buchheim. Directed by Wolfgang Petersen, and starring Jürgen Prochnow and Klaus Wennemann. Naval adviser, Kapitän zur See a.D. Hans-Joachim Krug. Introduced in ARD Television by Reinhart Müller-Freienfels.

1981: *Das Boot.* (300 min.) Bavaria Atelier GmbH, München Three-part TV-film based on the novel by Lothar-Günther Buchheim. Directed by Wolfgang Petersen, and starring Jürgen Prochnow and Klaus Wennemann.

1981: *Die Feindfahrt von U 96: Wie aus Buchheims Kriegsroman ein Film gemacht wird: ein Bericht von Wilhelm Bittorf.* (45 min.) Bavaria Atelier GmbH, München. ["The Making of Das Boot."] A report by Wilhelm Bittorf. Photography Franz Brandeis und Ernst Schmid. ARD-Fernsehn.

1985: *Jäger – Gejagte.* (54 min.) Produced by E.S. Mittler und Sohn Verlag, GmbH, with the assistance of Horst Bredow, Stiftung Traditionsarchiv Unterseeboote, und der Verband deutscher U-Bootfahrer. Based on Jochen Brennecke's book of the same title. Edited by Peter Krusko, narrated by Heinz-Detlev Bock.

1985: *Zu Tode Gesiegt – Der Untergang der U-Boote: Ein Film von Lothar-Günther Buchheim.* (79 min.) München.

1987: '... *gegen Engeland'* (105 min.) TV documentary about the U-boat war in the North Atlantic. A co-production of North German Radio and Radio Free Berlin (Sender Freies Berlin). Produced by Hans Brecht and Lothar Loewe. First broadcast on 22 April 1987 via ARD.

1990: *Die Grauen Wölfe: Feindfahrten deutscher U-Boote.* (54 min.) Production: History Films, 1990. Text and production by Karl-Heinz J. Geiger.

C.   SELECTED SECONDARY SOURCES

Ajax. *The German Pirate: His Methods and Record.* New York: George H. Doran Company, 1917.

Anon. "Fragen an Dieter Wellershoff, Admiral and Generalinspekteur der Bundeswehr." *Information für die Truppe.* Hrsgg. Bundesministerium der Verteidigung, Heft 6/90, 25–46.

Assmann, Kurt [Konteradmiral a.D.]. *Die Kämpfe der kaiserlichen Marine in den deutschen Kolonien.* [Teil I: *Tsingtau*; Teil II: *Deutsch-Ostafrika*] Bd 7 *Der Krieg zur See 1914–1918.* Hrsgg. vom Marine Archiv, Berlin: E.S. Mittler, 1935.

Assmann, K[urt]. "Der deutsche U-Bootskrieg und die Nürnberger Rechtssprechung." *Marine Rundschau,* Jg 50, Januar 1953, 2–8.

Baird, Jay W. *To Die for Germany: Heroes in the Nazi Pantheon.* Bloomington and Indianapolis: Indiana University Press, 1990.

Beesly, Patrick. *Very Special Intelligence: The Story of Admiralty's Operational Intelligence Centre in World War II.* London: Hamish Hamilton, 1977.

Beesly, Patrick. *Room 40: British Naval Intelligence 1914–18.* London: Hamish Hamilton, 1982.

Bethge, Hans-Georg. *Der Brandtaucher.* Bielefeld: Verlag Delius, Klasing & Co., 1968.

Bethmann Hollweg, Theobald von. *Betrachtungen zum Weltkriege,* Teil I: *Vor dem Kriege,* Berlin: Verlag von Reimar Hobbing, 1919; Teil II: *Während des Krieges,* Berlin: Verlag von Reiman Hobbing, 1922.

Campbell, Vice-Admiral Gordon, VC, DSO. *Wir jagen deutsche U-Boote.* trans. C. Freiherr von Spiegel. Gütersloh: Verlag C. Bertelsmann, 1937. [Orig. *My Mystery Ships,* London, 1937].

Carr, William Guy. *By Guess – and by God: The Story of British Submarines in the War.* With a preface by Admiral S.S. Hall. Garden City, NY: Doubleday, Doran & Co., 1930.

Clark, Ellery H. "Der Erste Weltkrieg: Die Operationen zu Beginn des Krieges," von K.J. Müller übersetzt und bearbeitet, in Potter, *Seemacht.*

Corbett, Julian, and Henry Newbolt. *Naval Operations,* 5 vols. London: Longmans, Green, 1929.

Doyle, A. Conan. *Danger and Other Stories.* London: John Murray, 1918. German edition: *England in Gefahr,* trans. Woldemar Schütze, frei nach dem Englischen. Berlin: Verlag von Karl Curtius, nd [pre-1919?].

Easton, Alan. *Fifty North: An Atlantic Battleground.* Toronto: Ryerson Press, 1963; Markham, Ontario: Paperjacks, 1980.

Eckart, Peter. *Marineblau und Khaki. Der Heldenkampf der "Königsberg."* Stuttgart: Franckh'sche Verlagsbuchhandlung [nd].

Edmonds, James M. *A Short History of World War I.* London: Oxford University Press, 1951.

Ehrensberger, Konrad. *100 Jahre Organisation der deutschen Marine.* Bonn: Bernhard & Graefe, 1993.

Eksteins, Modris. *Rites of Spring: The Great War and the Birth of the Modern Age.* London and New York: Bantam Press, 1989.

Ferber, Christian, Hrsg. *Hundert Jahre Ullstein: Ein Bilderbuch mit Randbemerkungen.* Berlin: Im Ullstein Verlag, 1977.

Ferber, Christian, ed., *Berliner Illustrirte Zeitung: Zeitbild, Chronik, Moritat für Jedermann 1892–1945.* Berlin: Ullstein Verlag, 1982.

Fock, Gorch. *Ein Schiff! Ein Schwert! Ein Segel! Kriegs- und Bordbuch des Dichters.* [First published as *Sterne überm Meer,* 1917]. Aus dem unveröffentlichten Nachlaß herausgegeben und bearbeitet von Jakob Rinau und Marie Luise Droop. J.F. Lehmanns Verlag, 1934.

Forester, C.S. *Konvoi 1942.* [Orig. *The Good Shepherd.* London: Michael Joseph, 1969]. Trans. Eugen v. Beulwitz. Hamburg: Eduard Kaiser Verlag, 1970.

Gannon, Michael. *Operation Paukenschlag: Der Deutsche U-Boot-Krieg gegen die USA.* [Orig. *Operation Drumbeat,* New York: Harper Collins, 1991]. Trans. Klaus-Dieter Schmidt. Berlin und Frankfurt a.M.: Ullstein, 1992.

Gebeschus, Kurt (KKpt a.D.). *Doggerbank. Kampf und Untergang des Panzerkreuzers Blücher.* Berlin: Brunnen-Verlag Willi Bischoff, 1935.

Gilson, Charles. *Submarine U-93: A Tale of the Great War, of German Spies, and Submarines, of Naval Warfare, and All Manner of Adventures.* London: "The Boy's Own Paper" Office [1917].

Glodschey, Erich. *Auf allen Ozeanen: Deutsche Handelsstörer, der Schrecken Englands.* Leipzig: National Verlagsgesellschaft, 1941.

Groos, Otto (Vizeadm Dr. h.c.). *Was jeder vom Seekrieg wissen muß.* Mit einem Geleitwort von Großadmiral Dr. h.c. Raeder. Berlin: Volk und Reich Verlag, 1940.

Gretton, Peter, [Vizeadmiral]. *Atlantik 1943: Wende im U-Bootkrieg.* Trans. Hans Berenbrok. Oldenburg und Stalling, Verlag Gerhard Stalling, 1974. [Orig. *Crisis Convoy: The Story of HX 231.* London: P. Davies, 1974].

Güth, Rolf. *Die Marine des Deutschen Reiches 1919–1939.* Frankfurt a.M.: Bernard & Graefe Verlag für Wehrwesen, 1972.

Hadley, Michael L. *U-Boats against Canada: German Submarines in Canadian Waters.* Montreal and Kingston: McGill-Queen's University Press, 1985 [paperback 1990].

Hadley, Michael L. "HMCS Sackville and the Myth of U-26." *Canadian Defence Quarterly,* 15/3 (1985/86), 47–50.

Hadley, Michael L. *Uboote gegen Kanada: Unternehmungen deutscher Uboote in kanadischen Gewässern.* Übertragen von Hans und Hanne Meckel. Herford und Bonn: E.S. Mitter & Sohn, 1990.

Hadley, Michael L. "'Rückwärtsschauende Propheten:' U-Bootgeschichten im Dienste der Zukunft," in Friedrich Gaede, Patrick O'Neal, und Ulrich Scheck, Hrsg. *Hinter dem schwarzen Vorhang: Die Katastrophe und die epische Tradition.* Festschrift für Anthony W. Riley. Tübingen und Basel: Francke Verlag, 1994, 217–29.

Hadley, Michael L., and Roger Sarty. *Tin-Pots and Pirate Ships: Canadian Naval Forces and German Sea Raiders 1880–1919.* Montreal and Kingston: McGill-Queen's University Press, 1991.

Harder, Hans-Joachim, and Norbert Wiggershaus, Hrsg. *Tradition und Reform in den Aufbaujahren der Bundeswehr,* Bd 2, *Entwicklung deutscher militärischer Tradition,* Herausgegeben vom Militärgeschichtlichen Forschungsamt. Herford und Bonn: Verlag E.S. Mittler, 1985.

Hattendorf, John B., ed. *The Influence of History on Mahan: The Proceedings of a Conference Marking the Centenary of Alfred Thayer Mahan's "The Influence of Sea Power upon History," 1660–1783.* Newport, Rhode Island: Naval War College Press, 1991.

Herwig, Holger H. "The Influence of A.T. Mahan upon German Sea Power," in Hattendorf, ed., *The Influence of History on Mahan*, 67–80.

Herwig, Holger H., and D.F. Trask, "Naval Operations Plans between Germany and the USA, 1898–1913." In *The War Plans of the Great Powers, 1880–1914*, edited by Paul M. Kennedy. London: George Allen & Unwin, 1979, 39–74.

Herzog, Bodo. "Admiral Hermann Bauer – der 'weise Mann' der U-Boot-Waffe – Zu seinem 25. Todestag." *Deutsches Soldatenjahrbuch 1983*. München, 1982, 11.

Hessler, Günther. *The U-Boat War in the Atlantic 1939–1945*. London: HM Stationery Office, 1989.

Hildebrandt, Hans H. *Die Deutschen Kriegsschiffe*. 7 Bde. 2. überarbeitete Aufl. Herford: Koehlers Verlagsgesellschaft, [1979] 1983.

Hollweg, [Carl] Adm. "Denkschrift einer Weiterentwicklung der Marine nach dem Krieg," and "Erster Etat nach Friedenschluß," [36–page document], Nachlaß Admiral Hollweg, BA-MA: RM3/11703.

Horn, Kapitän z. See. "Gesichtspunkte für die bisherige U-Bootskriegführung," 6 August 1918, BA-MA: RM5/6440, 180–5.

Horn, Daniel. *War, Mutiny and Revolution in the German Navy: The World War I Diary of Seaman Richard Stumpf*. New Brunswick, New Jersey: Rutgers University Press, 1967.

Horn, Daniel. *The German Naval Mutinies of World War I*. New Brunswick, New Jersey: Rutgers University Press, 1969.

Horten, Dirk, and Wolfgang Wilhelms. "Führung und Einsatz von U-Booten." In Gustav C. Liebig, Hrsg., *Die Deutsche Marine: Historisches Selbstverständnis und Standortbestimmung*. Herausgeber: Marine Institut und Deutsche Marine-Akademie. Herford: Verlag E.S. Mittler & Sohn, 1983, 271–81.

International Military Tribunal. *Trial of the Major War Criminals before the International Military Tribunal, Nuremberg, 14 November 1945–1 October 1946*. Nuremberg, 1947, I, 310–15.

Jackson, G. Gibbard. *The Romance of the Submarine*. London: Sampson Low, Marston & Co., 1931.

Jellicoe, Lord. *Lord Jellicoe's Erinnerungen: Zwischen Skagerrak und Scapa Flow*. [Orig. *Crisis of the Naval War*]. Trans. Kapitänleutnant a.D. Johannes Spieß. Berlin: Vorhut-Verlag Otto Schlegel, nd.

Jellicoe, Lord. *Der U-Boot-Krieg: Englands schwerste Stunde*. [Orig. *The Submarine Peril*]. Trans. Kapitänleutnant a.D. Johannes Spieß. 10. Aufl. Berlin: Vorhut-Verlag Otto Schlegel, nd.

Jeschke, Hubert. *U-Boottaktik: Zur deutschen U-Boottaktik 1900–1945*. Einzelschriften zur militärischen Geschichte des Zweiten Weltkrieges, Bd 9, Herausgegeben vom Militärgeschichtlichen Forschungsamt. Freiburg: Verlag Rombach, 1972.

Johannesson, Rolf. *Offizier in kritischer Zeit*, Hrsgg. vom Deutschen Marine-Institut mit Unterstützung des Militärgeschichtlichen Forschungsamtes. Herford und Bonn: E.S. Mittler, 1989.

Jung, Hermann A.K. *Die letzten Korsaren. Kriegsfahrten deutscher Hilfskreuzer.* Stuttgart: Franckh'sche Verlagsbuchhandlung, nd.

Karweina, Günter. *Geleitzug PQ 17: ein Tatsachenbericht.* Gütersloh: C. Bertelsmann, 1977. [Also paperback, München: Wilhelm Heyne, 1977.]

Kennedy, Ludovic. "War Crimes," *Telegraph Magazine,* 1 June 1991.

Kennedy, Paul. *The Rise of the Anglo-German Antagonism 1860–1914.* London: George Allen and Unwin, 1979.

Kirchhoff, Hermann [Vadm, a.D.] *Seekriegsgeschichte in ihren wichtigsten Abschnitten mit Berücksichtigung der Seetaktik.* 6. Teil: *Von 1910–1920.* Hannover: Hahnsche Buchhandlung, 1921.

Kludas, Arnold. *Die kaiserliche Marine auf alten Postkarten.* Hildesheim: Gerstenberg Verlag, 1983.

Köppen, Paul, Kapt.z S. (Ing) a.D. *Die Überwasserstreitkräfte und ihre Technik.* Bd 4, *Der Krieg zur See 1914–1918,* Hrsgg. von Marine-Archiv, Vizeadm. E. von Mantey. Berlin: Verlag von E.S. Mittler und Sohn, 1930.

Kreimeier, Klaus. *Die Ufa-Story: Geschichte eines Filmkonzerns.* München und Wien: Carl Hanser Verlag, 1992.

Krug, Hans-Joachim, Kapitän zur See, a.D., "Der Film 'Das Boot': Erfahrungen und Beobachtungen des Marinefachberaters," *Marine Forum,* 1/2, 1982, 11–17.

Kühlwetter, Friedrich von. *Skagerrak: Der Ruhmestag der deutschen Flotte.* Neubearbeitet und ergänzt von H.D. Philipp. Geleitwort v Konteradmiral a.D. Magnus v Levetzow (der an Bord des Flaggschiffs *Friedrich der Grosse* als Chef der Operationsabteilung der Hochseeflotte die Schlacht miterlebte). Berlin: Im Verlag Ullstein, 1933.

Lawrenz, Hans-Joachim. *Die Entstehungsgeschichte der U-Boote.* München: J.F. Lehmanns Verlag, 1968.

Liebig, Gustav C., Hrsg. *Die Deutsche Marine: Historisches Selbstverständnis und Standortbestimmung.* Herausgeber: Marine Institut und Deutsche Marine-Akademie. Herford: Verlag E.S. Mittler & Sohn, 1983.

Lützeler, Paul Michael. *Die Schriftsteller und Europa: Von der Romantik bis zur Gegenwart.* München: Piper Verlag, 1992.

Mallmann Showell, Jak. *Uboote gegen England: Kampf und Untergang der deutschen Uboot-Waffe 1939–1945.* [Orig. *U-Boats under the Swastika.* London: Ian Allan Ltd, 1973]. Trans. Hans Dehnert. Stuttgart: Motorbuch Verlag, 1974; 3. Aufl. 1978.

Marine-Amt. *Die Flotten-Manöver 1901.* Berlin: E.S. Mittler Verlag, 1901.

Martel, Gordon, ed. *Modern Germany Reconsidered, 1870–1945.* London and New York: Routledge, 1992.

Mason, David. *Deutsche U-Boote.* [Orig. *U-Boat – the Secret Menace,* 1968]. München: Moewig Verlag, 1980.

Messimer, Dwight R. "German Gunboats on the Yangtse." *Naval History* 1/1 (April 1987): 57–62.

Messimer, Dwight R. *The Merchant U-boat*. Annapolis, Maryland: Naval Institute Press, 1988.

Meyer, J. "Die Propaganda der deutschen Flottenbewegung 1897–1900." Inauguraldiss. Berne, 1967.

Michelsen, [Andreas], Vizeadmiral a.D. *Der U-Bootskrieg 1914–1918*. Leipzig: Verlag von K.F. Koehler, 1925.

Middlebrook, Martin. *Konvoi: U-Boot-Jagd auf die Geleitzüge SC-122 und HX-229 [1943]*. [Orig. *Convoy*. London: Allen Lane, 1976]. Berlin: Verlag Ullstein, 1977.

Mirow, Jürgen. *Der Seekrieg in Umrissen*. Zürich, Frankfurt: Musterschmidt Göttingen, 1976.

Mitscherlich, Alexander und Margarete. *Die Unfähigkeit zu trauern: Grundlage kollektiven Verhaltens*. [München: R. Piper Verlag, 1967, 1977.] Leipzig: Reclam, 1990.

Monsarrat, *Grausamer Atlantik*, trans. Arno Dohm. Klagenfurt: Eduard Kaiser Verlag – Buchgemeinde Alpenland, 1951; also in Berlin-Grunewald: Non Stop-Bücherei, Lizenzausgabe von Claasen Verlag, Hamburg, 1951. [Orig. *The Cruel Sea*. London: Cassel & Co., 1951; Penguin Books, 1954].

Padfield, Peter *Dönitz: The Last Führer*. London: Victor Gollanz, 1984. [German: *Dönitz: Des Teufels Admiral*, translated by Duncker, Erev, Nowel, and Rott-Illfeld. Berlin, Frankfurt, Wien: Verlag Ullstein, 1984].

Peillard, Léonce. *Geschichte des U-Bootkrieges 1939–45*. [Orig. *Histoire générale de la Guerre Sous-Marine 1939–1945*. Paris: Robert Laffont, 1970]. Aus dem Französischen übertragen von Fregattenkapitän Hans Sokol und Ing. Wilhelm Rudolf. Wien: Paul Neff Verlag, 1970.

Plievier, Theodor. *Des Kaisers Kulis* [1930]. Köln: Verlag Kiepenhauer & Witsch, 1981; München: Deutscher Taschenbuch Verlag, 1984.

Potter, E.B., Chester W. Nimitz, und J. Rohwer. *Seemacht*, Hrsgg. im Auftrag des Arbeitskreises für Wehrforschung von Jürgen Rohwer. Herrsching: Manfred Pawlak, 1986.

Raeder, Erich. *Das Kreuzergeschwader*, Bd 1 der Reihe *Der Kreuzerkrieg in den ausländischen Gewässern*. [In the official series *Der Krieg zur See 1914–1918*, hrsg. von E.v. Mantey]. Berlin: E.S. Mittler und Sohn, 1922.

Raeder, Erich. *Die Tätigkeit der kleinen Kreuzer "Emden," "Königsberg," und "Karlsruhe,"* mit einem Anhang "Die Kriegfahrt des kleinen Kreuzers 'Geier.'" 1923.

Raeder, Erich. *Mein Leben*. Tübingen-Neckar: Verlag Fritz Schlichtermayer, 1957.

Robertson, Terence. *Der Wolf im Atlantik: Die Kriegserlebnisse Otto Kretschmers, des erfolgreichsten U-Boot-Kommandanten im zweiten Weltkrieg*. 5. Aufl. Wels: Verlag Welsermühl, 1969. [Orig. *The Golden Horseshoe*. London: Evans Brothers, 1955; American edition, *Night Raiders of the Atlantic*. New York: Dutton, 1956].

Rohwer, Jürgen, und G. Hümmelchen. *Chronik des Seekrieges 1939–45*. Hrsgg. vom Arbeitskreis für Wehrforschung und von der Bibliothek für Zeitgeschichte. [Oldenburg und Hamburg: Stalling Verlag], Herrsching: Manfred Pawlak Verlagsgesellschaft, 1968.

Rohwer, Jürgen. "Herbert A. Werner: 'Iron Coffins.'" *Schaltung Küste*, Heft 38, 1970, 502–5.

Rohwer, Jürgen. *Der Krieg zur See 1939–1945*. Gräfelfing/München: Urbes Verlag Hans Jürgen Hansen, 1992.

Roth, Karl Jürgen. "Deutschlands Ehr' im Weltmeer: Marineagitation in Jugendpublikationen aus der Zeit des Kaiserreiches," *Schiff und Zeit*, Hrsgg. von der Deutschen Gesellschaft für Schiffahrts- und Marinegeschichte e.V., No. 39 (1994), 1–11.

Ruge, Friedrich. *In Vier Marinen: Lebenserinnerungen als Beitrag zur Zeitgeschichte*. München: Bernard & Graefe Verlag, 1979.

Salewski, Michael, "Selbstverständnis und historisches Bewußtsein der deutschen Kriegsmarine." *Marine-Rundschau*, 67, Jahrgang, Heft 2 (1970), 65–122.

Salewski, Michael. *Von der Wirklichkeit des Krieges: Analysen und Kontroversen zu Buchheims "Boot."* München: Deutscher Taschenbuch Verlag [1976], 2. Aufl. 1985.

Saunders, Thomas. "Weimar, Hollywood and the Americanization of German Culture, 1917–1933." PhD dissertation, University of Toronto, 1985.

Saunders, Thomas. "Politics, the Cinema, and Early Revisitations of War in Weimar Germany." *Canadian Journal of History*, 23 (April 1988), 25–48.

Saunders, Thomas. "Nazism and Social Revolution." In Gordon Martel, ed., *Modern Germany Reconsidered, 1870–1945*. London and New York: Routledge, 1992, 159–77.

Scheer, Reinhard, Hrsg. *Die deutsche Flotte in grosser Zeit*. Unter Mitwirkung deutscher Seehelden. Wohlfeile Ausgabe. Braunschweig und Berlin: Georg Westermann, 1926.

Scheer, Admiral [Reinhard]. *Deutschlands Hochseeflotte im Weltkrieg: Persönliche Erinnerungen*. Berlin: Verlag Scherl, 1937.

Scholl, Lars U. *Claus Bergen 1885–1964: Marinemalerei im 20. Jahrhundert*. Mit Beiträgen von Michael Salewski und Gert Schlechtriem. Sonderausstellung im Deutschen Schiffahrtsmuseum 24.4.–26.9 1982. Bremerhaven: Deutsches Schiffahrtsmuseum, 1982.

Sethe, Paul. *Die ausgebliebene Seeschlacht. Eine Betrachtung der englischen Flottenführung 1911–1915*. Berlin: Verlag von E.S. Mittler und Sohn, 1933.

Sohler, Herbert. *U-Bootkrieg und Völkerrecht*. Beiheft 1 der *Marine Rundschau*. Frankfurt a.M.: Verlag E.S. Mittler & Sohn, September 1956.

Stockfisch, Dieter. "Vom schwierigen Umgang mit der Tradition." *Marine Forum*, 4, 1987, 120–2.

Tirpitz, Alfred von. *Erinnerungen* [1919]. Leipzig: Verlag von K.F. Koehler, 1920.

Treue, Wilhelm, Eberhard Möller, and Werner Rahn. *Deutsche Marinerüstung 1919–1942: Die Gefahren der Tirpitz-Tradition.* Herford und Bonn: E.S. Mittler & Sohn, 1992.

Vincent, C. Paul. *The Politics of Hunger: The Allied Blockade of Germany 1915–1919.* Athens, Ohio: Ohio University Press, 1985.

Wegener, Edward. "Selbstverständnis und historisches Bewußtsein der deutschen Kriegsmarine." *Marine-Rundschau,* 67, Jahrgang, Heft 6 (1970), 321–39.

Wegener, Wolfgang [VADM a.D.]. *Die Seestrategie des Weltkrieges.* Berlin: E.S. Mittler und Sohn, 1929.

Weir, Gary E. *Building the Kaiser's Navy: The Imperial Naval Office and German Industry in the von Tirpitz Era, 1890–1919.* Annapolis, Maryland: Naval Institute Press, 1992.

Wislicenus, Georg. *Deutschlands Seemacht sonst und jetzt.* [1895]. Leipzig: Fr. Wilh. Grunow [1901], Mit Bildern von Willy Stöwer, 3. Aufl. 1909.

Witschetzky, KKpt F. *Das schwarze Schiff. Kriegs- und Kaperfahrten des Hilfskreuzers "Wolf."* Reihe "Vaterländische Volks- und Jugendbücher des Unionverlags." 19. Aufl. Stuttgart, Berlin, Leipzig: Union Deutsche Verlagsgesellschaft [1930].

Index